STUDY GUIDE TO ACCOMPANY MORRIS HAMBURG'S

STATISTICAL ANALYSIS FOR DECISION MAKING

FIFTH EDITION

STUDY GUIDE TO ACCOMPANY MORRIS HAMBURG'S

STATISTICAL ANALYSIS FOR DECISION MAKING

FIFTH EDITION

JOSEPH P. FUHR
WIDENER UNIVERSITY

HARCOURT BRACE JOVANOVICH, PUBLISHERS
AND ITS SUBSIDIARY, *ACADEMIC PRESS*
SAN DIEGO   NEW YORK   CHICAGO   AUSTIN   WASHINGTON, D.C.
LONDON   SYDNEY   TOKYO   TORONTO

Requests for permission to make copies of any part of the work should be mailed to: Permissions, Harcourt Brace Jovanovich, Publishers, Orlando, Florida 32887.

ISBN: 0-15-583461-4

Library of Congress Catalog Card Number: 90-80976

Printed in the United States of America

PREFACE

This Study Guide is a supplement to *Statistical Analysis for Decision Making*, Fifth Edition, by Morris Hamburg. Each chapter consists of a brief discussion of a statistical concept, followed by an example and a problem. At the end of each chapter are review problems. The answers to all problems are at the end of the Study Guide. There are statistical tables in the appendix.

The following people have contributed to the creation of the Study Guide: Dr. Erwin Blackstone of Temple University and Dr. Hamid Zangenehzadeh of Widener University made many helpful comments; at Harcourt Brace Jovanovich I would like to thank Dee Salisbury for her editorial assistance, Lori J. Mc Thomas for implementing the new design, and Jacqui Parker for helping the book through production. Last but not least, I thank my family–especially my wife, Kathy–for their tolerance during this project.

Joseph P. Fuhr, Jr.

CONTENTS

Preface   **v**

1   Frequency Distributions and Summary Measures   1

2   Introduction to Probability   16

3   Discrete Random Variables and Probability Distributions   33

4   Statistical Investigations and Sampling   47

5   Sampling Distributions   49

6   Estimation   61

7   Hypothesis Testing   70

8   Chi-Square Tests and Analysis of Variance   91

9   Regression Analysis and Correlation Analysis   107

10   Multiple Regression and Correlation Analysis   120

11   Time Series   135

12   Index Numbers   146

13   Nonparameteric Statistics   156

14   Decision Making Using Prior Information   171

15   Decision Making with Posterior Probabilities   182

16   Devising Optimal Strategies Prior to Sampling   193

17   Comparison of Classical and Bayesian Statistics   205

Appendix   Statistical Tables   213

Answers to Problems and Review Problems   241

STATISTICAL ANALYSIS FOR DECISION MAKING

FIFTH EDITION

1

FREQUENCY DISTRIBUTION AND SUMMARY MEASURES

FREQUENCY DISTRIBUTION

Data Classification

If you have 1,000 pieces of data, you may want to summarize the data to obtain a better picture. This can be achieved by putting the data into classes. The criteria for classifying data are that the classes are both mutually exclusive and all inclusive.

- **Mutually exclusive:** Each element of the data set must fall in only *one* class which means the classes do not overlap.
- **All inclusive:** Each element of the data set *must* fall in a class.

To meet these two criteria, each element must fall in one and only one class.

Frequency distribution is the classification of the elements of a data set by quantitative characteristics. The purpose of a frequency distribution is to summarize the data so that one can obtain a better picture. Thus, a frequency distribution makes it easier to work with the data. The number of elements in a given class of a frequency distribution is called the **frequency** of the class.

Example 1: grouping raw data in a frequency distribution

Raw Data				
56	12	18	30	41
25	27	43	14	29
47	23	19	36	55
21	37	23	33	24
11	26	35	12	21
31	48	20	41	17

x	f
10 and under 20	7
20 and under 30	10
30 and under 40	6
40 and under 50	5
50 and under 60	2

Each value of x in the frequency distribution represents a class of values. Each value of f represents the frequency of the class. For example, there are 7 values between 10 and under 20.

Remember that the classes need to be mutually exclusive and all inclusive. The preceding frequency distribution meets both criteria.

Example 2: classes that are not mutually exclusive

10 and under 15
14 and under 20

Fourteen is in both classes. Therefore, the classes are not mutually exclusive.

Example 3: classes that are not all inclusive

10 and under 15
16 and under 20
20 and under 25

Fifteen is not in any class. Therefore, the classes are not all inclusive.

Some Terminology

Class limits are the lower and upper bounds of each class.

10 and under 20
20 and under 30

- The lower class limit of the first class is 10
- The higher class limit of the first class is 20*
- The lower class limit of the second class is 20
- The higher class limit of the second class is 30*

The class limits can be used to find the class size or **class interval** (i), which is the width of the class.

Rule:
$$i = \frac{\text{Higher}}{\text{class limit}} - \frac{\text{Lower}}{\text{class limit}}$$

From the frequency distribution in Example 1, the first class has a class size of 10.

$$\text{first class}\quad i = 20 - 10 = 10$$

The class limits can be used to find the **midpoint** (m) of the class.

Rule:
$$m = \frac{\frac{\text{higher}}{\text{class limit}} + \frac{\text{lower}}{\text{class limit}}}{2}$$

The midpoint of the first class (in Example 1) is 15.

$$m = \frac{20 + 10}{2} = 15$$

* The higher class limit is actually $19.\overline{99}$ and $29.\overline{99}$ respectively.

Problem 1: Given the following frequency distribution, find the class limits, the class size, and the class midpoints.

x	f
10 and under 20	2
20 and under 30	14
30 and under 40	19
40 and under 50	11
50 and under 60	4

Problem 2: Do the following classes meet the criteria of mutually exclusive and all inclusive? If not, why?

x	x	x
a. 0 and under 10	b. 100 and under 150	c. 10 and under 20
9 and under 19	150 and under 200	15 and under 30
20 and under 30	200 and under 250	30 and under 40

Graphic Presentations of Frequency Distribution

1. histogram
2. frequency polygon
3. ogive

The **histogram** is a bar graph. The frequency is represented on the y axis and the class limits are on the x axis. The frequency of each class is represented by a bar between the class limits of each class. The histogram for the data in Example 1 is shown in Figure 1-1.

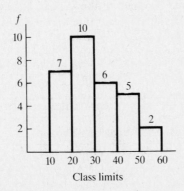

FIGURE 1-1

Histogram for data in Example 1

The **frequency polygon** has the frequency on the y axis and the class midpoints on the x axis. The frequency of each class is represented by a dot at the midpoint of each class. The graph is completed by having a frequency of zero for values that are a class size from the midpoint of the first and the last class respectively. The frequency polygon for the data in Example 1 is shown in Figure 1-2.

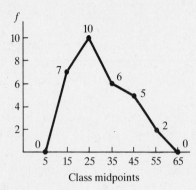

FIGURE 1-2
Frequency polygon for data in Example 1

The **ogive** is a cumulative frequency distribution. It has the cumulative frequency on the y axis and the class limits on the x axis. The cumulative frequency is represented by a dot at the higher class limit (except for the frequency of zero which is represented by the lower limit of the first class) of each class and then the dots are connected. The ogive for the data in Example 1 is shown in Figure 1-3.

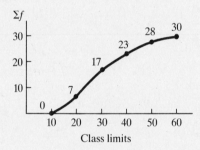

FIGURE 1-3
Ogive for data in Example 1

Now that we have discussed graphing frequency distributions, let's take a look at Table 1-1 for a comparison of procedures used in creating the various kinds of graphical presentations of frequency distributions. Note how the data are set up on each axis and how the connecting line is formed.

TABLE 1-1
Comparison of axis labels and procedures for graphical presentation of frequency distributions

	Histogram	**Frequency Polygon**	**Ogive**
y axis	Frequency	Frequency	Cumulative frequency
x axis	Class limits	Class midpoints	Class limits
Procedure	Bar graph	Connect the dots with straight lines	Connect the dots with a smooth curve

Problem 3: Find the histogram, polygon, and ogive for the frequency distribution in Problem 1.

MEASURES OF CENTRAL TENDENCY

There are three basic measures of central tendency: the *mean*, the *median*, and the *mode*.

The Mean

The simple mean and weighted mean are the two types of means that we examine. In the *simple mean* each observation carries the same weight. In the *weighted mean* each observation carries different weights.

The rules in this chapter are for *sample data*. In the last section of this chapter, we deal with the rules for *population data*.

Simple Mean The **simple mean** ($\bar{X}$) is the sum of the values of the items divided by the number of items.*

Rule:
$$\bar{X} = \Sigma X/n$$

$\bar{X}$ = sample mean

X = value of each observation

n = sample size

Example 4: Find the mean for the following sample data: 3, 6, 12, 9, 15.

$$n = 5$$
$$\Sigma X = 3 + 6 + 12 + 9 + 15 = 45$$
$$\bar{X} = \Sigma X/n = 45/5 = 9$$

Problem 4: Find the simple mean for the following data: 10, 13, 21, 17, 14, 22, 18, 21.

The mean is the most commonly used measure of central tendency because it has many convenient mathematical properties. One major problem is that the mean is heavily influenced by extreme observations.

Example 5: Find the mean for the following data: 3, 6, 12, 9, 15, 75.

$$\bar{X} = \Sigma X/n = 120/6 = 20$$

The mean is equal to 20, but the single extreme value of 75 increases considerably the value of the mean. Without that 75, the mean equals 9 (see Example 4).

---

* The rule for $\bar{X}$ is actually

$$\bar{X} = \frac{\sum_{i=1}^{n} X_i}{n}$$

However, for simplicity we omit the subscript notation and use $\bar{X} = \Sigma X/n$. The same is true for most of the other rules in the book.

Weighted Average   The **weighted average** is calculated by multiplying each observation by its appropriate weight, totaling these products, and then dividing the total by the sum of the weights.

Rule:

$$\bar{X}_w = \Sigma wX / \Sigma w$$

w = weight of each observation

X = value of each observation

$\bar{X}_w$ = weighted mean

Example 6: A new student obtains an A in a three-credit course, a B in a four-credit course and a D in a one-credit course. What is the student's grade point average if $A = 4$, $B = 3$, and $D = 1$? Each course carries different weights (credits), so the weighted mean is the appropriate measure.

Grade X	Credit w	wX
A = 4	3	12
B = 3	4	12
D = 1	1	1
	$\Sigma w = 8$	$\Sigma wX = 25$

w = credit hours

X = grade earned

$$\bar{X}_w = \Sigma wX / \Sigma w = 25/8 = 3.125$$

The advantage of the weighted average is that it takes into account the different weights and is, therefore, a better measure than the simple average when the observations carry different weights.

Note: An alternative method would be to weight the credits by a percentage breakdown of the denominators (in this case, a percentage breakdown of total credits). Using this method for the data in Example 6, we obtain:

Grade X	Credit w	wX
A = 4	0.375	1.500
B = 3	0.500	1.500
D = 1	0.125	0.125
	1.000	3.125

Problem 5: Three communities with populations of 100,000, 50,000, and 1 million have unemployment rates of 2%, 4%, and 6% respectively. What is the weighted average unemployment rate of these 3 communities? Why is the weighted average the appropriate measure in this problem?

The Median

The **median** is the geographic center of the distribution when ranking the observations of the data from the lowest to highest. The same number of observations are to the right of the median as to the left of the median. There are three steps in finding the value of the median.

a. Find the position of the median.

b. Rank the data from lowest to highest.

c. Find the value of the median.

Example 7: Using the same data as Example 4 (listed below), find the median for 3, 6, 12, 9, 15. Compare this answer with that of Example 4.

a. Find the position of the median.

Rule:
$$\frac{n+1}{2}$$

$$\text{Median} = \frac{5+1}{2}$$

$$= \text{3rd position}$$

b. Rank the data from lowest to highest

$$\begin{array}{ccccc} 3 & 6 & 9 & 12 & 15 \\ P_1 & P_2 & P_3 & P_4 & P_5 \end{array}$$

c. The value of median is the value of the observation in the third position: Value of median = 9.

If the size of the sample is even, then a slight adjustment must be made.

Example 8: Find the median for the following data: 3, 10, 10, 7, 12, 13.

a. Position of the median

$$\frac{n+1}{2} = \frac{6+1}{2} = \text{3.5th position}$$

b. Rank from lowest to highest

$$\begin{array}{cccccc} 3 & 7 & 10 & 10 & 12 & 13 \\ P_1 & P_2 & P_3 & P_4 & P_5 & P_6 \end{array}$$

c. The value of the median is the value of the observation in the 3.5th position. Given there is no value in the 3.5th position, one is created by adding the value in the position before the median position (P_3) to that of the value in the position after the median position (P_4) and dividing by 2.

$$\text{Value of median} = \frac{P_3 + P_4}{2} = \frac{10 + 10}{2} = 10$$

The median is not influenced by extreme values. For example, if we replace the highest observation (13) in Example 8 with a value of 500 (that is, 3, 7, 10, 10, 12, 13, 500), the value of the median is still 10.

Problem 6: Find the median for the data in Problem 4.

Problem 7: Find the median for the following data: 8, 5, 4, 12, 19, 21, 7, 10, 12.

The Mode

The mode is the value that occurs most frequently.

Example 9: Using the data from Example 8, find the mode.

$$3, 10, 10, 7, 12, 13$$

Note that 10 occurs twice and 3, 7, 12, 13 occur only once. The mode is 10.

Problem 8: Find the mode for the data in Problem 4.

MEASURES OF DISPERSION

Besides determining the center of the distribution, we are also interested in how spread out the distribution is. There are two basic measures of dispersion (variability), the *range* and the *variance* (standard deviation).

The Range

The **range** is the difference between the highest and lowest values in a data set.

Rule: Range = Highest value − Lowest value

Example 10: Given the following data, find the range: 8, 3, 27, 9, 14, 11.

Rule: Range = Highest value − Lowest value

$$\text{Range} = 27 - 3 = 24$$

Because the range is based on only two observations (and, like the mean, it is heavily influenced by extreme values), it does not give a true representation of the data.

Problem 9: Find the range for the data in Problem 4.

The Variance and the Standard Deviation

The variance and the standard deviation take into account all of the values in the data set and measure dispersion around the mean.

Variance rule:
$$s^2 = \frac{\Sigma(X - \bar{X})^2}{n - 1}$$

The standard deviation (s) is the positive square root of the variance.

The **variance** is computed by taking the sum of the squared deviations around the mean and dividing by the sample size (actually, $n - 1$ is used). The reason for the $n - 1$ instead of n is to make the standard deviation an unbiased estimator.

Example 11: Using the data from Example 4, find the variance and standard deviation for 3, 6, 12, 9, 15.

$$n = 5 \quad \text{so } (n - 1) = 4$$
$$\bar{X} = 9$$
$$\Sigma(X - \bar{X})^2 = (3 - 9)^2 + (6 - 9)^2 + (12 - 9)^2 + (9 - 9)^2 + (15 - 9)^2$$
$$= (-6)^2 + (-3)^2 + 3^2 + 0^2 + 6^2$$
$$= 36 + 9 + 9 + 0 + 36$$
$$= 90$$
$$s^2 = 90/4 = 22.5$$
$$s = \sqrt{22.5} = 4.74$$

Problem 10: Find the variance and standard deviation for the data in Problem 4.

The greater the dispersion, the greater the value of the variance. Also, if all values in a sample are the same, there is no dispersion and the variance is zero.

MEASURES OF CENTRAL TENDENCY AND DISPERSION FOR A FREQUENCY DISTRIBUTION

We have examined the measures of central tendency and dispersion for raw data. We next look at these measures for a frequency distribution.

Note: When finding these measures for a frequency distribution, we are approximating the values. The only way we can obtain the actual values is to compute them using the raw data. However, these rules allow for good approximations while decreasing the amount of computation needed to obtain the measures.

Mean of Frequency Distribution

Rule:
$$\bar{X} = \Sigma fm/n$$

where n = sample size
m = midpoint of each class
f = frequency of each class

Example 12: Using the frequency distribution from Example 1, find the mean.

(1) x	(2) f	(3) m	(4) fm
10 and under 20	7	15	105
20 and under 30	10	25	250
30 and under 40	6	35	210
40 and under 50	5	45	225
50 and under 60	2	55	110
	30		900

$$\bar{X} = \Sigma fm/n = 900/30 = 30$$

- Columns (1) and (2) are given.
- Column (3) is the midpoint of each class (see the rule preceding Problem 1 for computation of midpoint).
- Column (4) is obtained by multiplying column (2) by column (3).
- Σfm is the summation of the observations in column (4).

Median of Frequency Distribution

Rule:
$$Md = L_{Md} + \left(\frac{n/2 - \Sigma f_p}{f_{Md}} \right) i$$

where Md = the median

L_{Md} = the (real) lower limit of the class containing the median

n = the total number of observations in the distribution

Σf_p = the sum of the frequencies of the class preceding the one containing the median.

f_{Md} = the frequency of the class containing the median

i = the size of the class interval

Example 13: Using the frequency distribution from Example 12, find the median.

x	f	Σf	Positions
10 and under 20	7	7	1–7
20 and under 30	10	17	8–17
30 and under 40	6	23	18–23
40 and under 50	5	28	24–28
50 and under 60	2	30	29–30

$$\text{Position of median} = \frac{n+1}{2} = \frac{30+1}{2} = \frac{31}{2} = 15.5\text{th position}$$

The median class is the one that contains the median position (in this case, the 15.5th position). By using the cumulative frequency, the median class can be determined.

- Positions 1–7 contain numbers between 10 and under 20.
- Positions 8–17 contain numbers between 20 and 30.

- Positions 18–23 contain numbers between 30 and 40.
- The 2nd class contains the 15.5th position and is the median class.
- The lower limit of the median class (2nd class) is 20, $L_{Md} = 20$
- The sample size (n) is 30: $n/2 = 15$
- The cumulative frequency of the classes preceding the median class is 7, $\Sigma f_p = 7$
- The frequency of the median class (2nd class) is 10, $f_{Md} = 10$
- The class size is 10, $i = 10$

Substituting these values into the rule for the median we obtain:

$$Md = L_{Md} + \left(\frac{n/2 - \Sigma f_p}{f_{Md}} \right) i$$

$$= 20 + \left(\frac{15 - 7}{10} \right) 10$$

$$= 28$$

Mode of a Frequency Distribution

The **mode of a frequency distribution** is the midpoint of the modal class. The modal class is the class with the highest frequency.

Example 14: Using the frequency distribution from Example 1, find the mode.

x	f	m
10 and under 20	7	15
20 and under 30	10	25
30 and under 40	6	35
40 and under 50	5	45
50 and under 60	2	55

The modal class is the class with the highest frequency, in this case the 2nd class with a frequency of 10. The mode is the midpoint of the modal class (in this case, 25).

The mode = 25

Review: We have computed the mean, median, and mode for the frequency distribution in Example 1.

Mean = 30

Median = 28

Mode = 25

The Variance and the Standard Deviation of a Frequency Distribution

Rule:

$$s^2 = \frac{\Sigma f(m - \bar{X})^2}{n - 1} \quad \text{(variance)}$$

$$s = \sqrt{\frac{\Sigma f(m - \bar{X})^2}{n - 1}} \quad \text{(standard deviation)}$$

Example 15: Find the variance and standard deviation for the frequency distribution in Example 1.

(1) x	(2) f	(3) m	(4) $(m - \bar{X})$	(5) $(m - \bar{X})^2$	(6) $f(m - \bar{X})^2$
10 and under 20	7	15	-15	225	1,575
20 and under 30	10	25	-5	25	250
30 and under 40	6	35	5	25	150
40 and under 50	5	45	15	225	1,125
50 and under 60	2	55	25	625	1,250
	$n = 30$				$\Sigma f(m - \bar{X})^2 = 4{,}350$

- Columns (1) and (2) are given.
- Column (3) is the midpoint of each class.
- Column (4) is obtained by subtracting $\bar{X}$ (in this case, 30) from the observations in column (3).
- Column (5) is obtained by squaring the observations in column (4).
- Column (6) is obtained by multiplying the observations in column (2) by the observations in column (5).
- The $\Sigma f(m - \bar{X})^2$ is obtained by summing the observation in column (6).

$$\bar{X} = 30 \quad \text{(for computation see Example 12)}$$

$$s^2 = \frac{\Sigma f(m - \bar{X})^2}{n - 1} = \frac{4{,}350}{29} = 150$$

$$s = 12.247$$

Another possible rule for the variance and the standard deviation of a frequency distribution is mathematically equivalent to the preceding rule.

Rule:
$$s^2 = \frac{n\Sigma fm^2 - (\Sigma fm)^2}{n(n - 1)}$$

Example 16: Find the variance and standard deviation using the above rule for the frequency distribution in Example 1.

(1) x	(2) f	(3) m	(4) fm	(5) fm^2
10 and under 20	7	15	105	1,575
20 and under 30	10	25	250	6,250
30 and under 40	6	35	210	7,350
40 and under 50	5	45	225	10,125
50 and under 60	2	55	110	6,050
	30		900	31,350

- Columns (1) and (2) are given.
- Column (3) is the midpoint of each class.
- Column (4) is obtained by multiplying the observations in column (2) by the observations in column (3).
- The Σfm is obtained by summing the observations in column (4).

- Column (5) is obtained by multiplying the observations in column (3) by the observations in column (4).
- The Σfm^2 is obtained by summing the observations in column (5).

$$s^2 = \frac{n\Sigma fm^2 - (\Sigma fm)^2}{n(n-1)}$$

$$= \frac{30(31,350) - (900)^2}{30(29)} = \frac{940,500 - 810,000}{870} = \frac{130,500}{870} = 150$$

$$s = 12.247$$

Problem 11: Find the mean, median, mode, variance, and standard deviation for the frequency distribution in Problem 1.

Relative Dispersion: Coefficient of Variation

The standard deviation measures the absolute variability. The **coefficient of variation** (CV) is a measure of relative dispersion. It measures dispersion in relationship to the mean.

Rule:
$$CV = s/\bar{X}$$

Example 17: From the data in Example 1, find the coefficient of variation.

$$s = 12.247$$
$$\bar{X} = 30$$
$$CV = s/\bar{X} = 12.247/30 = 0.408$$

Problem 12: Find the coefficient of variation, using the data in Problem 1.

MEAN AND VARIANCE OF A POPULATION

We have examined the rules for the mean and variance for sample data. In this section we look at the rules for the mean and variance of a population.

Rule: $\mu = \dfrac{\Sigma X}{N}$ The mean of the population

where X = the value of the observations

N = the number of items in the population

Rule: $\sigma^2 = \dfrac{\Sigma(X - \mu)^2}{N}$ The variance of the population

Example 18: Find the mean and the variance for the following data: 15, 22, 21, 25, 17.

$$N = 5$$
$$\Sigma X = 15 + 22 + 21 + 25 + 17 = 100$$
$$\mu = \Sigma X/N = 100/5 = 20$$
$$\Sigma(X - \mu)^2 = (15 - 20)^2 + (22 - 20)^2 + (21 - 20)^2 + (25 - 20)^2 + (17 - 20)^2$$
$$= (-5)^2 + 2^2 + 1^2 + 5^2 + (-3)^2$$
$$= 25 + 4 + 1 + 25 + 9$$
$$= 64$$

$$\sigma^2 = \Sigma(X - \mu)^2/N = 64/5 = 12.8$$

Problem 13: Find the mean and the variance of the following data: 20, 22, 26, 28, 30, 36.

CHAPTER 1 REVIEW PROBLEMS

1. Find the mean, median, mode, range, and standard deviation for the following sample data: 18, 22, 15, 27, 35, 19, 21, 22, 19, 22.

2. Find the mean, median, mode, and standard deviation for the following sample data: 20, 20, 20, 20, 20.

3. Find the mean and the variance for the following sample:

   Sample 1: 51, 52, 53, 54, 55.

   Sample 2: 45, 65, 53, 41, 61.

4. Company Z produces four products. Its profit per item and quantity sold are as follows:

Product	Profit per Item	Quantity Sold
A	$50	1,000
B	100	5,000
C	400	500
D	1,000	200

   What is the average profit per item sold?

5. Find the mean, median, mode, and standard deviation for the following sample data of test scores on a math exam:

x	f
0 and under 20	2
20 and under 40	5
40 and under 60	12
60 and under 80	25
80 and under 100	6

6. Find the mean, median, mode, and standard deviation for the following sample data of production of workers per shift.

x	f
0 and under 100	10
100 and under 200	40
200 and under 300	120
300 and under 400	25
400 and under 500	5

7. Find the mean, median, mode, and standard deviation for the following sample data of passenger ages on an airline.

x	f
0 and under 10	5
10 and under 20	25
20 and under 30	30
30 and under 40	85
40 and under 50	50
50 and under 60	25
60 and under 70	13
70 and over	12

8. Using the data in Review Problem 5, construct a histogram, a frequency polygon, and an ogive.

9. Using the data in Review Problem 5, find the coefficient of variation.

10. Using the data in Review Problem 6, find the coefficient of variation.

2
Introduction to Probability

FUNDAMENTALS OF PROBABILITY

Probability is the relative frequency with which an event occurs or can be expected to occur.

Rule: $P(A) = \dfrac{a}{a + b}$

a = number of favorable outcomes (number of outcomes of interest)
b = number of unfavorable outcomes
$a + b$ = number of possible outcomes

Another way of looking at probability is to define A as a success. Then

$$P(A) = \frac{\text{Number of ways of obtaining a success}}{\text{Total number of possible outcomes}}$$

Example 1: If a fair coin is tossed once, what is the probability of obtaining a head?

$$P(\text{Head}) = P(A) = \frac{a}{a + b}$$

There is only one way to obtain a head, so $a = 1$. There is only one way not to obtain a head, so $b = 1$. There are two possible outcomes, so $a + b = 2$. Thus, $P(\text{Head}) = 1/2$.

Example 2: A card is drawn from a regular deck of cards. What is the probability of obtaining a heart?

$$P(\text{Heart}) = \frac{a}{a + b}$$

There are 13 hearts in the deck, so $a = 13$. The total number of cards in the deck is 52, so $a + b = 52$.

$$P(\text{Heart}) = 13/52 = 1/4$$

It is important to remember that probability applies only before the event or trial occurs. Once the event or trial has taken place, the rules of probability no longer apply. For example, one can talk about the probability of winning before an event takes place; once you have played the game you have either won or lost, and probability no longer applies.

Problem 1: Find the probability of the following events occurring as a card is drawn from a regular deck of cards.

a. drawing a king

b. drawing a black card

c. drawing a card whose inclusive value is between 3 and 7

Some Terminology

Sample space (S) is the set of all possible outcomes.

Example 3: Roll a fair die

$$S = \{1, 2, 3, 4, 5, 6\}$$

Event (E) is any set of possible outcomes.

Example 4: Use the sample space data in Example 3.

$$\text{Event } 1 = E_1 = \text{Roll an odd number} = E_1 = \{1, 3, 5\}$$
$$\text{Event } 2 = E_2 = \text{Roll a number less than } 3 = E_2 = \{1, 2\}$$

Complementary event $(\bar{E})$ is the set of all possible outcomes not contained in the event (E).

Example 5: From the events in Example 4.

$$\overline{\text{Event}_1} = \bar{E}_1 = \{2, 4, 6\}$$
$$\overline{\text{Event}_2} = \bar{E}_2 = \{3, 4, 5, 6\}$$

Event intersection $(E_1 \text{ and } E_2)$ is the set of all possible outcomes that belong to both E_1 and E_2 (the outcomes that are common to both events).

Example 6: From the events in Example 4.

$$(E_1 \text{ and } E_2) = \{1\}$$

Event union $(E_1 \text{ or } E_2)$ is the set of outcomes that belongs to at least one of the events.

Example 7: From the events in Example 4.

$$(E_1 \text{ or } E_2) = \{1, 2, 3, 5\}$$

Postulates of Probability: There are two basic postulates of probability.

1. $$0 \leq P(E) \leq 1$$

This states that the probability of any event is between 0 and 1. If something is certain to occur, then the probability of that event is 1. If something cannot occur, then the probability of that event is 0. The probability of an event cannot be greater than 1, and probabilities cannot be negative (less than 0).

2.
$$P(S) = 1$$

The sample space is defined as the set of all possible outcomes. If the event is the sample space, then the probability of the event is 1.

Example 8: Look at the sample space in Example 3. If the event is $E_1 = \{1, 2, 3, 4, 5, 6\}$, then the event is the sample space and it is certain to occur. If you roll a die, the probability of rolling a 1, 2, 3, 4, 5, or 6 is 1: You cannot roll any other number.

$$P(E_1) = P(S) = 1$$

Concepts Concerning Probability

Before the various rules of probability are examined, let's look at some of the concepts concerning probability.

Suppose a coin is tossed twice. What is the sample space? Figure 2-1 shows a tree diagram that can be used to find the sample space.

On the first toss, one can obtain either a head (H_1) or a tail (T_1). On the second toss, one can obtain either a head (H_2) or a tail (T_2). By going from branch to branch, we can obtain the sample space.

$$S = \{(H_1, H_2)(H_1, T_2)(T_1, H_2)(T_1, T_2)\}$$

What is the probability of each event? There are four events that are equally likely to occur. So, using the rule of

$$P(H_1, H_2) = \frac{a}{a + b}$$

we obtain $a = 1$ and $a + b = 4$. Thus

$$P(H_1, H_2) = 1/4$$

The same is true for the other possible outcomes.

$$P(H_1, T_2) = 1/4 \qquad P(T_1, H_2) = 1/4 \qquad P(T_1, T_2) = 1/4$$

The tossing of the coins are independent events; that is, the outcome of the first toss does not influence the outcome of the second.

The probability of obtaining 2 heads if we toss a fair coin twice is 1/4. Suppose we change the problem: Instead of tossing coins, we draw two cards from a regular deck. What is the probability

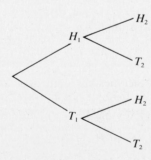

FIGURE 2-1
Tree diagram

that both are red?

The sample space is $\{(R_1\,R_2)(R_1\,B_2)(B_1\,R_2)(B_1\,B_2)\}$

In this case, the answer depends on how the trials are set up—that is, whether or not the first card is replaced before the second card is drawn.

Sampling with Replacement   There are 52 cards in the deck, of which 26 are red, so

$$P(R_1) = 26/52$$

If the first card is replaced, then there are again 52 cards in the deck—and 26 are red, so

$$P(R_2) = 26/52 = 1/2$$
$$P(R_1 \text{ and } R_2) = P(R_1)P(R_2) = (1/2)(1/2) = 1/4$$

The outcome of the first draw does not influence the second outcome. The events are independent: The outcome of the first trial does not affect the outcome of the second.

Sampling without Replacement   Suppose, however, we draw without replacement; that is, we draw the second card without replacing the first. What is the probability of two reds?

There are 52 cards in the deck, of which 26 are red, so

$$P(R_1) = 26/52 = 1/2$$

If the second card is drawn without replacing the first card, then the sample space changes. (Given the first card was red). There are now only 51 cards left in the deck, of which only 25 are red; so the probability of a red on the second, given a red on the first, is $P(R_2\,|\,R_2) = 25/51$.

$$P(R_1 \text{ and } R_2) = P(R_1)P(R_2\,|\,R_1) = (1/2)(25/51) = 25/102$$

If a black card was drawn on the first card, then the probability of a red on the second (given a black was drawn on the first) would be $P(R_2\,|\,B_1) = 26/51$. In this case, the outcome of the first draw influences the outcome of the second draw. If the outcome of one trial influences the outcome of another trial, then the events are dependent.

REVIEW OF CONCEPTS

Sampling with replacement deals with independent events; the outcome of the first event has no influence on the outcome of the second.

Sampling without replacement deals with dependent events; the outcome of the first event influences the outcome of the second.

Whether events are independent or dependent influences which rules of probability are used. These concepts should be understood before we proceed to the rules of probability.

Another important concept concerning the rules of probability is that of mutually exclusive events. Events are **mutually exclusive** if the outcome of one event precludes the occurrence of the other event; both events cannot occur at the same time.

Example 9: If we draw a single card from a deck of 52, what is the probability of a black and a heart?

$$P(\text{Black and Heart}) = 0$$

You cannot draw a black and a heart on the same draw. Thus, the events are mutually exclusive— that is if one occurs, the other cannot. The probability of the intersection of two mutually exclusive events is zero.

Independent events: Events are independent if the outcome of one event has no effect on the outcome of the other events.

Dependent events: Events are dependent if the outcome of one event influences the outcome of another event.

Mutually exclusive: Events are mutually exclusive if the occurrence of one event means that the other event cannot occur.

RULES OF PROBABILITY

Addition Rule

The addition rule is useful in obtaining the probability that at least one of the events occurs.

General Rule: $P(A \text{ or } B) = P(A) + P(B) - P(A \text{ and } B)$

The term $(A \text{ or } B)$ means the probability of A or B or both. Another way of stating the rule is to say that at least one of the events must occur. The intersection $(A \text{ and } B)$ is subtracted out to avoid the problem of double counting, as illustrated in Example 11.

Suppose we roll 2 dice and are interested in the possible sum.

Sample Space for Sum of 2 Dice					
(1, 1)	(1, 2)	(1, 3)	(1, 4)	(1, 5)	(1, 6)
(2, 1)	(2, 2)	(2, 3)	(2, 4)	(2, 5)	(2, 6)
(3, 1)	(3, 2)	(3, 3)	(3, 4)	(3, 5)	(3, 6)
(4, 1)	(4, 2)	(4, 3)	(4, 4)	(4, 5)	(4, 6)
(5, 1)	(5, 2)	(5, 3)	(5, 4)	(5, 5)	(5, 6)
(6, 1)	(6, 2)	(6, 3)	(6, 4)	(6, 5)	(6, 6)

There are 36 possible outcomes.

Example 10: What is the probability of rolling a sum of 2 or 8?

$$P(A \text{ or } B) = P(A) + P(B) - P(A \text{ and } B)$$
$$P(2 \text{ or } 8) = P(2) + P(8) - P(2 \text{ and } 8)$$
$$= 1/36 + 5/36 - 0 = 6/36 = 1/6$$

The sample above shows 36 possible outcomes, one of which yields a sum of 2: (1, 1). Therefore, $P(2) = 1/36$. There are 36 possible outcomes, 5 of which yield a 8: (2, 6), (3, 5), (4, 4), (5, 3), (6, 2); hence, $P(8) = 5/36$.

It is impossible to roll a 2 and an 8 on the same roll. So, $P(2 \text{ and } 8) = 0$. The events 2 and 8 are mutually exclusive.

Example 11: What is the probability of rolling a 6 or a double? (A "double" is defined as showing the same value on both dice.) There are 36 possible outcomes, 5 of which will yield a sum of 6: (1, 5), (2, 4), (3, 3), (4, 2), and (5, 1). Therefore, $P(6) = 5/36$. Six of the 36 possible outcomes will yield a double: (1, 1), (2, 2), (3, 3), (4, 4), (5, 5), and (6, 6). Therefore, $P(\text{Double}) = P(D) = 6/36$.

There are only 10 distinct possible outcomes, because the possible outcome (3, 3) is common to both series. It has been counted twice, once as a 6 and once as a double. So, to avoid double counting, we must subtract the $P(6 \text{ and } D)$.

$$P(6 \text{ and } D) = 1/36$$
$$P(6 \text{ or } D) = P(6) + P(D) - P(6 \text{ and } D)$$
$$= 5/36 + 6/36 - 1/36 = 10/36 = 5/18$$

The general addition rule is $P(A \text{ or } B) = P(A) + P(B) - P(A \text{ and } B)$. However, if A and B are mutually exclusive then $P(A \text{ and } B) = 0$, and we can use the addition rule for mutually exclusive events: $P(A \text{ or } B) = P(A) + P(B)$.

Note: If it is not known whether A and B are mutually exclusive, then the general rule should be used. It will take more time, but it will yield the right answer provided everything else is done correctly. However, if A and B are mutually exclusive, then the mutually exclusive rule can be used.

Problem 2: Using sample space for the sum of 2 dice, find the probability of a sum of 5 or a double.

Problem 3: Using sample space for the sum of 2 dice, find the probability of a sum of 12 or a double.

Complement Rule

As mentioned earlier, the **complement** is the set of all possible outcomes not contained in the event.

The probability of a sample space is equal to 1; the sample space is made up of the event and its complement, so $P(E) + P(\bar{E}) = 1$. If we define A as an event, then the complement rule is $P(A) = 1 - P(\bar{A})$ or $P(\bar{A}) = 1 - P(A)$.

Sometimes it is easier to find the probability of the complement than it is to find the probability of the event.

Example 12: Using the sample space for the sum of 2 dice, what is the probability that the sum is greater than 2?

$$P(\text{Sum} > 2) = P(3 \text{ or } 4 \text{ or } 5 \text{ or} \dots \text{or } 12)$$

Let's look at the complement: The complement of Sum > 2 would be Sum ≤ 2.

$$A = \text{Sum} > 2$$
$$\bar{A} = \text{Sum} \leq 2$$
$$P(\bar{A}) = P(\text{Sum} \leq 2) = P(2) = 1/36$$

Thus, the $P(\text{Sum} > 2) = 1 - P(\text{Sum} = 2) = 1 - 1/36 = 35/36$.

When it is easier to obtain the probability of the complementary event than the event itself, the complement rule should be used.

Problem 4: If you roll 2 dice, what is the probability of not rolling a double?

Joint Probability

Joint probability is the probability of two or more events occurring at the same time. A joint probability table is often used to determine the joint probability.

Example 13: We have classified 500 people by gender and marital status.

	Married B_1	Unmarried B_2	Total
Male A_1	100	50	150
Female A_2	200	150	350
Total	300	200	500

We can use the information in this table to obtain the joint and marginal probabilities. There are 500 possible outcomes, of which 100 have the attributes of A_1 and B_1, that is, male and married. If someone is drawn at random, then the probability of that person being both male and married is 0.2.

$$P(A_1 \text{ and } B_1) = 100/500 = 0.2 \qquad P(\text{Male and married}) = 0.2$$

Similarly

$$P(A_1 \text{ and } B_2) = 50/500 \qquad P(\text{Male and unmarried}) = 0.1$$
$$P(A_2 \text{ and } B_1) = 200/500 \qquad P(\text{Female and married}) = 0.4$$
$$P(A_2 \text{ and } B_2) = 150/500 \qquad P(\text{Female and unmarried}) = 0.3$$

The joint probability can be obtained from the preceding table by dividing each cell (number) by the sample size (in this case, 500).

	B_1	B_2	Total
A_1	100/500	50/500	150/500
A_2	200/500	150/500	350/500
Total	300/500	200/500	500/500

which gives you

Joint Probability Table

	B_1	B_2	Total
A_1	0.2	0.1	0.3
A_2	0.4	0.3	0.7
Total	0.6	0.4	1.0

In addition to the joint probabilities, the marginal probabilities can also be obtained from the joint probability table. **Marginal probabilities** are so named because they are in the margins of the table. They actually represent the probabilities of $A_1, A_2, B_1,$ and B_2—the probability of drawing a male (A_1), female (A_2), married (B_1), and unmarried (B_2). The marginal probabilities are:

$$P(A_1) = 0.3 \qquad P(A_2) = 0.7 \qquad P(B_1) = 0.6 \qquad P(B_2) = 0.4$$
$$P(\text{Male}) = 0.3 \quad P(\text{Female}) = 0.7 \quad P(\text{Married}) = 0.6 \quad P(\text{Unmarried}) = 0.4$$

The marginal probabilities can be obtained by using the Addition Rule. There are two ways that A_1

can occur—with B_1 or with B_2—so

$$P(A_1) = P(A_1 \text{ and } B_1) + P(A_1 \text{ and } B_2)$$
$$P(A_1) = 0.2 + 0.1$$
$$P(A_1) = 0.3$$

We obtain $P(A_1 \text{ and } B_1)$ and $P(A_1 \text{ and } B_2)$ from the joint probability table.

Problem 5: Given the following table of 500 students classified by gender and student status, find the joint and marginal probabilities.

	Graduate B_1	Undergraduate B_2	Total
Male A_1	100	200	300
Female A_2	50	150	200
Total	150	350	500

Conditional Probability

Conditional probability is the probability that an event occurs given that another event has already occurred. A conditional probability is a probability assigned after additional information has been obtained. The rules for conditional probability are

$$P(A \mid B) = \frac{P(A \text{ and } B)}{P(B)} \quad \text{or} \quad P(B \mid A) = \frac{P(A \text{ and } B)}{P(A)}$$
$$\text{(the probability of } A \text{ given } B) \qquad \text{(the probability of } B \text{ given } A)$$

Example 14: From the joint probability table in Example 13,

a. Find the probability of a male, given that the person is married.

b. Find the probability of married, given that the person is a male.

Joint Probability Table			
	Married B_1	Unmarried B_2	Total
Male A_1	0.2	0.1	0.3
Female A_2	0.4	0.3	0.7
Total	0.6	0.4	1.0

a. The rule for the probability of a male (A_1), given someone who is married (B_1), is

$$P(A_1 \mid B_1) = \frac{P(A_1 \text{ and } B_1)}{P(B_1)} = \frac{0.2}{0.6} = 0.33$$

b. The rule for the probability of married (B_1), given a male (A_1), is

$$P(B_1 \mid A_1) = \frac{P(A_1 \text{ and } B_1)}{P(A_1)} = \frac{0.2}{0.3} = 0.67$$

Note: Unlike the $P(A \text{ and } B)$ which equals $P(B \text{ and } A)$ and the $P(A \text{ or } B)$ which equals $P(B \text{ or } A)$, the $P(A \mid B)$ does not have to nor does it usually equal $P(B \mid A)$.

Example 15: From the results of Example 14,

$$P(A_1 \mid B_1) = 0.33 \qquad P(B_1 \mid A_1) = 0.67$$

So $P(A_1 \mid B_1)$ does not have to equal $P(B_1 \mid A_1)$.
The $P(A_1 \mid B_1)$ can equal $P(B_1 \mid A_1)$, but this does not usually occur.

Problem 6: Using the joint probability table in Problem 5, find the probability of

      a. a graduate student, given a male

      b. a male, given a graduate student

Complement of a Conditional Probability

Determining the complement of a conditional probability often causes problems for students. The complement of the $P(A_1 \mid B_1)$ is $P(A_2 \mid B_1)$. The rationale is that, given B_1 occurs, then either A_1 or A_2 occurs.

Example 16: The complement of the probability of a male given married $P(A_1 \mid B_1)$ is the probability of a female given married $P(A_2 \mid B_1)$.

$$P(A_1 \mid B_1) = \frac{P(A_1 \text{ and } B_1)}{P(B_1)} \qquad P(A_2 \mid B_1) = \frac{P(A_2 \text{ and } B_1)}{P(B_1)}$$

$$= \frac{0.2}{0.6} = 0.33 \qquad\qquad = \frac{0.4}{0.6} = 0.67$$

Problem 7: Using the joint probability table in Problem 5, find the complement of the probability of a graduate student, given a male.

Multiplication Rule

The **multiplication rule** enables us to find the probability that two or more events occur.

General rule:

$$P(A \text{ and } B) = P(A) \cdot P(B \mid A) \quad \text{or} \quad P(A \text{ and } B) = P(B) \cdot P(A \mid B)$$

Either rule can be used, depending on the information in the problem.

Example 17: The probability that a child chews gum is 0.5. The probability that a woman chews gum is 0.4. The probability that a child chews gum given his mother does is 0.8. Find the probability that the child and mother chew gum.

$$P(A) = P(\text{Child}) = 0.5$$
$$P(B) = P(\text{Mother}) = 0.4$$
$$P(A \mid B) = P(\text{Child} \mid \text{Mother}) = 0.8$$

so
$$P(A \text{ and } B) = P(B) \cdot P(A \mid B) = (0.4)(0.8) = 0.32$$

If A_1 and B_1 are independent events—the outcome of one does not influence the outcome of the other—then the multiplication rule can be expressed as

$$P(A_1 \text{ and } B_1) = P(A_1) \cdot P(B_1)$$

Example 18: If you toss a coin twice, what is the probability of two heads?

The outcome of the first toss does not influence the outcome of the second, so they are independent events.

$$P(A) = P(H_1) = 1/2 \qquad P(B) = P(H_2) = 1/2$$

and $P(B \mid A) = P(H_2 \mid H_1) = 1/2$ because the outcome of the first has no influence on the outcome of the second.

$$P(A \text{ and } B) = P(A) \cdot P(B)$$
$$P(H_1 \text{ and } H_2) = P(H_1) \cdot P(H_2) = 1/2 \cdot 1/2 = 1/4$$

Previously we examined the drawing of 2 cards from a 52-card deck. We discussed the meaning of statistical independence. We can now express it mathematically. Two events are statistically ·independent if

$$P(B_1 \mid A_1) = P(B_1) \quad \text{and} \quad P(A_1 \mid B_1) = P(A_1)$$

Going back to the drawing of 2 cards from a deck, we use the multiplication method to solve for each scenario.

Example 19: If you draw 2 cards from a deck, what is the probability that they are both red? Given that replacement occurs, we have independent events; so, the rule is

$$P(R_1 \text{ and } R_2) = P(R_1) \cdot P(R_2) = 1/2 \cdot 1/2 = 1/4$$

If we draw without replacement, then we have dependent events and the rule is

$$P(R_1 \text{ and } R_2) = P(R_1) \cdot P(R_2 \mid R_1)$$
$$= 1/2 \cdot 25/51 = 25/102$$

Note: If you are not sure whether A and B are statistically independent, use the general rule. If they are independent, then $P(A) = P(A \mid B)$ will give you the right answer (provided you do not make a mistake anywhere else). However, if you are certain that A and B are statistically independent, use the independent rule.

Problem 8: Penny buys 2 tickets to a drawing in which 200 tickets are sold. There are two prizes. What is the probability that Penny will win both prizes if the drawing is done with replacement?

Problem 9: Penny buys 2 tickets to a drawing in which 200 tickets are sold. There are two prizes. What is the probability that Penny will win both prizes if the drawing is done without replacement?

Relationship between Mutually Exclusive and Independent and Dependent Events

Students frequently have the misconception that *mutually exclusive* and *independent* are the same. This is not true. In Example 19, the drawing of 2 cards with replacement involves independent events, as does the tossing of 2 coins in Example 18. However, these are not mutually exclusive events, because $P(A \text{ and } B) \neq 0$. In both cases $P(A \text{ and } B) = 1/4$, so independent events do not have to be *and for the most part are not* mutually exclusive.

Dependent events can be mutually exclusive: $P(7 \text{ and } 11) = 0$ and the events $P(7 \mid 11) = 0$ and $P(11 \mid 7) = 0$ are dependent, whereas $P(7) = 6/36$ and $P(11) = 2/36$.

However, dependent events do not have to be mutually exclusive: In Example 19 (when the two cards are drawn without replacement), R_1 and R_2 are dependent, but $P(R_1 \text{ and } R_2) = 25/102$.

REVIEW OF RULES

Rules for 2 Events

General rule:
$$P(A \text{ or } B) = P(A) + P(B) - P(A \text{ and } B)$$

$$P(A \text{ or } B) = P(A) + P(B) \quad \text{(if } A \text{ and } B \text{ are mutually exclusive)}$$

General rule:
$$P(A \text{ and } B) = P(A) \cdot P(B \mid A) = P(B) \cdot P(A \mid B)$$

$$P(A \text{ and } B) = P(A) \cdot P(B) \quad \text{(if } A \text{ and } B \text{ are independent)}$$

$$P(A \mid B) = \frac{P(A \text{ and } B)}{P(B)}$$

$$P(B \mid A) = \frac{P(A \text{ and } B)}{P(A)}$$

$$P(A) = 1 - P(\bar{A})$$

Rules for n Events

$$P(A_1 \text{ or } A_2 \text{ or} \ldots \text{or } A_n) = P(A_1) + P(A_2) + \cdots + P(A_n) \quad \text{(if all the } A\text{'s are mutually exclusive)}$$

$$P(A_1 \text{ and } A_2 \text{ and} \ldots \text{and } A_n) = P(A_1) \cdot P(A_2) \cdots P(A_n) \quad \text{(if all the } A\text{'s are independent)}$$

BAYES' THEOREM

Bayes' Theorem is an expansion of the rule for conditional probability.

General rule:
$$P(A_1 \mid B) = \frac{P(A_1) \cdot P(B \mid A_1)}{\Sigma P(A_i) \cdot P(B \mid A_i)}$$

If $n = 3$ then

$$P(A_1 \mid B) = \frac{P(A_1) \cdot P(B \mid A_1)}{P(A_1) \cdot P(B \mid A_1) + P(A_2) \cdot P(B \mid A_2) + P(A_3) \cdot P(B \mid A_3)}$$

Example 20: There are three identical cylinders: The first cylinder contains 2 red balls and 1 white ball, the second contains 3 red balls, and the third contains 3 white balls. One cylinder is chosen at random, and a ball is taken from it. The ball is white. What is the probability that the ball came from the first cylinder?

Let C_1 = cylinder 1, C_2 = cylinder 2, and C_3 = cylinder 3; let R = red and W = white. Then:

$$P(C_1) = P(C_2) = P(C_3) = 1/3$$
$$P(W \mid C_1) = 1/3$$
$$P(W \mid C_2) = 0$$
$$P(W \mid C_3) = 1$$

$$P(C_1 \mid W) = \frac{P(C_1) \cdot P(W \mid C_1)}{P(C_1) \cdot P(W \mid C_1) + P(C_2) \cdot P(W \mid C_2) + P(C_3) \cdot P(W \mid C_3)}$$

$$= \frac{(1/3) \cdot (1/3)}{(1/3) \cdot (1/3) + (1/3) \cdot 0 + (1/3) \cdot (1)} = \frac{1/9}{4/9} = 1/4$$

If there are only 2 possible outcomes A_1 and A_2, then we can use the following rule for Bayes.

$$P(A_1 \mid B) = \frac{P(A_1) \cdot P(B \mid A_1)}{P(A_1) \cdot P(B \mid A_1) + P(A_2) \cdot P(B \mid A_2)}$$

Example 21: There are 2 decks of cards. Deck 1 contains all kings, deck 2 is a regular deck. A deck is drawn at random and a card is drawn. It is a king. What is the probability that it came from deck 1?

$$P(\text{Deck 1}) = P(D_1) = 1/2$$
$$P(\text{Deck 2}) = P(D_2) = 1/2$$
$$P(\text{King} \mid \text{Deck 1}) = P(K \mid D_1) = 52/52 = 1$$
$$P(\text{King} \mid \text{Deck 2}) = P(K \mid D_2) = 4/52 = 1/13$$

$$P(D_1 \mid K) = \frac{P(D_1) \cdot P(K \mid D_1)}{P(D_1) \cdot P(K \mid D_1) + P(D_2) \cdot P(K \mid D_2)}$$

$$= \frac{(1/2) \cdot (1)}{(1/2) \cdot (1) + (1/2) \cdot (1/13)} = \frac{1/2}{1/2 + 1/26} = 13/14$$

Problem 10: A quality control inspector examines microchips produced by different machines. Machine 1 produces 40% of the microchips, machine 2 and machine 3 each produce 30%. One percent of machine 1's output is defective, 2% of machine 2's output is defective, and 4% of machine 3's output is defective. The inspector picks a microchip and finds it to be defective. What is the probability that it came from machine 2?

COUNTING PRINCIPLES AND TECHNIQUES

Counting principles and techniques are useful in determining the sample space or the number of possible outcomes for multistage trials.

Multiplication Principle

Distinct possible outcomes over a number of trials means that the multiplication principle can be used to find the number of possible outcomes.

Example 22: Roll one die twice.

First Roll   2nd Roll
$$6 \quad \times \quad 6 \quad = 36 \text{ possible outcomes}$$

Example 23: Toss a coin and roll a die.

Toss   Roll
$$2 \quad \times \quad 6 \quad = 12 \text{ possible outcomes}$$

Example 24: Toss a coin, roll a die, and draw a card from a deck.

Toss   Roll   Draw
$$2 \quad \times \quad 6 \quad \times \quad 52 \quad = 624 \text{ possible outcomes}$$

Problem 11: A company wants to start an identification code system for its clients. If it uses a letter in the first slot and a number in the next two slots, how many possible identification codes are available?

Permutations and Combinations

Two other techniques that can be used to find the number of possible outcomes are permutations and combinations. In **permutations**, the rank or order of the elements is important. In **combinations**, order is not important, only the composition matters.

Example 25: Permutations and combination for a group of 3: (A, B, C).

Permutations			Combination
A, B, C	B, A, C	C, A, B	A, B, C
A, C, B	B, C, A	C, B, A	

There are 6 different ways to arrange the letters A, B, and C. When order is important, there are 6 permutations. However, the 3 letters comprise only one combination because the order in which the letters occur does not matter—only the end result of having the letters A, B, and C is important.

Permutations for Entire Group   Suppose we have a group of n different objects. In how many ways can these n objects be arranged in order?

Example 26: There are 5 horses in a race. You want to pick the order in which they will finish. How many possible outcomes are there?

$$\underset{\substack{\text{first} \\ \text{place}}}{5} \times \underset{\substack{\text{2nd} \\ \text{place}}}{4} \times \underset{\substack{\text{3rd} \\ \text{place}}}{3} \times \underset{\substack{\text{4th} \\ \text{place}}}{2} \times \underset{\substack{\text{5th} \\ \text{place}}}{1} = 120$$

There are 5 possible outcomes for 1st place. However, once the first horse finishes there are only 4 horses left in the race for 2nd place.

General Rule: $\qquad\qquad\qquad n(n - 1)(n - 2)\ldots(2)(1) = n!$

From Example 26, $n = 5$, so $n! = 5!$

$$\begin{aligned} \text{Factorials} \quad &0! = 1 \text{ by definition} \\ &1! = 1 \text{ by definition} \\ &2! = 2 \times 1 = 2 \\ &3! = 3 \times 2 \times 1 = 6 \end{aligned}$$

Problem 12: Joe the delivery man has 6 stops on his route. He wants to take a different route each day. How many possible routes can he schedule (order is important)?

Permutations for Subgroups Sometimes we are interested in arranging in order a subgroup x of n different objects.

Rule: $\qquad {}_nP_x = \dfrac{n!}{(n - x)!}$ where n = total number of objects

$\qquad\qquad\qquad\qquad\qquad\qquad\quad x$ = number of objects in the subgroup

Example 27: From a group of 8 job applicants 3 are to be hired: each will be assigned to a different division. How many possible outcomes are there? Note that each person chosen will go to a different division. Rank or order is important. So we are dealing with permutations.

$${}_nP_x = \frac{n!}{(n - x)!} \qquad n = 8 \quad \text{and} \qquad x = 3$$

$${}_8P_3 = \frac{8!}{(8 - 3)!} = \frac{8!}{5!} = \frac{8 \times 7 \times 6 \times 5!}{5!} = 336 \text{ possible outcomes}$$

Combinations Combinations differ from permutations; in combinations, order is not important.

Rule: $\qquad {}_nC_x = \dbinom{n}{x} = \dfrac{n!}{(n - x)!x!}$ where n = total number of objects

$\qquad\qquad\qquad\qquad\qquad\qquad\qquad\qquad\quad x$ = number of objects in the subgroup

Example 28: From Example 27, suppose you want to choose a subcommittee of 3 where order is not important. How many possible outcomes are there?

$$n = 8 \quad \text{and} \quad x = 3$$

$$_8C_3 = \binom{8}{3} = \frac{8!}{(8-3)!3!} = \frac{8 \times 7 \times 6 \times 5!}{5!3!} = 56 \text{ possible outcomes}$$

One can see from Examples 27 and 28 that there are 336 permutations and 56 combinations. The difference in the rule for permutations and combinations is the added $x!$ in the denominator of the combination rule. In this case, it is 3! or a factor of 6. So, in this case, for every 6 permutations there is one combination.

Problem 13: The Pennsylvania Lotto consists of 30 balls numbered 1 to 30 in a container. Five numbers are chosen without replacement.

   a. How many possible outcomes are there, if order is not important?

   b. How many possible outcomes are there, if order is important?

We can use combinations to determine probability.

$$P(A) = \frac{\text{Number of possible successes}}{\text{Total number of possible outcomes}}$$

Example 29: Suppose we draw 2 cards from a deck without replacement. What is the probability of obtaining 2 hearts?

$$P(2 \text{ hearts}) = \frac{\text{Number of ways of obtaining 2 hearts}}{\text{Total number of possible outcomes}}$$

There are $n = 52$ cards in the deck and we are drawing $x = 2$ cards from the deck. So, the total number of possible outcomes are $_nC_x = {}_{52}C_2$.

$$_nC_x = \binom{n}{x} = \frac{n!}{(n-x)!x!}$$

$$_{52}C_2 = \binom{52}{2} = \frac{52!}{(52-2)2!} = \frac{52 \times 51 \times 50!}{50!2!}$$

$$= 1{,}326 \text{ possible outcomes}$$

There are $n = 13$ hearts in the deck, and we are drawing $x = 2$ hearts. So, that the total number of ways of obtaining 2 hearts are:

$$_nC_x = \binom{n}{x} = \frac{n!}{(n-x)!x!}$$

$$_{13}C_2 = \binom{13}{2} = \frac{13!}{(13-2)!2!} = \frac{13 \times 12 \times 11!}{11!2!}$$

$$= 78 \text{ possible ways of obtaining 2 hearts}$$

$$P(2 \text{ hearts}) = \frac{78}{1{,}326} = 0.059$$

Problem 14: Three cards are drawn from a regular deck. What is the probability that they are all aces?

CHAPTER 2 REVIEW PROBLEMS

1. Find the probability for the following events:

   a. Draw a card from a regular deck and get a two.

   b. Roll a die and get an even number.

   c. Given that a person was born in June, what is the probability that person was born on the 21st?

2. Use the following data to answer parts (a) through (f).

	Unemployed ($\bar{E}$)	Employed (E)
Skilled (S)	25	280
Unskilled ($\bar{S}$)	175	20

   a. Find the joint probability table.

   b. Find the probability of skilled and employed.

   c. Find the probability of skilled.

   d. Find the probability of employed, given they are skilled.

   e. Are skilled and employed independent events?

   f. Are skilled and employed mutually exclusive events?

3. The probability that Kathy will become a doctor is 0.5. The probability that Joan will become a doctor is 0.6. (Assume independent events.) What is the probability of the following outcomes?

   a. They both become doctors.

   b. Neither becomes a doctor.

   c. Joan becomes a doctor, given Kathy becomes a doctor.

   d. At least one becomes a doctor.

4. Given A and B are mutually exclusive events, with $P(A) = 0.3$ and $P(B) = 0.6$, find

   a. $P(A \mid B)$ b. $P(B \mid A)$ c. $P(A \text{ and } B)$ d. $P(A \text{ or } B)$

5. The probability that a married man drinks tea is 0.5. The probability that a married woman drinks tea is 0.7. If a woman drinks tea, the probability that her husband does is 0.6. Find the probability of the following events.

   a. They both drink tea.

   b. The women drinks tea, given her husband does.

   c. That at least one drinks tea.

   d. That neither drinks tea.

6. An urn contains 6 blue balls, 3 red balls, and 1 white ball.

   a. If a ball is drawn at random, what is the probability that it is red?

   b. If two balls are drawn at random with replacement, what is the probability that they both are red?

   c. If two balls are drawn at random without replacement, what is the probability that they both are red?

7. If 90% of people like pizza, 60% of people like hotdogs, and 55% like pizza and hotdogs, what percentage of people like at least one of these foods?

8. An accounting firm has personal and business accounts. Thirty percent of the accounts are business. Given it is a business account, the probability of an error is 0.02; Given it is a personal account, the probability of an error is 0.03. Given a mistake is found, what is the probability that it is in a business account?

9. A state's license plate must have 6 characters. How many possible different licenses can be issued if the following limits exist?

   a. Numbers must be in the first 3 slots, and letters must be in the last 3 slots.

   b. You can have numbers or letters in all of the slots.

10. A head table at a banquet has 12 seats. In how many ways can the 12 guests at the head table be seated?

11. From a group of 12 students, 4 are chosen for a committee. How many different committees are possible?

3

DISCRETE RANDOM VARIABLES AND PROBABILITY DISTRIBUTIONS

INTRODUCTION TO PROBABILITY DISTRIBUTIONS

An assignment of probabilities to each of the basic outcomes in a sample space is called the **probability distribution** of that sample space. A probability distribution is a combination of frequency distributions (discussed in Chapter 1) and probability (discussed in Chapter 2).

A **random variable** is a variable whose value depends on chance. There are two types of random variables—discrete and continuous. A **discrete random variable** is usually a count (like the rolling of a die). The sample space is 1, 2, 3, 4, 5, 6. The fact that there are no possible outcomes between 2 and 3 is what makes it discrete. A **continuous random variable** is one that takes on any value in a continuum (like the weight of people). Between the weights of 180 and 181 there is an infinite number of weights (180.1, 180.11, etc.). In this chapter, we discuss discrete probability distributions.

Example 1: Calculate the probability distribution of the tossing of a fair coin twice.

Elements of Sample Space	Number of Heads	Probability
T_1, T_2	0	1/4
H_1, T_2	1	1/4
T_1, H_2	1	1/4
H_1, H_2	2	1/4

Converting this to a probability distribution, x = the number of heads and $f(x)$ = probability.

Probability Distribution	
Number of Heads x	Probability $f(x)$
0	1/4
1	1/2
2	1/4

Characteristics of a Probability Distribution

1. The term $f(x)$ represents probability. The same rules apply for $f(x)$ as for the $P(E)$ in Chapter 2—that is, the probability cannot be negative and cannot be greater than 1. So each individual probability must be between

$$0 \leq f(x) \leq 1$$

2. The term $\Sigma f(x)$ is the sum of the individual probabilities and represents the sample space. As in Chapter 2 the $P(S) = 1$, one is also the sum of the individual probabilities

$$\Sigma f(x) = 1$$

Reviewing Example 1, we see that the criteria for a probability distribution are met, each individual $f(x)$ is between 0 and 1 $(1/4, 1/2, 1/2)$ and the $\Sigma f(x) = 1$ $(1/4 + 1/2 + 1/4)$.

Example 2: What is the probability distribution of the rolling of a die?

$$f(x) = 1/6 \quad x = 1, 2, 3, 4, 5, 6$$

x	$f(x)$
1	1/6
2	1/6
3	1/6
4	1/6
5	1/6
6	1/6
	$6/6 = 1 = \Sigma f(x)$

This is a probability distribution because the individual probabilities are betweeen zero and one and the sum of the individual probabilities is equal to 1 $(\Sigma f(x) = 1)$.

In a probability distribution, it is understood that x's are defined for certain values and for all other values of x, $f(x) = 0$.

In Example 2, it should be stated that:

$$f(x) = 1/6 \quad x = 1, 2, 3, 4, 5, 6$$

$$f(x) = 0 \quad x = \text{any other value}$$

However, not all functions are probability distributions.

Example 3: Now let's look at a function that is not a probability distribution.

$$f(x) = \frac{x + 2}{14} \quad x = 1, 2, 3$$

x	$f(x)$
1	3/14
2	4/14
3	5/14
	$12/14 \neq 1$

This is not a probability distribution.

Each individual probability is between zero and one, so the first criterion is met. However, the $\Sigma f(x) \neq 1$, and the second criterion is not met. Therefore, the function in Example 3 is not a probability distribution. When a function is not a probability distribution, $f(x)$ does not represent probability.

Cumulative Distribution Function

A cumulative distribution function is used to determine the probability that the random variable X is less than or equal to x.

Example 4: From the frequency distribution in Example 2, find the probability of rolling a number less than or equal to a 4.

$$P(X \leq x) = P(x \leq 4)$$
$$P(x \leq 4) = f(1) + f(2) + f(3) + f(4)$$
$$= 1/6 + 1/6 + 1/6 + 1/6$$
$$= 4/6 = 2/3$$

Problem 1: Determine whether the following are probability distributions.

    a. $f(x) = \dfrac{x}{10}$ $x = 1, 2, 3, 4$

    b. $f(x) = \dfrac{x-1}{2}$ $x = 0, 1, 2, 3$

    c. $f(x) = \dfrac{x^2 + 1}{35}$ $x = 1, 2, 3, 4$

Problem 2: **a.** Show that the following is a probability distribution.

$$f(x) = \frac{x+1}{20} \qquad x = 1, 2, 3, 4, 5$$

    b. Then find the probability that $x \leq 3$.

THE UNIFORM DISTRIBUTION

Characteristic

Equal probabilities are assigned to all of the possible outcomes.

Rule: $\qquad\qquad f(x) = \dfrac{1}{s}$ $s =$ number of possible outcomes

Example 5: The production of a bricklayer is uniformly distributed between 200 and 300 bricks an hour. Find the probability that the number of bricks laid next hour will be

a. exactly 225 bricks.

b. between 200 and 250 bricks (inclusive).

Rule: $f(x) = 1/s$ s = number of possible outcomes

In this case, $s = 101$, with $x = 200, 201, \ldots, 300$

$$f(x) = 1/101$$

a. $f(225) = 1/101$

b. $f(200 \leq x \leq 250) = 51/101$

Problem 3: An envelope stuffer's productivity is uniformly distributed between 300 and 325 an hour. What is the probability that he stuffs

    a. exactly 300 envelopes?

    b. between 310 and 320 envelopes (inclusive)?

    c. less than 315 envelopes?

    d. exactly 295 envelopes?

THE BINOMIAL DISTRIBUTION

Characteristics

1. There are two mutually exclusive possible outcomes to each trial.

2. The outcome of one trial does not affect the outcome of any other trial (independent trials).

3. The probability of success stays constant over all trials.

If these three conditions hold, then we can define one of the two mutually exclusive possible outcomes as a **success** and the other as a **failure**. Also, given that each trial is independent, then the probability of a success $[P(S)]$ can be defined as p, $P(S) = p$, and the probability of a failure $[P(F)]$ which is the complement of a success can be defined as $(1 - p)$; $P(F) = (1 - p)$ for each trial.

Rule: $f(x) = \binom{n}{x} p^x (1 - p)^{n-x}$

where n = number of trials

       x = number of successes wanted

       $p = P(S)$ = probability of a success on any given trial

   $1 - p = P(F)$ = probability of a failure

   $\binom{n}{x}$ represents the combination symbol

Example 6: A fair coin is tossed 4 times. What is the probability of obtaining exactly 2 heads?

The first step is to determine if the criteria for a binomial are met. There are two mutually exclusive possible outcomes (Head, Tail) to each trial, so criterion one is met. Also, the outcome of any one trial (toss) has no effect on the outcome of any other trial (toss). The trials are independent and criterion two is met. Also, the $P(H)$ does not change from one trial to another.

Since we have a binomial distribution, we can use the binomial rule to determine the probability.

$$n = \text{number of trials (tosses)} = 4$$
$$x = \text{number of successes (heads) wanted} = 2$$
$$p = P(S) = P(\text{Head}) = 1/2$$
$$1 - p = P(F) = P(\text{Tail}) = 1/2$$

Substituting this information into the binomial rule, we obtain

$$f(x) = \binom{n}{x} p^x (1-p)^{n-x} \qquad f(2) = \binom{4}{2}\left(\frac{1}{2}\right)^2\left(\frac{1}{2}\right)^2$$

Computation of

$$\binom{4}{2} = \frac{4!}{(4-2)!2!} = \frac{4 \cdot 3 \cdot 2!}{2 \cdot 2!} = \frac{12}{2} = 6$$

$$f(2) = \binom{4}{2}\left(\frac{1}{2}\right)^2\left(\frac{1}{2}\right)^2 = (6)(1/4)(1/4) = \frac{6}{16} = \frac{3}{8} = 0.375$$

So, the probability of obtaining exactly 2 heads is 3/8.

Problem 4: A phone survey is taken. The probability that the person answering the phone will provide information is 0.3. Ten calls are completed. What is the probability that exactly four people will provide information? (Assume independent trials.)

In the Appendix at the back of the book, there are binomial probability tables that make it easier to compute probabilities of binomial distributions. Table A-1 gives selected values of a cumulative binomial distribution, whereas Table A-2 gives selected values of the binomial distribution.

We first look at Table A-2, which allows us to compute the probability for any exact value: for example, $f(x = 5)$.

Example 7: From Example 6, we have $n = 4$, $x = 2$, $p = 0.5$. With this information, we can read directly from Table A-2 the probability of exactly 2 heads.

The first column gives us the number of trials n (in this case, $n = 4$), the second column gives us the number of successes x (in this case, $x = 2$). The p value is obtained by going across the top (in this case, $p = 0.50$). By looking at the value that corresponds to $n = 4$, $x = 2$, and $p = 0.50$, we obtain $f(x = 2) = 0.3750$.

This is the same result as in Example 7.

Problem 5: Using Table A-2, find the answer for Problem 4.

Table A-1 allows us to compute the probability for a cumulative binomial distribution function: $f(x \leq 5)$.

Example 8: From Example 6, what is the probability of obtaining less than or equal to 2 heads—$f(x \leq 2)$?

In this case, $n = 4$, $x \leq 2$, and $p = 0.5$. With this information, we can read directly from Table A-1 the probability of less than or equal to 2 heads.

As in Example 7, the first column gives us the number of trials (in this case, $n = 4$), the second column gives the cumulative number of successes wanted x (in this case, $x \leq 2$). The p value is found by going across the top (in this case, $p = 0.50$). By looking at the value that corresponds to $n = 4$, $x \leq 2$, and $p = 0.50$, we obtain $f(x \leq 2) = 0.6875$.

Table A-1 can also be used to find the probability that x is greater than some value.

Example 9: From Example 6, find the probability of at least two heads: $P(x \geq 2)$. This can be found by using the complement rule.

$$P(A) = 1 - P(\bar{A})$$
$$P(x \geq 2) = 1 - P(x < 2)$$

which, given a discrete probability distribution, can be expressed as

$$P(x \geq 2) = 1 - P(x \leq 1)$$

Using Table A-1, the $P(x \leq 1) = 0.3125$.

$$P(x \geq 2) = 1 - 0.3125$$
$$= 0.6875$$

Table A-1 can also be used to find the probability of obtaining between a and b successes: thus, $P(a \leq x \leq b)$.

Example 10: From Example 6, find the probability of obtaining between 1 and 3 successes, inclusive: $P(1 \leq x \leq 3)$.

This can be obtained by subtracting $x \leq 0$ from $x \leq 3$.

$$(x \leq 3) = 0, 1, 2, 3$$
$$\underline{-(x \leq 0) = 0}$$
$$(1 \leq x \leq 3) = 1, 2, 3$$

We subtract $f(x \leq 0)$ from $f(x \leq 3)$ because $f(x \leq 3) = f(0) + f(1) + f(2) + f(3)$ and $f(x \leq 0) = f(0)$. This would leave $f(1 \leq x \leq 3)$. If $f(x \leq 1)$ was subtracted from $f(x \leq 3)$, then only $f(1)$ and $f(2)$ would remain and we would have $P(1 \leq x \leq 2)$.

From Table A-1

$$f(x \leq 3) = \quad 0.9375$$
$$\underline{-f(x \leq 0) = -0.0625}$$
$$f(1 \leq x \leq 3) = \quad 0.8750$$

Problem 6: A student takes a test with 10 multiple choice questions. Each question has four possible answers but only one correct answer. The student guesses all the answers. Find the probability that he gets

    a. exactly 3 right.

    b. at least 7 right.

    c. at most 5 right.

    d. less than 6 right.

    e. between 2 and 4 right (inclusive).

    f. more than 6 right.

MULTINOMIAL DISTRIBUTION

The multinomial distribution is a generalization of the binomial. Unlike the binomial distribution, which is limited to only two mutually exclusive outcomes on each trial, the multinomial distribution allows more than two mutually exclusive possible outcome to each trial.

Characteristics

1. There are k mutually exclusive possible outcome to each trial where $k \geq 2$.

2. The outcome of one trial does not affect the outcome of any other trial (independent trials).

3. The probability of each outcome stays constant over all trials.

If these three conditions hold, then we can define the k mutually exclusive outcomes as $x_1, x_2, \ldots, x_k$. Also, given each trial is independent, then the probability of each individual x occurring is the same for each trial. Thus, the probability of x_1 $[p(x_1)]$ is equal to p_1 for each trial.

Rule:
$$f(x_1, x_2, \ldots, x_k) = \frac{n!}{x_1! x_2! \cdots x_k!} p_1^{x_1} p_2^{x_2} \cdots p_k^{x_k}$$

where n = number of trials

    x_1 = number of x_1 wanted

    $\vdots$

    x_k = the number of x_k wanted

    p_1 = probability of x_1 on each trial

    $\vdots$

    p_k = probability of x_k on each trial

Example 11: Five dice are tossed. What is the probability of obtaining two 5's and three 6's?

There are six mutually exclusive outcomes $(1, 2, 3, 4, 5, 6)$ to each trial, so $k = 6$. Because the trials are independent, the multinomial distribution should be used.

$$f(x_1, x_2, x_3, x_4, x_5, x_6) = \frac{n!}{x_1! x_2! x_3! x_4! x_5! x_6!} p_1^{x_1} p_2^{x_2} p_3^{x_3} p_4^{x_4} p_5^{x_5} p_6^{x_6}$$

where n = number of dice tossed = 5

    x_1 = number of 1's wanted = 0

    x_2 = number of 2's wanted = 0

$$x_3 = \text{number of 3's wanted} = 0$$
$$x_4 = \text{number of 4's wanted} = 0$$
$$x_5 = \text{number of 5's wanted} = 2$$
$$x_6 = \text{number of 6's wanted} = 3$$
$$p_1 = \text{probability of rolling a 1 on each trial} = 1/6$$
$$p_2 = \text{probability of rolling a 2 on each trial} = 1/6$$
$$p_3 = \text{probability of rolling a 3 on each trial} = 1/6$$
$$p_4 = \text{probability of rolling a 4 on each trial} = 1/6$$
$$p_5 = \text{probability of rolling a 5 on each trial} = 1/6$$
$$p_6 = \text{probability of rolling a 6 on each trial} = 1/6$$

Substituting these values into the rule, we obtain

$$f(0,0,0,0,2,3) = \frac{5!}{0!0!0!0!2!3!}(1/6)^0(1/6)^0(1/6)^0(1/6)^0(1/6)^2(1/6)^3$$

$$= \frac{5!}{(1)(1)(1)(1)(2!)(3!)}(1)(1)(1)(1)(1/36)(1/216) = 0.0013$$

Problems 7: A company manufactures transistors of which 92% are good, 5% are defective (but can be fixed), and 3% are defective. If 6 transistors are chosen at random, what is the probability that

    a. 4 are good, 1 is defective (but can be fixed), and 1 is defective.

    b. 5 are good and 1 is defective?

HYPERGEOMETRIC DISTRIBUTION

Unlike the binomial and multinomial distributions, which have independent trials, the hypergeometric distribution deals with dependent trials. If you think of the binomial distribution as appropriate for sampling with replacement, then the **hypergeometric distribution** is appropriate for sampling without replacement.

Characteristics

1. There are k mutually exclusive possible outcomes to each trial where $k \geq 2$.

2. The outcome of one trial is affected by the outcome of the other trials (dependent trials).

General rule:

$$f(x_1, x_2, \ldots, x_k) = \frac{\binom{X_1}{x_1}\binom{X_2}{x_2}\cdots\binom{X_k}{x_k}}{\binom{N}{n}}$$

where $X_1 = \text{total number of } X_1$

$$\vdots$$

$$X_k = \text{total number of } X_k$$

x_1 = number of x_1 wanted

⋮

x_k = number of x_k wanted

N = total number of items

n = number of items chosen.

Example 12: A group of 10 doctors consists of 5 general practitioners, 3 pediatricians, and 2 surgeons. If a committee of three is chosen at random what is the probability of obtaining exactly one of each?

There are three mutually exclusive possible outcomes (general practitioner, pediatrician, and surgeon) to each trial, so $k = 3$ since we are sampling without replacement, the hypergeometric is used.

$$f(x_1, x_2, x_3) = \frac{\binom{X_1}{x_1}\binom{X_2}{x_2}\binom{X_3}{x_3}}{\binom{N}{n}}$$

where X_1 = total number of general practitioners = 5

X_2 = total number of pediatricians = 3

X_3 = total number of surgeons = 2

x_1 = total number of general practitioners wanted = 1

x_2 = total number of pediatricians wanted = 1

x_3 = total number of surgeons wanted = 1

N = total number of doctors = 10

n = total number of doctors chosen = 3

$$f(1, 1, 1) = \frac{\binom{5}{1}\binom{3}{1}\binom{2}{1}}{\binom{10}{3}} = \frac{5 \times 3 \times 2}{120} = 0.25$$

Problem 8: The student government association consists of 15 students—of which 4 are seniors, 5 are juniors, 3 are sophomores, and 3 are freshmen. The president of the SGA wants to pick 4 students at random. What is the probability that each class will be represented?

A variant of the hypergeometric rule can be used when there are only two possible outcomes to each trial ($k = 2$). In this case, one of the possible outcomes can be labeled a success and the other outcome can be labeled a failure.

Rule: $$f(x) = \frac{\binom{N-X}{n-x}\binom{X}{x}}{\binom{N}{n}}$$

where N = total number of items

n = number of items chosen

X = total number of successes

$N - X$ = total number of failures

x = number of successes wanted

$n - x$ = number of failures wanted

Example 13: A television repairman has 6 transistors, 4 of which are good. If 3 transistors are picked at random what is the probability of obtaining exactly 2 good transistors?

There are 2 mutually exclusive possible outcomes to each trial, so $k = 2$. Because we are sampling without replacement, the special rule for the hypergeometric distribution can be used.

$$f(x) = \frac{\binom{N-X}{n-x}\binom{X}{x}}{\binom{N}{n}}$$

where N = total number of transistors = 6

n = number of transistors chosen = 3

X = total number of good transistors = 4

$N - X$ = total number of bad transistors = 2

x = number of good transistors wanted = 2

$n - x$ = number of bad transistors wanted = 1

$$f(2) = \binom{4}{2}\binom{2}{1} \bigg/ \binom{6}{3} = \frac{(6)(2)}{20} = \frac{12}{20} = 0.6$$

Problem 9: A subcommittee of 4 is chosen from a group of 10—6 of which are management and the rest are union members. What is the probability that there are exactly two from management?

POISSON DISTRIBUTION

The Poisson distribution can be used to describe the probability function of product demand or demand for services in a given time period—for example, the number of people coming into a hospital emergency room or the number of customers coming into a bank. It can be used in terms of space instead of time—for example, the number of mistakes on a typed page.

Characteristics

1. The probability of any event is independent of what happened in previous time (space) periods.
2. The probability of an event occurring is the same throughout each interval of the time period—that is, the probability of someone arriving in the first minute is the same as in the second minute and as in the third minute, and this is true to the nth minute.

Rule: $f(x) = \dfrac{\mu^x e^{-\mu}}{x!}$ where x = the number of successes

μ = the mean of the distribution

e = natural log = 2.71828...

Example 14: If a superior secretary makes an average of 0.5 mistakes per typed page, what is the probability that she makes exactly one mistake on a page?

Rule: $\qquad f(x) = \dfrac{\mu^x e^{-\mu}}{x!}$ $\qquad\qquad\qquad\qquad$ where $\quad \mu = 0.5$ per page

$\qquad\qquad\qquad\qquad\qquad\qquad\qquad\qquad\qquad\qquad\qquad\qquad x = 1$ mistake

$$f(1) = \frac{0.5^1 e^{-0.5}}{1!} = 0.5e^{-0.5} = 0.303$$

Instead of computing the results, we can use Table A-3 (which is a cumulative Poisson distribution table) to find the probability. Using Table A-3, we can find $P(x \le c)$, where $c \ge 0$, directly from the table: $\mu = 3$, $P(x \le 2) = 0.423$.

This is similar to the binomial table (Table A-1), which is also a cumulative table. To find the probability $x = 2$, when $\mu = 3$

$$P(x \le 2) = 0.423$$
$$\underline{P(x \le 1) = 0.199}$$
$$P(x = 2) = 0.224$$

From Example 14, the probability that $x = 1$, $\mu = 0.5$ is

$$P(x \le 1) = 0.910$$
$$\underline{P(x \le 0) = 0.607}$$
$$P(x = 1) = 0.303$$

Problem 10: An average of 5 customers arrive every hour at Tony's barber shop. What is the probability that

    a. fewer than or exactly 5 customers arrive in an hour?

    b. exactly 5 arrive in an hour?

    c. between 4 and 6 arrive in an hour (inclusive)?

    d. more than 3 arrive in an hour?

EXPECTED VALUE (MEAN) AND VARIANCE OF A RANDOM VARIABLE

Just as with a frequency distribution, one can find the mean (expected value) and variance of a probability distribution. The rule for the mean μ is also referred to as the expected value.

Rule for the mean: $\qquad\qquad\qquad \mu = E(X) = \Sigma x f(x)$

Rule for the variance σ^2:

$$\sigma^2 = E(X^2) - [E(X)]^2 \quad \text{or} \quad \sigma^2 = E(X^2) - \mu^2$$

Rule for the standard deviation:

$$\sigma = \sqrt{\sigma^2} \quad \text{(the positive square root of the variance)}$$

Example 15: If a fair coin is tossed twice, what is the expected value and variance? From Example 1, we obtain the frequency distribution.

x	$f(x)$	$xf(x)$	$x^2f(x)$
0	1/4	0	0
1	1/2	1/2	1/2
2	1/4	1/2	1
	4/4 = 1	1	1.5

$$E(X) = \mu = \Sigma xf(x) = 1$$
$$E(X^2) = \Sigma x^2 f(x) = 1.5$$
$$\sigma^2 = E(X^2) - [E(X)]^2 = 1.5 - 1 = 0.5$$
$$\sigma = \sqrt{\sigma^2} = \sqrt{0.5} = 0.7$$

Example 16: Frank is given the following option: (1) if he draws an ace, he is given $25. (2) If he draws a face card, he is given $15. (3) If he draws anything else he receives nothing. He must pay $10 to draw a card. What is the expected value of this game of chance?

If Frank draws an ace, his net winnings are $15 ($25 − $10). The probability of drawing an ace is 4/52. If he draws a face card, his net winnings are $5 ($15 − $10). The probability of drawing a face card is 12/52. If he draws anything else, his net winnings are $ − 10 ($0 − $10). The probability of drawing anything else is 36/52.

This gives the following probability distribution:

x	$f(x)$	$xf(x)$
15	4/52	60/52
5	12/52	60/52
−10	36/52	−360/52

$$E(x) = \mu = \Sigma xf(x) = -240/52 = \$-4.62$$

Problem 11: A roulette wheel has 2 green, 18 red, and 18 black numbers. You receive $10 if you pick the right color and nothing if you pick the wrong color. You must pay $5 to play. What is the expected value of this game?

Problem 12: Given

$$f(x) = \frac{x}{10} \qquad x = 1, 2, 3, 4$$

Find the mean (expected value) and variance.

EXPECTED VALUE AND VARIANCE OF SUMS OF RANDOM VARIABLES

The expected value of a sum of random variables is equal to the sum of their expected values.

$$E(X_1 + X_2 + \cdots + X_n) = E(X_1) + E(X_2) + \cdots + E(X_n)$$

The same is true for the variance of a sum of independent random variables.

$$\sigma^2(X_1 + X_2 + \cdots + X_n) = \sigma^2(X_1) + \sigma^2(X_2) + \cdots + \sigma^2(X_n)$$

Example 17: Myron owns 3 bakeries. The expected value and variance of birthday cakes sold per week at each store are listed below. Find the expected value and variance for the three bakeries combined.

Store	Expected Value	Variance
1	1,500	2,000
2	400	500
3	200	300

$$E(X_1 + X_2 + X_3) = E(X_1) + E(X_2) + E(X_3)$$
$$= 1,500 + 400 + 200$$
$$= 2,100$$

$$\sigma^2(X_1 + X_2 + X_3) = \sigma^2(X_1) + \sigma^2(X_2) + \sigma^2(X_3)$$
$$= 2,000 + 500 + 300$$
$$= 2,800$$

Problem 13: From Problem 11, what is the expected value if you played the roulette game 5 times?

CHAPTER 3 REVIEW PROBLEMS

1. Find the mean and variance of the following function:
$$f(x) = (x + 1)/20 \quad (x = 1, 2, 3, 4, 5)$$

2. Find the mean and variance of the following function:
$$f(x) = x/9 \quad (x = 1, 2, 3, 4)$$

3. Two dice are rolled. If the sum is 2 or 12 you win $100. If the sum is anything else you receive nothing. It cost $10 to roll. What is the expected value of this game?

4. Using the information in Review Problem 3, if you played this game 10 times, how much on average would you expect to win or lose?

5. A resort restaurant has a record of customer payment of 5% by traveler's check, 20% by cash, and 75% by credit card. Determine the probability that the next 6 customers will pay as follows:

   a. one by traveler's check, 2 by cash, and 3 by credit card
   b. all by credit card

6. Historically, 10% of the oranges in a shipment are bad. From a lot of 50 oranges, a sample of 4 is taken. Find the probability that

   a. all four are bad

   b. exactly three are bad

7. Suppose that on average there are 5 accidents a day on the Sure Kill Expressway. What is the probability that on any given day there are

   a. exactly 5 accidents

   b. fewer than 3 accidents

   c. between 2 and 6 accidents, inclusive

   d. more than 10 accidents

8. The probability that an item is returned to a department store is 5%. If 10 items are sold what is the probability that at most 2 will be returned. (Assume independence.)

9. A secretary's typing is uniformly distributed between 50 and 65 words per minute (wpm). Find the probability that she will type

   a. exactly 55 wpm

   b. less than 60 wpm

   c. between 50 and 55 wpm, inclusive

10. The success rate for drilling for oil is 10%. If 10 wells are drilled (assume independence), what is the probability that

    a. exactly 3 wells will contain oil

    b. all the wells will contain oil

    c. none of the wells will contain oil

    d. at least 6 will contain oil

11. In poker, if a person is dealt 5 cards from a regular deck of 52 cards, what is the probability that

    a. all of the cards are black

    b. he gets 3 aces and 2 kings

    c. exactly 3 are hearts

    d. all are spades

12. The cure rate for a certain drug is 20%. If 5 people who take this drug are chosen at random, what is the probability that

    a. all are cured

    b. none are cured

    c. exactly 3 are cured

    d. at least 3 are cured

    e. between 2 and 4 are cured, inclusive

13. A bank has an average of 20 customers per hour. What is the probability that

    a. exactly 20 customers will arrive in the next hour

    b. more than 20 customers will arrive in the next hour

    c. between 15 and 25, inclusive, will arrive in the next hour

4

STATISTICAL INVESTIGATIONS AND SAMPLING

A **population** is the entire set of elements of interest for a given problem. A **finite population** is one in which you can count the number of elements in the population. An **infinite population** is one in which you cannot count the number of elements in the population.

A **census** looks at the entire population. A **sample** is a portion (subset) of the population that is selected and examined so that inferences can be made about the population. Because a sample gives only a partial picture of the population, there is always some error involved in using a sample to infer something about the entire population. **Sampling error** is the difference between the results obtained from a sample and the results that would be obtained if a census were taken.

Why Sampling?

1. It is costly in both time and money to take a census of a large population.
2. It is impossible to take a census of an infinite population.
3. It is impractical to take a census of a product that is damaged or destroyed during the testing of the product: in testing how long light bulbs last, the light bulbs that are tested are rendered useless. Thus, if one took a census there would be nothing to sell after the test was completed.

   There are many different kinds of samples, but we'll concentrate on the simple random sample.

Finite Population of N Elements

A random sample of n elements is drawn from the population N in such a way that every combination of n elements (sample) has an equal chance of being the sample selected. (Most sampling is done without replacement.)

Rule: $\binom{N}{n}$ (number of possible samples)

The probability of any particular sample being chosen is $1 \left/ \binom{N}{n} \right.$.

Example 1: Suppose we take a sample of 3, from a population of size 5 with elements 3, 6, 9, 12, 15. How many different samples can we obtain?

Using the rule

$$\binom{N}{n} = \binom{5}{3} = \frac{5!}{(5-3)!3!} = 10$$

Here is a list of the 10 different samples that can be obtained in Example 1.

3, 6, 9	3, 9, 12	6, 9, 12	9, 12, 15
3, 6, 12	3, 9, 15	6, 9, 15	
3, 6, 15	3, 12, 15	6, 12, 15	

Each one of these 10 samples has a 1/10 probability of being the one chosen. After this brief introduction to sampling, let's examine sampling distributions (Chapter 5).

Problem 1: Given the following population (2, 4, 6, 8), find the number of samples of size 2 that can be taken and list them.

CHAPTER 4 REVIEW PROBLEMS

1. From a population of 15, a sample of 5 is taken. How many possible samples can be obtained?

2. From a population of 5 (A, B, C, D, E), a sample of 3 is taken. What is the probability that the sample BCD is the one chosen?

3. From a population of 6 (1, 3, 5, 7, 9, 11), a sample of 3 is chosen. Find the number of possible samples and list them.

5

SAMPLING DISTRIBUTIONS

SAMPLING DISTRIBUTION OF A NUMBER OF OCCURRENCES

We can best illustrate the meaning and the properties of a sampling distribution of a number of occurrences by using an example: Assume that a manufacturing process produces articles, of which 5% are defective. A random sample drawn from this population would be done without replacement. However, if we have an infinite population, we cannot use the hypergeometric rule because N is infinity. Given the large size of the population, the probability of drawing a defective article will change very little (negligible, for all practical purposes) with the outcome of the first draw. Thus, we can assume that the trials are independent and use the binomial distribution.

Example 1: A manufacturing process produces articles, 5% of which are defective. A sample of 4 is drawn. Find the sampling distribution of a number of occurrences (defectives).

$$n = 4; \quad P(\text{Defective}) = P(\text{Success}) = p = 0.05$$

Using Table A-2, we can find the binomial distribution for $n = 4$ and $p = 0.05$.

x	$f(x)$
0	0.8145
1	0.1715
2	0.0135
3	0.0005
4	0.0000^+

The probability of getting no defectives $f(0)$ is 0.8145. The probability of getting 3 defectives $f(3)$ is 0.0005.

Problem 1: A company knows that 30% of the population uses its product. If a sample of 5 people is taken, find the sampling distribution of the number of occurrences.

SAMPLING DISTRIBUTION OF A PROPORTION

The sampling distribution of the number of occurrences can easily be converted into a sampling distribution of a proportion by converting occurrences into proportions.

Rule: $\bar{p} = \dfrac{x}{n}$

$\bar{p} =$ sample proportion

$x =$ number of occurrences

$n =$ sample size

From Example 1

$$x = 0 \Rightarrow \bar{p} = 0/4 = 0.00$$
$$x = 1 \Rightarrow \bar{p} = 1/4 = 0.25$$
$$x = 2 \Rightarrow \bar{p} = 2/4 = 0.50$$
$$x = 3 \Rightarrow \bar{p} = 3/4 = 0.75$$
$$x = 4 \Rightarrow \bar{p} = 4/4 = 1.00$$

Example 2: From the data in Example 1, we can obtain the sampling distribution of a proportion.

$\bar{p}$	$f(\bar{p})$
0.00	0.8145
0.25	0.1715
0.50	0.0135
0.25	0.0005
1.00	0.0000$^+$

Problem 2: Convert the sampling distribution of a number of occurrences in Problem 1 to a sampling distribution of proportions.

Mean and Variance of the Sampling Distribution of Occurrences and Proportions (Assuming a Binomial Distribution)

	Number of Occurrences	Proportions
Mean	$\mu_{n\bar{p}} = np$	$\mu_{\bar{p}} = p$
Variance	$\sigma^2_{n\bar{p}} = np(1 - p)$	$\sigma^2_{\bar{p}} = \dfrac{p(1 - p)}{n}$
Standard deviation	$\sigma_{n\bar{p}} = \sqrt{np(1 - p)}$	$\sigma_{\bar{p}} = \sqrt{\dfrac{p(1 - p)}{n}}$

Example 3: From data in Example 1

$$\mu_{n\bar{p}} = np = 4 \cdot 0.05 = 0.20$$
$$\sigma^2_{n\bar{p}} = np(1 - p) = 4(0.05)(0.95) = 0.19$$
$$\sigma_{n\bar{p}} = \sqrt{np(1 - p)} = \sqrt{0.19} = 0.436$$

Example 4: From data in Example 2

$$\mu_{\bar{p}} = p = 0.05$$
$$\sigma^2_{\bar{p}} = \frac{p(1 - p)}{n} = \frac{(0.05)(0.95)}{4} = 0.012$$
$$\sigma_{\bar{p}} = \sqrt{0.012} = 0.11$$

Problem 3: Using data in Problems 1 and 2, find the mean and standard deviation for the number of occurrences and proportions.

CONTINUOUS DISTRIBUTIONS

So far, we have examined only discrete probability distributions. In this section, we look at continuous probability distributions. Unlike a *discrete distribution* where we could find the probability at a point or an exact value of the random variable (for example, rolling a 6 on a die), in a *continuous probability distribution* the probability of the exact value of the random variable is zero. Therefore, we have to find the probability over an interval. For example, find the probability that someone weighs between 180 and 200 pounds. Unlike the discrete case, there are people who weigh between 181 and 182. Also, the probability that someone weighs *exactly* 180 pounds is zero. So, in terms of continuous probability distribution, we must find the area under a curve. Calculus is generally used to find the area under a curve; however, there are various tables in the Appendix that allow us to find the area without the use of calculus.

Rule: The area under the curve of a continuous distribution represents the probability of the sample space; thus, the area under the curve of a continuous distribution is 1.

Rule: The probability that x equals any particular value is zero: $P(x = 180) = 0$ because no one weighs exactly 180 pounds.

The rule for area is *length* multiplied by *width*. A point has a width of zero. Thus $A = l \times w = 1 \times 0 = 0$ for any point.

Normal Distribution

The most commonly used continuous distribution is the normal distribution. One important feature of the normal distribution is that all we need is the mean μ and standard deviation σ of the distribution to compute any probabilities concerning the distribution.

Characteristics of a Normal Distribution

1. The area under the curve is equal to 1.
2. It is a symmetric distribution with the center at μ. Half the distribution (0.5000) is to the left of the center, and half the distribution is to the right of the center, as shown in Figure 5.1.

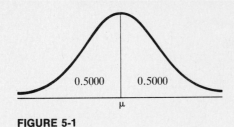

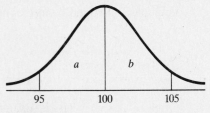

FIGURE 5-1

FIGURE 5-2

3. Given the symmetry of a normal curve, an equal distance to the left and to the right of the mean will have the same area. As shown in Figure 5-2, area a (between 95 and 100) and area b (between 100 and 105) are the same.

In order to calculate probabilities, it is necessary to transform a normally distributed variable into a form so that a single table can be used. This transformation is known as the standardized normal.

Rule:
$$z = \frac{X - \mu}{\sigma}$$

where X = value of observation

μ = mean of distribution

σ = standard deviation of distribution

z = number of standard deviations away from the mean that X is

The standardized normal distribution has a mean of zero ($\mu = 0$) and a standard deviation of 1 ($\sigma = 1$).

Figure 5-3 shows the graph of a normal distribution using both the z and x scale with $\mu = 50$ and $\sigma = 5$ while Figure 5-4 shows the graph of a normal distribution using the number of standard deviations as the scale.

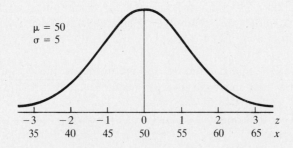

FIGURE 5-3

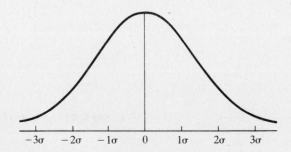

FIGURE 5-4

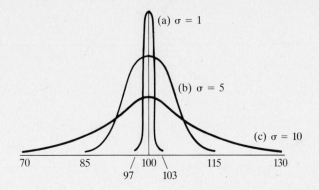

FIGURE 5-5

For all normal curves, approximately

- 68% of the area is within one standard deviation of the mean
- 95.5% of the area is within 2 standard deviations of the mean
- 99.7% of the area is within 3 standard deviations of the mean

The shape of the normal distribution depends on the standard deviation of the distribution. The greater the value of the standard deviation, the greater is the dispersion of the normal distribution.

Example 5: Normal distribution with mean $\mu = 100$. As Figure 5-5 demonstrates, the greater the standard deviation, the greater the spread of the distribution.

a. When $\sigma = 1$, approximately 99.7% of the observations are between 97 and 103.

b. When $\sigma = 5$, approximately 99.7% of the observations are between 85 and 115.

c. When $\sigma = 10$, approximately 99.7% of the observations are between 70 and 130.

Reading the Standardized Normal Distribution z. (See Table A-5.)

1. Remember that $P(X = \text{any particular value}) = 0$.
2. There is an equal probability that z is greater than or less than zero (μ), as shown in Figure 5-6.
3. The table is set up so that areas between zero and some positive value k ($z = k$) can be read directly: $P(0 \leq z \leq k)$.

Example 6: Figure 5-7 shows graphically $P(0 < z < 1) = 0.3413$.

Example 7: Figure 5-8 demonstrates that, given symmetry

$$P(-1 < z < 0) = P(0 < z \leq 1) = 0.3413$$

Example 8: Figure 5-9 shows graphically how to find the $P(z > 0.99)$. First separate the probabilities into 3 areas: A, B, and C.

$$A = P(z > 0) = 0.5000$$
$$B = P(0 < z < 0.99) = 0.3389$$

This can be read directly from Table A-5.

$$C = P(z > 0.99)$$

$$C = A - B$$
$$P(z > 0.99) = 0.5000 - P(0 < z < 0.99)$$
$$P(z > 0.99) = 0.5000 - 0.3389$$
$$P(z > 0.99) = 0.1611$$

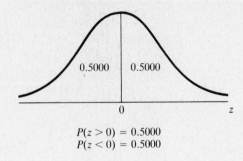

$$P(z > 0) = 0.5000$$
$$P(z < 0) = 0.5000$$

FIGURE 5-6

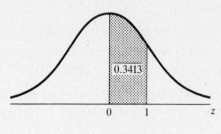

$$P(0 < z < 1) = 0.3413$$

FIGURE 5-7

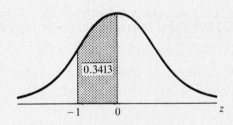

$$P(-1 < z < 0) = 0.3413$$

FIGURE 5-8

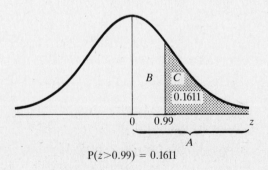

$$P(z > 0.99) = 0.1611$$

FIGURE 5-9

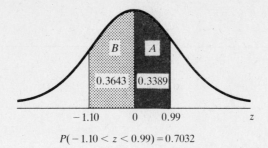

$$P(-1.10 < z < 0.99) = 0.7032$$

FIGURE 5-10

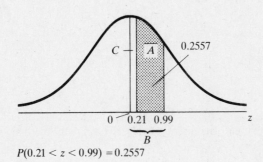

$$P(0.21 < z < 0.99) = 0.2557$$

FIGURE 5-11

Example 9: Figure 5-10 shows graphically how to find the $P(-1.10 < z < 0.99)$. First, separate the probabilities into 2 areas, A and B.

$$A = P(0 < z < 0.99) = 0.3389$$

this can be read directly from the Table A-5.

Because of symmetry $\quad B = P(-1.10 < z < 0) = P(0 < z < 1.10) = 0.3643$

So

$$P(-1.10 < z < 0.99) = P(-1.10 < z < 0) + P(0 < z < 0.99)$$
$$= 0.3643 + 0.3389$$
$$= 0.7032$$

Example 10: Figure 5-11 shows graphically how to find the $P(0.21 < z < 0.99)$. First, separate the probabilities into 3 areas: A, B, and C.

$$A = P(0.21 < z < 0.99)$$
$$B = P(0 < z < 0.99) = 0.3389 \quad \text{(read directly from the table)}$$
$$C = P(0 < z < 0.21) = 0.0832 \quad \text{(read directly from the table)}$$

$$A = B - C$$
$$P(0.21 < z < 0.99) = P(0 < z < 0.99) - P(0 < z < 0.21)$$
$$= 0.3389 - 0.0832$$
$$= 0.2557$$

Problem 4: Using Table A-5, find

    a. $P(z > 2)$

    b. $P(0 \leq z \leq 3)$

    c. $P(0 < z < 3)$

    d. $P(-2 < z < 2)$

    e. $P(-1.86 < z < 1.86)$

    f. $P(z < -0.75)$

    g. $P(z < 3)$

    h. $P(-2 \leq z < -1)$

    i. $P(-1.8 \leq z \leq 2.31)$

    j. $P(1.26 \leq z \leq 1.89)$

    k. $P(z > -2.11)$

Now that we know how to read the normal table, the next step is to show how to apply this to a normal distribution problem.

    Example 11: Suppose we have a normal distribution with mean 50 and standard deviation 8: If we pick one item at random, what is the probability

a. $(X > 50)$

b. $(54 < X < 58)$

c. $(30 < X < 58)$

a. Figure 5-12 shows graphically the $P(X > 50)$. The rule for the standardized normal is

$$z = \frac{X - \mu}{\sigma}$$

$$= \frac{50 - 50}{8}$$

$$= 0$$

$$P(X > 50) = P(z > 0) = 0.5000$$

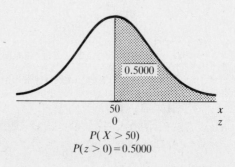

$$P(X > 50)$$
$$P(z > 0) = 0.5000$$

FIGURE 5-12

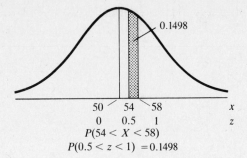

$P(54 < X < 58)$
$P(0.5 < z < 1) = 0.1498$

FIGURE 5-13

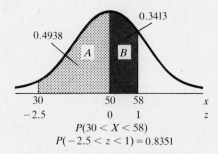

$P(30 < X < 58)$
$P(-2.5 < z < 1) = 0.8351$

FIGURE 5-14

b. Figure 5-13 shows graphically the $P(54 < X < 58)$. Converting to z

$$z = \frac{X - \mu}{\sigma} = \frac{54 - 50}{8} = 0.5$$

$$z = \frac{X - \mu}{\sigma} = \frac{58 - 50}{8} = 1$$

Thus

$$P(54 < X < 58) = P(0.5 < z < 1) = P(0 < z < 1) - P(0 < z < 0.5)$$
$$= 0.3413 - 0.1915$$
$$P(0.5 < z < 1) = 0.1498$$

c. Figure 5-14 shows graphically the $P(30 < X < 58)$. Converting to z

$$z = \frac{X - \mu}{\sigma} = \frac{30 - 50}{8} = -2.5$$

$$z = \frac{X - \mu}{\sigma} = \frac{58 - 50}{8} = 1$$

Thus

$$\qquad\qquad\qquad\qquad\qquad\qquad A + B$$
$$P(30 < X < 58) = P(-2.5 < z < 1) = P(-2.5 < z < 0) + P(0 < z < 1)$$
$$= 0.4938 + 0.3413$$
$$= 0.8351$$

Problem 5: The contents of canned sodas are normally distributed with a mean of 12 ounces and a standard deviation of 0.2 ounces. Find

    a. $P(X \geq 11.8)$

    b. $P(11.6 \leq X \leq 11.8)$

    c. $P(X > 12.1)$

SAMPLING DISTRIBUTION OF THE MEAN

Characteristics

1. The mean of sampling distributions of the mean $\mu_{\bar{x}}$ is equal to the mean of the population:
$\mu_{\bar{x}} = \mu$

2. The standard deviation of the sampling distribution of the mean $\sigma_{\bar{x}}$ is equal to

$$\sigma_{\bar{x}} = \sqrt{\frac{N - n}{N - 1}} \cdot \frac{\sigma}{\sqrt{n}} \quad \text{(for a finite population)}$$

$$\sigma_{\bar{x}} = \frac{\sigma}{\sqrt{n}} \quad \text{(for an infinite population)}$$

If X is a normally distributed random variable with mean μ and standard deviation σ, the sampling distribution of the mean will be normal with mean $\mu_{\bar{x}}$ and standard deviation $\sigma_{\bar{x}}$.

Central Limit Theorem:

If the population is not normal, the sampling distribution of the mean approaches normally as n increases.

It should be noted that as the n sample size increases, the standard error $\sigma_{\bar{x}}$ decreases. Thus, as the sample size increases, the dispersion of the sampling distribution of means decreases.

    Example 12: Suppose an infinite population is normally distributed with $\mu = 100$ and standard deviation of 10. Find the standard error when

a. $n = 25$

b. $n = 100$

a. $\sigma_{\bar{x}} = \dfrac{\sigma}{\sqrt{n}} = \dfrac{10}{\sqrt{25}} = 2$

b. $\sigma_{\bar{x}} = \dfrac{\sigma}{\sqrt{n}} = \dfrac{10}{\sqrt{100}} = 1$

Figure 5-15 shows the difference in the distributions graphically. To determine the probability related to $\bar{X}$, the rule for the standardized normal is

Rule: $\qquad z = \dfrac{\bar{X} - \mu}{\sigma_{\bar{x}}} \qquad$ where $\quad \bar{X}$ = sample mean

μ = mean of the population

$\sigma_{\bar{x}}$ = standard error

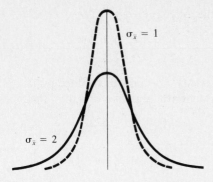

FIGURE 5-15

Example 13: Using the data in Example 12 and a sample size of 25, find the probability that $(100 \leq \bar{X} \leq 101)$.

Rule:
$$z = \frac{\bar{X} - \mu}{\sigma_{\bar{x}}}$$

$$P(100 \leq \bar{X} \leq 101) = P(0 \leq z \leq 0.5) = 0.1915 \quad \text{(Using Table A-5)}$$

$$\bar{X} = 101$$

$$\mu = 100$$

$$\sigma_{\bar{x}} = \frac{\sigma}{\sqrt{n}} = \frac{10}{\sqrt{25}} = 2$$

$$z = \frac{\bar{X} - \mu}{\sigma_{\bar{x}}} = \frac{101 - 100}{2} = 0.5$$

Problem 6: Using the data in Example 13 and a sample size of 400, find the probability that $(100 \leq \bar{X} \leq 101)$.

CHAPTER 5 REVIEW PROBLEMS

1. In a large state, 40% of the people think that the governor is doing a good job. If a sample of 5 is taken, find the sampling distribution of the number of occurrences. (Assume independence.)

2. Using the data in Review Problem 1, find the sampling distribution of a proportion.

3. Using the data in Review Problem 1, find the mean and standard deviation of the sampling distribution of the number of occurrences.

4. Using the data in Review Problem 2, find the mean and standard deviation of the sampling distribution of a proportion.

5. Student grades are normally distributed with a mean of 70 and a standard deviation of 5.

   a. If one student is chosen at random, what is the probability that the student's grade is greater than 72?

   b. If a sample of 25 is taken, what is the probability that the average is greater than 72?

6. Find the probability for the following:

   a. $z \leq 0$ c. $z \geq 1$ e. $-1 \leq z \leq 2$

   b. $z < 0$ d. $-1.23 \leq z \leq 1.23$ f. $-3 \leq z \leq -1$

7. If a sample of 16 is taken from a normally distributed population of 400 women with a mean height of 66 inches and a standard deviation of 4, find the probability that

   a. $\bar{X} \geq 66$ b. $\bar{X} \leq 68$ c. $65 \leq \bar{X} \leq 67$

8. A sample of 49 is taken from a normally distributed infinite population with a mean of 100 and a standard deviation of 7. Find the probability that

   a. $\bar{X} \geq 98$ c. $\bar{X} > 102$

   b. $99 \leq \bar{X} \leq 101$ d. $98 \leq \bar{X} \leq 99$

9. Using the data in Review Problem 8, find the probabilities if the sample size is 196.

10. Bags of potatoes are normally distributed with a mean of 50 and a standard deviation of 1. If we draw one bag at random, what is the probability that

    a. $X > 52$ c. $48 \leq X \leq 53$ e. $49.5 \leq X \leq 49.8$

    b. $50 \leq X \leq 54$ d. $X > 49$ f. $48 \leq X \leq 50$

11. A machine produces parts that are normally distributed with a mean of 12 inches and a standard deviation of 0.1 inch. If one item is drawn at random, find the probability that

    a. $X > 12.11$ c. $12.1 \leq X \leq 12.2$

    b. $X < 11.87$ d. $12.15 < X < 12.25$

12. Given a normally distributed population with a mean of 50 and a standard deviation of 5. Find the probability that the sample mean is greater than 51 if the sample size is

    a. 16   b. 25   c. 64

6
ESTIMATION

We have assumed that the mean and the standard deviation of the population are known, but this is not always true. If we do not know the population parameters, we can estimate them by using information obtained from a sample.

There are two different types of estimates of population parameters: point and interval. A **point estimate** is a single number that is used to estimate the unknown population parameter. An **interval estimate** is a statement of two values between which it is estimated that the population parameter may lie.

CONFIDENCE INTERVALS

A confidence interval is found by building an interval around the point estimate; it is called a **confidence interval** because it gives the degree of confidence. For example, a 95% confidence interval means that if we take 100 samples of the same size and construct 100 confidence intervals, 95 of the confidence intervals will contain the population mean. The procedure is set up so that 95% of the time, we are right. However, once a specific confidence interval is found, it either contains or does not contain the mean of the population. Remember, probability applies only before an event occurs.

Confidence Interval for One Mean Large Sample (σ Known)

Note: A sample is large if it is greater than or equal to 30.

Rule: $$\bar{X} \pm z\sigma_{\bar{x}}$$

where $\bar{X}$ = sample mean

z = normal distribution

$1 - \alpha$ = level of confidence

α = level of significance

$\sigma_{\bar{x}} = \sigma/\sqrt{n}$ = standard error

σ = standard deviation of population

n = sample size

Finding the value for z in a confidence interval

$$1 - \alpha = \text{level of confidence}$$
$$\alpha = \text{level of significance}$$

Example 1: For a 95% confidence interval, $1 - \alpha = 0.95$, $\alpha = 0.05$, and $\alpha/2 = 0.025$. Given a normal distribution, we want to build a 95% confidence interval around $\bar{X}$ and have 5% outside— half (0.025) on each tail.

In Chapter 5, we had a value for z and wanted to determine the probability. In this case, we want to determine the value for z given a probability value. So, $P(0 \leq z \leq z_0) = 0.4750$.

Looking inside the normal table (Table A-5), we find 0.4750 to equal 1.96, so for a 95% confidence interval $z = 1.96$.

Example 2: For a 90% confidence interval where $1 - \alpha = 0.90$, $\alpha = 0.10$, and $\alpha/2 = 0.05$, $P(0 < z < z_0) = 0.4500$. Looking up 0.4500 inside the z table, we see that 0.4495, $z_0 = 1.64$ and for 0.4505, $z_0 = 1.65$. We then interpolate 0.4500, for $z_0 = 1.645$, so for a 90% confidence interval $z_0 = 1.65$.

Problem 1: Find the z value that corresponds to

    a. 98% confidence interval

    b. 99% confidence interval

Example 3: A random sample of 100 students is taken to estimate the average SAT scores of the students in the school. A mean of 1,000 is found for the sample. It is known that the standard deviation of all students is 100. Find the 95% confidence interval for the mean SAT score.

95% confidence interval for μ

$$n = 100 \quad \bar{X} = 1,000 \quad \sigma = 100 \quad 1 - \alpha = 0.95 \quad \alpha = 0.05 \quad \alpha/2 = 0.025 \quad z = 1.96$$
$$\sigma_{\bar{x}} = \sigma/\sqrt{n} = 100/\sqrt{100} = 10$$

$$\bar{X} \pm z\sigma_{\bar{x}} = 1,000 \pm 1.96(10) = 1,000 \pm 19.6 \quad \text{or} \quad (980.4 \text{ to } 1,019.6)$$

Interpretation and Use of the Confidence Interval

The confidence interval is often misinterpreted. So let's first explain what it isn't and then explain what it is.

1. From Example 3: The 95% confidence interval does not mean that 95% of all observations are between 980.4 and 1,019.6. This can be shown from the normal distribution of a population. If $\sigma = 100$, then 95.5% of the area is within 2 standard deviations of the mean. The 95% range would be 400; so if μ was actually equal to 1,000, then approximately 95% of the observations would be between 800 and 1,200, if the population was normally distributed.

2. From Example 3: The 95% confidence interval does not mean that there is a 95% probability that the mean is between 980.4 and 1,019.6. Once the sample is chosen and the confidence interval is built, probability no longer applies.

A 95% confidence interval actually means that 95% of the confidence intervals would include the mean of the population.

Confidence Interval for a Mean in a Large Sample (σ Unknown)

If we do not know μ, then we usually don't know σ. If σ is unknown, we can use s as a point estimator of σ and $s_{\bar{x}}$ as a point estimator of $\sigma_{\bar{x}}$.

Rule:
$$s_{\bar{x}} = \frac{s}{\sqrt{n}} \quad \text{(for an infinite population)}$$

$$s_{\bar{x}} = \sqrt{\frac{N-n}{N-1}} \cdot \frac{s}{\sqrt{n}} \quad \text{(for a finite population)}$$

Rule: The rule for the confidence interval for a mean in a large sample (σ unknown) is

$$\bar{X} \pm z s_{\bar{x}}$$

Example 4: A sample of 64 bags of flour is taken to estimate the average weight of all the bags. The sample results are a mean of 49 and a standard deviation of 4.

a. Find the 95% confidence interval for μ.

b. Find the 99% confidence interval for μ.

a. 95% confidence interval for μ:

$n = 64 \quad \bar{X} = 49 \quad s = 4 \quad 1 - \alpha = 0.95 \quad \alpha = 0.05 \quad \alpha/2 = 0.025 \quad z = 1.96$

$s_{\bar{x}} = s/\sqrt{n} = 4/\sqrt{64} = 0.5$

$$\bar{X} \pm z s_{\bar{x}} = 49 \pm 1.96(0.5) = 49 \pm 0.98 \quad \text{or} \quad (48.02 \text{ to } 49.98)$$

b. 99% confidence interval for μ:

$1 - \alpha = 0.99 \quad \alpha = 0.01 \quad \alpha/2 = 0.005 \quad z = 2.58$

$$\bar{X} \pm z s_{\bar{x}} = 49 \pm 2.58(0.5) = 49 \pm 1.29 \quad \text{or} \quad (47.71 \text{ to } 50.29)$$

Problem 2: A sample of 400 students is taken to estimate the average amount of hours all students study per week. A mean of 20 hours and a standard deviation of 10 was found. Find the 95% confidence interval for the mean of all students.

Confidence Interval for a Proportion (Large Samples)

Rule: $\bar{p} \pm z s_{\bar{p}}$ $\bar{p} = x/n$

$$s_{\bar{p}} = \sqrt{\bar{p}(1 - \bar{p})/n}$$

Example 5: A survey is taken to determine how well-liked a soap product is. A sample of 100 is taken and 60 people like the product. Find the 95% confidence interval for the proportion of people who like the product.

95% confidence interval for $\bar{p}$:

$n = 100 \quad x = 60 \quad \bar{p} = x/n = 60/100 = 0.60 \quad \alpha = 0.05 \quad \alpha/2 = 0.025 \quad z = 1.96$

$s_{\bar{p}} = \sqrt{\bar{p}(1 - \bar{p})/n} = \sqrt{(0.6)(0.4)/100} = 0.049$

$$\bar{p} \pm zs_{\bar{p}} = 0.6 \pm 1.96(0.049) = 0.6 \pm 0.096 \quad \text{or} \quad (0.504 \text{ to } 0.696)$$

Problem 3: A sample of 200 televisions is taken and 5% are found to be defective. Find the 98% confidence interval for the proportion of defective televisions.

Confidence Interval for the Difference between Two Means (Large Samples)

Rule:
$$(\bar{X}_1 - \bar{X}_2) \pm zs_{\bar{x}_1 - \bar{x}_2} \qquad s_{\bar{x}_1 - \bar{x}_2} = \sqrt{\frac{s_1^2}{n_1} + \frac{s_2^2}{n_2}}$$

where $\quad \bar{X}_1 = $ mean of sample 1

$\bar{X}_2 = $ mean of sample 2

$s_1^2 = $ variance of sample 1

$s_2^2 = $ variance of sample 2

$n_1 = $ size of sample 1

$n_2 = $ size of sample 2

Example 6: A sample of 50 women yields an average height of 65 inches and a standard deviation of 4. A sample of 50 men yields a mean of 70 inches and a standard deviation of 5. Find the 90% confidence interval for the differences in the two population means.

90% confidence interval for $(\mu_1 - \mu_2)$:

$n_1 = 50 \quad \bar{X}_1 = 65 \quad s_1 = 4 \quad n_2 = 50 \quad \bar{X}_2 = 70 \quad s_2 = 5 \quad \alpha = 0.10 \quad \alpha/2 = 0.05 \quad z = 1.65$

$s_{\bar{x}_1 - \bar{x}_2} = \sqrt{s_1^2/n_1 + s_2^2/n_2} = \sqrt{16/50 + 25/50} = .91$

$$(\bar{X}_1 - \bar{X}_2) \pm zs_{\bar{x}_1 - \bar{x}_2} = (65 - 70) \pm 1.65(.91) = (-5) \pm 1.50 \quad \text{or} \quad (-6.5 \text{ to } -3.5)$$

Problem 4: A simple random sample of 64 female smokers finds that they smoke on average 14 cigarettes a day, with a standard deviation of 4, whereas a sample of 100 male smokers finds a mean of 20 and a standard deviation of 5. Find the 90% confidence interval for the difference in the two population means.

Confidence Interval for the Difference between Two Proportions (Large Samples)

Rule:
$$\bar{p}_1 - \bar{p}_2 \pm zs_{\bar{p}_1 - \bar{p}_2}$$

$$s_{\bar{p}_1 - \bar{p}_2} = \sqrt{\frac{(\bar{p}_1)(1 - \bar{p}_1)}{n_1} + \frac{(\bar{p}_2)(1 - \bar{p}_2)}{n_2}}$$

where $\bar{p}_1$ = sample proportion of sample 1

$\bar{p}_2$ = sample proportion of sample 2

n_1 = size of sample 1

n_2 = size of sample 2

Example 7: In city A, a random sample of 400 is taken and 250 people prefer Bernie Beer. In city B, a random sample of 200 is taken and 100 people prefer Bernie Beer. Find the 99% confidence interval for the differences in the population proportions.

99% confidence interval for $(p_1 - p_2)$

$n_1 = 400 \quad x_1 = 250 \quad \bar{p}_1 = 250/400 = 0.625 \quad n_2 = 200 \quad x_2 = 100 \quad \bar{p}_2 = 100/200 = 0.50$

$\alpha = 0.01 \quad \alpha/2 = 0.005 \quad z = 2.58$

$$s_{\bar{p}_1 - \bar{p}_2} = \sqrt{\frac{\bar{p}_1(1 - \bar{p}_1)}{n_1} + \frac{\bar{p}_2(1 - \bar{p}_2)}{n_2}} = \sqrt{\frac{(0.625)(0.375)}{400} + \frac{(0.5)(0.5)}{200}} = 0.043.$$

$$\bar{p}_1 - \bar{p}_2 \pm z s_{\bar{p}_1 - \bar{p}_2} = (0.625 - 0.5) \pm 2.58(0.043) = 0.125 \pm 2.58(0.043)$$
$$= 0.125 \pm 0.111 \quad \text{or} \quad (0.014 \text{ to } 0.236)$$

Problem 5: In a sample of 100 parts taken from factory A, 6% are found to be defective. In a sample of 64 parts from factory B, 4% are found to be defective. Find the 95% confidence interval for the differences in the population proportions.

THE STUDENT'S t DISTRIBUTION

We have stated that if the sample is sufficiently large $(n \geq 30)$, we can use the normal distribution. However, in certain cases, it is not feasible to take a sample of at least 30. (This may be true when the cost of sampling is high.) In cases where the sample is less than 30 and we are looking for the confidence interval for the mean, we can use the t distribution.

Characteristics of the t distribution as shown in Figure 6-1.

1. continuous

2. symmetric

3. centered with $\mu = 0$

4. The smaller the sample size the greater the dispersion (variance).

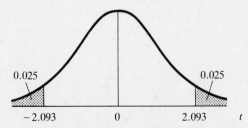

FIGURE 6-1

Graph of t distribution for 19 degrees of freedom and $\alpha = 0.05$

We use the t table (Table A-6), with degrees of freedom $= n - 1$. Also, Table A-6 gives the area in both tails, so for a 95% confidence interval, $1 - \alpha = 0.95$ and $\alpha = 0.05$ (area in both tails).

Example 8: Find the t value for $n = 15$, $\alpha = 0.05$.

$$t = 2.145$$

Example 9: Find the t value for $n = 20$, $\alpha = 0.01$

$$t = 2.861$$

Problem 6: Find the t value for $n = 18$, $\alpha = 0.02$.

Problem 7: Find the t value for $n = 23$, $\alpha = 0.10$.

Confidence Interval for a Mean (Small Sample), σ Unknown

Rule: $$\bar{X} + t s_{\bar{x}}$$

Example 10: A random sample of size 20 is taken from the weights of babies born at a hospital last year. A mean of 6.87 pounds and a standard deviation of 1.76 pounds was found. Estimate the mean weight of all babies born in the hospital with a 95% confidence interval.

95% confidence interval for μ

$$n = 20 \quad \bar{X} = 6.87 \quad s = 1.76 \quad \alpha = 0.05 \quad t = 2.093 \quad s_{\bar{x}} = s/\sqrt{n} = 1.76/\sqrt{20} = 0.39$$

$$\bar{X} \pm t s_{\bar{x}} = 6.87 \pm 2.093(0.39) = 6.87 \pm 0.82 \quad \text{or} \quad (6.05 \text{ to } 7.69)$$

Problem 8: A sample of 25 doctors yields an average income of \$90,000, with a standard deviation of \$10,000. Find the 98% confidence interval for the average income of all doctors.

DETERMINATION OF SAMPLE SIZE

In the previous examples, we have assumed that the sample size was given. However, we can determine the sample size needed to meet certain specifications. These specifications are degree of confidence and tolerated deviation D.

Determining Sample Size for Estimation of a Mean

Remember the rule for the confidence interval for one mean is

Rule:
$$\bar{X} \pm z \cdot \frac{\sigma}{\sqrt{n}}$$

The tolerated deviation D is what comes after the $\pm$ signs.

$$D = z \cdot \frac{\sigma}{\sqrt{n}}$$

Solving for n, one obtains the rule for determining the sample size.

$$n = \frac{z^2 \sigma^2}{D^2}$$

Note: When determining the required sample size, always round up: for example, 20.2 is rounded to 21.

If we don't know σ and given the sample has not been taken, we cannot use s as the point estimator. Thus, σ must be estimated in another way. If we assume that the distribution is normal, then approximately 99.7% of the observations are within 3 standard deviations of the mean. A rough estimate of σ can be determined by dividing the range of the population observations by 6. (The range of a normal distribution is approximately 6 standard deviations.)

Rule:
$$6\sigma = \text{Range} \qquad \sigma = \frac{\text{Range}}{6}$$

Example 11: If we have a normal distribution whose highest observation is 200 and whose lowest observation is 20, what is the approximate value of σ?

$$6\sigma = \text{Range} = 200 - 20 = 180$$
$$\sigma = 30$$

Given we can find σ, we can determine the sample size by specifying the level of confidence and tolerated deviation.

Example 12: Adding to the information in Example 11, we want to have a tolerated deviation of 5 and a 95% confidence level. Find the minimum sample size that will meet these requirements.

$$n = \frac{z^2 \sigma^2}{D^2}$$

$$= \frac{(1.96)^2 (30)^2}{(5)^2} = \frac{3.84(900)}{25} = \frac{3,456}{25} = 138.24$$

$$= 139$$

Problem 9: A company, for quality control purposes, wants to determine how large a sample is needed to meet the following specifications: a tolerated deviation of 10 and a confidence level of 98%. It is estimated that the range of the population is 210.

Determining the Sample Size for Estimation of Proportion

Rule: $n = \dfrac{z^2(p)(1-p)}{D^2}$ where p = estimated population proportion

D = tolerated deviation

Similar to the case of the mean, the values for z and D are determined by the specifications desired by the statistician. However, just like σ, the value for p is unknown and must be estimated. When estimating p, we should use past experience. If past experience is lacking, then the most conservative estimate is the proper approach.

Example 13: In a manufacturing process, past experience shows that 2% of the population is defective. What size sample is required to ensure that the proportion is within 1% with a 95% confidence level?

$$n = \frac{z^2(p)(1-p)}{D^2}$$

$$= \frac{(1.96)^2(0.02)(0.98)}{(0.01)^2} = \frac{(3.8416)(0.02)(0.98)}{(0.01)^2} = \frac{0.075295}{0.0001} = 752.9$$

$$= 753$$

Problem 10: An auditor knows from past experience that Lucy's books have mistakes 2% of the time. He wants a precision of 1% and a 95% confidence level. How large a sample must he take to meet these specifications?

CHAPTER 6 REVIEW PROBLEMS

1. Company data shows lightbulbs last from 80 to 200 hours. A 98% confidence interval is desired with a precision of 5. How large a sample should be taken to estimate the average life of lightbulbs that meet the above criteria?

2. A professor wants to estimate the difference in the proportion of evening and day students who fail a course. From a sample of 30 evening students and 50 day students, only 3 evening students and 7 day students failed the class. Find the 95% confidence interval for the difference between the proportion of day and evening students who fail the course.

3. The president of Savas Supermarkets wants to estimate the difference in average stores sales in 2 regions. In region 1, a sample of 30 stores yields a mean of $50,000 and a standard deviation

of $10,000. In Region 2, a sample of 30 stores yields a mean of $30,000 and a standard deviation of $6,000. Find the 95% confidence interval for the difference in population means.

4. A lawn service company wants to determine what percentage of its customers are satisfied with its performance. A sample of 80 customers is taken; 75 are satisfied. Find the 95% confidence interval for the true proportion of customers who are satisfied.

5. A college student wants to estimate the average cost of books for a student each year. She takes a sample of 100 students and finds a mean of $600 and a standard deviation of $200. Find the 95% confidence interval for the population mean.

6. An airline wants to estimate the proportion of roundtrip travelers who stay longer than a week. How large a sample should the airline take if it wants a 90% confidence interval and a 1% precision? Industry-wide studies have estimated p to be 0.25.

7. A production manager wants to estimate the average productivity of all employees. A sample of 81 workers reveals a mean of 65 and a standard deviation of 9. Find the 98% confidence interval for the average productivity of all the employees.

8. A statistics professor who has 200 exams to mark takes a sample of 10 and finds a mean of 70 and a standard deviation of 8. Find the 95% confidence interval for the mean of all the students.

9. An owner of two stores wants to estimate the difference in the average sales at the stores. A sample of 50 days' receipts from each store yields a mean of $10,000 and a variance of 20,000 in the first store and a mean of $11,000 and a variance of 25,000 at the second store. Find the 99% confidence interval for the difference in the average sales at the stores.

10. A farmer takes a sample of 10 tomato plants to estimate the average yield of the plants, with the following results: 20, 30, 25, 29, 30, 32, 40, 21, 30, and 33. Find the 95% confidence interval for the average yield of all the tomato plants.

11. A pollster wants to estimate if there is any difference between the proportion of women and men who like a certain television program. A sample of 50 women results in 22 who like the program; a sample of 40 men indicates 16 who like the program. Construct the 90% confidence interval for the difference in the population proportion of men and women who would like the show.

12. A sample of 64 mail carriers reveals that they walk an average of 4 miles a day on their route. Find the 98% confidence interval for the average of all mail carriers. Assume $\sigma = 3$.

13. A political poll is taken to estimate the proportion of people who will vote for a candidate. A sample of 300 is taken and 140 will vote for the candidate. Find the 95% confidence interval for the true proportion of voters who favor this candidate.

7
HYPOTHESIS TESTING

A hypothesis test is used in testing claims about the value of a population parameter. For example, a manufacturer claims its light bulbs have an average life of 1,000 hours. We take a sample and use statistical analysis and probability to test whether we believe this claim to be true. Suppose we took a sample and found the average life of the bulbs was 20 hours. We would probably not believe the claim of an average life of 1,000 hours. However, suppose the sample mean was 999.9; it does not equal 1,000 but it is very close and, given there is some error involved with the estimate, we would probably believe the claim. A hypothesis test gives us criteria so we can set up a decision rule to decide under what conditions we believe or don't believe the hypothesis.

No matter what population parameter we are testing, there are 5 basic steps to all hypothesis tests.

THE 5 STEPS OF A HYPOTHESIS TEST

1. Formulate the null hypothesis
2. Formulate the alternative hypothesis
3. Determine the test criteria and decision rule
4. Determine the value of the test statistic
5. Make the decision and interpret the results

An elaboration of the 5 basic steps follows.

1. Formulate the null hypothesis (H_0): This states that the population parameter has a specific value (for example, $H_0: \mu = 1,000$).
2. Formulate the alternative hypothesis (H_1): This states that the population parameter has a value different from that specified in H_0 (for example, $H_1: \mu \neq 1000$).
3. Determine the test criteria

   a. Determine the relevant probability distribution (for example, normal).
   b. Specify a level of α (for example, $\alpha = 0.05$).
   c. Determine the critical value (for example, $z = 1.96$) and the decision rule (for example, reject H_0 if $z < -1.96$ or $z > 1.96$).

4. Determine the value of the test statistic: This is done by examining how much the sample statistic differs from the population parameter in terms of the standard error of the distribution.

5. Compare the value obtained in Step 4 with the decision rule. Make a decision and interpret the results.

Before developing an example of a hypothesis test, we discuss certain characteristics of hypothesis testing. There are 4 possible outcomes to all hypothesis tests.

- If H_0 is true and we accept H_0, then we made a correct decision.
- If H_0 is true and we reject H_0, then we made a Type I error.
- If H_0 is false and we accept H_0, then we made a Type II error.
- If H_0 is false and we reject H_0, then we made a correct decision.

The following table summarizes these outcomes.

	H_0 is True	H_0 is False
Accept H_0	Correct decision	Type II error (β)
Reject H_0	Type I error (α)	Correct decision

Since we are dealing with sample data and don't have all the information concerning the population, we won't always make the right decision. The only way to make the correct decision all of the time is to examine the population. However, for various reasons (discussed in Chapter 4), it may not be feasible to examine the entire population.

TYPE I AND TYPE II ERRORS

Alpha α is the Type I error; this is the probability of rejecting H_0 when H_0 is true.

Beta β is the Type II error; this is the probability of accepting H_0 when H_0 is false.

You may ask, why distinguish between mistakes? A mistake is a mistake and who cares whether it is of the Type I or Type II variety? The following example shows the importance in distinguishing between a Type I and Type II error.

Example 1: Consider the following null and alternative hypothesis.

$$H_0: \text{The parachute will open.}$$
$$H_1: \text{The parachute will not open.}$$

The Type I error would be to return a good parachute. The Type II error would be to jump with a parachute that will not open. In this case, you would obviously want to minimize the Type II error.

Problem 1: Given the following null and alternative hypotheses, verbally express the Type I and Type II error.

$$H_0: \text{The shipment of apples is good.}$$
$$H_1: \text{The shipment of apples is bad.}$$

Setup of the Null Hypothesis

The null hypothesis can take one of three forms. However, the null hypothesis must always contain an equal sign. We use Q to represent the population parameter and v represents the assumed (hypothesized) value of the parameter.

	Two-Tailed	One-Tailed Lower	One-Tailed Upper
1.	$H_0: Q = v$	$H_0: Q \geq v$	$H_0: Q \leq v$
2.	$H_1: Q \neq v$	$H_1: Q < v$	$H_1: Q > v$

Discussion of Null Hypothesis

Two-Tailed Test   We reject H_0 only if the sample statistic is significantly different from the assumed value of the population parameter. So, we reject H_0 if the sample statistic is significantly less than v, as shown in area a of Figure 7-1(a), or significantly greater than v, as shown in area b of Figure 7-1(a). Because the rejection can occur in either tail, it is known as a two-tailed test.

Example 2: Given

$$H_0: \mu = 50$$
$$H_1: \mu \neq 50$$

we reject H_0 if the sample mean is significantly less than 50 (for example, 5) or significantly greater than 50 (for example, 500).

One-Tailed Lower   We reject H_0 only if the sample statistic is significantly less than the assumed value of the population parameter. Thus, the rejection can occur only on the lower tail, as shown in area a of Figure 7-1(b).

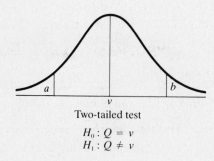

Two-tailed test

$$H_0: Q = v$$
$$H_1: Q \neq v$$

FIGURE 7-1(a)

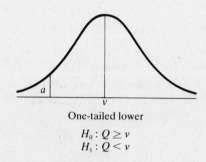

One-tailed lower

$$H_0: Q \geq v$$
$$H_1: Q < v$$

FIGURE 7-1(b)

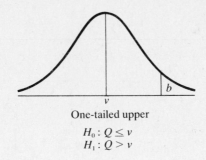

One-tailed upper

$$H_0 : Q \leq v$$
$$H_1 : Q > v$$

FIGURE 7-1(c)

Example 3: Given

$$H_0 : \mu \geq 50$$
$$H_1 : \mu < 50$$

we reject H_0 only if the sample mean is significantly less than 50 (for example, 5). We do not reject H_0 if the sample mean is significantly greater than 50 (for example, 1,000) because it supports the hypothesis than $\mu \geq 50$.

One-Tailed Upper   We reject H_0 only if the sample statistic is significantly greater than the claimed value of the population parameter. Thus, the rejection can occur only on the upper tail, as shown in area b of Figure 7-1(c).

Example 4: Given

$$H_0 : \mu \leq 50$$
$$H_1 : \mu > 50$$

we reject H_0 only if the sample mean is significantly greater than 50 (for example, 5,000). We do not reject H_0 if the sample mean is significantly lower than 50 (for example, 1) because it supports the hypothesis that $\mu \leq 50$.

HYPOTHESIS TEST FOR A MEAN WHEN σ IS KNOWN

First, we examine the two-tailed test. After that, we look at the one-tailed test.

Setup for Two-Tailed Test

Step 1. $H_0 : \mu = 100$

Step 2. $H_1 : \mu \neq 100$

Step 3. (Test criteria)

    a. relevant probability distribution ⇒ in this case the normal so use z

    b. level of significance (α) ⇒ in this case use $\alpha = 0.05$

    c. Determine the critical value and the decision rule.

Critical value: $z = 1.96$. We use the same procedure for finding the value of z that was used in confidence interval development (see Chapter 6).

Decision rule: Reject H_0 if $z < -1.96$ or $z > 1.96$. This expresses the decision rule in terms of z. So you reject H_0 if the sample mean is more than 1.96 standard errors away from the assumed population mean.

Step 4. Find value of test statistic

Rule:

$$z = \frac{\bar{X} - \mu}{\sigma_{\bar{x}}}$$

where $\sigma_{\bar{x}}$ = standard error

$\bar{X}$ = sample mean

μ = assumed population mean

σ = standard deviation of population

n = sample size

Step 5. Make a decision and interpret the results.

Setup of Decision Rule in Terms of $\bar{X}$ The critical value or decision rule can be expressed in terms of $\bar{X}$ instead of z. In that case, the rule for Step 3 changes.

Step 1. $H_0: \mu = 100$
Step 2. $H_1: \mu \neq 100$
Step 3. $\bar{X}_c = \mu \pm z\sigma_{\bar{x}}$ where $\bar{X}_c$ = the critical value of $\bar{X}$.

Decision rule: Reject H_0 if $\bar{X} < Y$ or $\bar{X} > Z$, where $Z > Y$.

Step 4. The value of the test statistic is $\bar{X}$.
Step 5. Make a decision and interpret the results.

Setup for One-Tailed Test   If a one-tailed test is employed, step 3 changes, but the rest of the steps are unchanged. The entire level of significance is in one tail; this changes the critical value and the decision rule.

	For One-Tailed Lower	**For One-Tailed Higher**
Step 1.	$H_0: \mu \geq 100$	$H_0: \mu \leq 100$
Step 2.	$H_1: \mu < 100$	$H_1: \mu > 100$
Step 3. Critical value:	$z = 1.65$	$z = 1.65$
Decision Rule:	Reject H_0 if $z < -1.65$.	Reject H_0 if $z > 1.65$.
	or $\bar{X}_c = \mu - z\sigma_{\bar{x}}$	or $\bar{X}_c = \mu + z\sigma_{\bar{x}}$

Steps 4 and **5** are the same as in a two-tailed test.

HYPOTHESIS TEST FOR A MEAN WHEN σ IS UNKNOWN AND $n \geq 30$

Just as with the confidence interval, the population standard deviation σ is usually unknown. If this is the case, then the standard deviation of the sample s can replace the population standard deviation, provided $n \geq 30$.

Setup for Two-Tailed Test

Step 1. $H_0: \mu = 100$
Step 2. $H_1: \mu \neq 100$
Step 3. Critical value: $z = k$

Decision rule: Reject H_0 if $z < -k$ or $z > k$.

Step 4. $z = \dfrac{\bar{X} - \mu}{s_{\bar{x}}}$ $\quad s_{\bar{x}} = \dfrac{s}{\sqrt{n}}$

Step 5. Make a decision and interpret the results.

Setup for One-Tailed Test

	For One-Tailed Lower	For One-Tailed Higher
Step 1.	$H_0: \mu \geq 100$	$H_0: \mu \leq 100$
Step 2.	$H_1: \mu < 100$	$H_1: \mu > 100$
Step 3. Critical value:	$z = k$	$z = k$
Decision Rule:	Reject H_0 if $z < -k$.	Reject H_0 if $z > k$.

Steps **4** and **5** are the same as in a two-tailed test.

Remember the z value changes because of the one-tailed test.

Example 5: Let's look at an example of a two-tailed test for a mean, σ unknown, $n \geq 30$. Joanie states that on average her strawberry-rhubarb pies weigh 4 pounds. A sample of 36 pies is taken, and an average weight of 3.9 pounds with a standard deviation of 0.6 is found. Test Joanie's statement at $\alpha = 0.05$.

$$n = 36, \quad \bar{X} = 3.9, \quad s = 0.6, \quad \alpha = 0.05$$

$$s_{\bar{x}} = \frac{s}{\sqrt{n}} = \frac{0.6}{\sqrt{36}} = 0.1$$

Step 1. $H_0: \mu = 4$

Step 2. $H_1: \mu \neq 4$

Given $n \geq 30$, use z for Steps 3 & 4.

Step 3. Critical value: $z = 1.96$ or $\bar{X}_c = 3.8$ and 4.2.

$$4 \pm 1.96(0.1) = 3.8 \text{ and } 4.2$$

Decision rule: Reject H_0, if $z < -1.96$ or $z > 1.96$ or if $\bar{X} < 3.8$ or $\bar{X} > 4.2$.

Step 4. $z = \dfrac{\bar{X} - \mu}{s_{\bar{x}}} = \dfrac{3.9 - 4}{0.1} = -1$

Step 5. $z = -1$; accept H_0.

Interpretation: The statistical evidence supports the hypothesis that Joanie's pies weigh an average of 4 pounds at $\alpha = 0.05$.

SOME OBSERVATIONS CONCERNING HYPOTHESIS TESTING

In Example 5, even though the sample mean is only 3.9, it is not significantly different from the claimed population mean of 4 and therefore H_0 is accepted.

Also, the hypothesis test doesn't prove anything. There is always the possibility of making a mistake, like a Type I or a Type II error. However, using probability and statistical techniques we attempt to use sample data to infer something about the population parameter.

When taking a hypothesis test, we are really testing both the null and alternative hypotheses. H_0 and H_1 are complementary statements: If one is true, then the other must be false. If we reject H_0, then at the same time we are accepting H_1. Conversely, if we accept H_0, then we reject H_1.

Hypothesis tests are purely objective; they are not trying to accept H_0 and reject H_1. Their purpose is to use the information provided by the sample and make a decision based solely on this information.

A hypothesis test is only valid if the criteria such as the sample size, the level of significance, and the null hypothesis are determined before the sample is taken. One should *never* take the sample and then adjust one of the criteria, such as the level of significance α, to obtain the conclusion that the person doing the test desires. When criteria are adjusted after the sample has been taken, the hypothesis test is no longer valid.

Example 6: Let's take a look at an example of a one-tailed lower test for one mean (large sample). Jack and Jimmy claim that their diet pizza has less than 100 calories on average. A sample of 64 pizzas is taken, and a mean of 97 is found with a standard deviation of 16. Test this hypothesis at $\alpha = 0.0228$.

$$n = 64; \quad \bar{X} = 97; \quad s = 16; \quad \alpha = 0.0228$$

$$s_{\bar{x}} = \frac{s}{\sqrt{n}} = \frac{16}{\sqrt{64}} = 2$$

1. $H_0: \mu \geq 100$
2. $H_1: \mu < 100$
3. Critical value: $z = 2$

Decision rule: Reject H_0 if $z < -2$.

4. $z = \dfrac{\bar{X} - \mu}{s_{\bar{x}}} = \dfrac{97 - 100}{2} = -1.5$

5. $z = -1.5$, accept H_0.

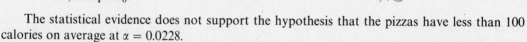

The statistical evidence does not support the hypothesis that the pizzas have less than 100 calories on average at $\alpha = 0.0228$.

We can also express the decision rule in terms of $\bar{X}$.

Step 1. $H_0: \mu \geq 100$
Step 2. $H_1: \mu < 100$
Step 3. Critical value: $\bar{X}_c = \mu - z s_{\bar{x}} = 100 - 2(2) = 96$

Decision rule: Reject H_0 if $\bar{X} < 96$.

Step 4. $\bar{X} = 97$
Step 5. Accept H_0.

So, either way we obtain the same results.

Problem 2: A production manager claims that the average production of employees is more than 50 units an hour. A sample of 64 workers is taken; a mean of 53 and a standard deviation of 8 is found. Test at $\alpha = .02$.

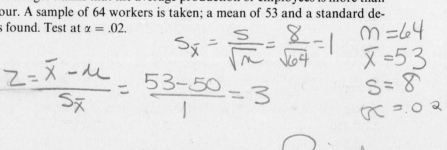

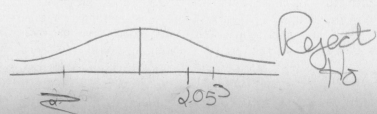

FINDING THE LEVELS OF THE TYPE II ERROR

The **Type I error** α is the probability of rejecting H_0 when H_0 is true and there is only one level of α for each problem (for example, $\alpha = 0.05$). This means that there is a 5% probability of rejecting H_0 when H_0 is true.

The **Type II error** β is the probability of accepting H_0 when H_0 is false. There are different levels of β for the same problem. The levels of β can be shown either by the use of a chart or by the use of a graph known as the power curve.

Example 7: We can show the levels of β by using the data in Example 6 and assuming various values of the parameter μ.

$$H_0: \mu \geq 100$$
$$H_1: \mu < 100$$

We can make a Type II error only if H_0 is false. In this case, H_0 is false if $\mu < 100$. Thus, we can obtain the level of β for particular values of μ less than 100.

We don't know the mean of the population. If we did we wouldn't need to do a hypothesis test. However, we can assume certain values for the population mean, which we shall call the true mean μ_T.

The first step in obtaining the levels of β is to determine the critical value $\bar{X}_c$. This will tell us under what conditions we will accept H_0.

$$\mu = 100; \quad \alpha = 0.0228; \quad n = 64; \quad s = 16; \quad s_{\bar{x}} = 16/\sqrt{64} = 2; \quad z = 2$$

Rule: $\qquad\qquad \bar{X}_c = \mu - zs_{\bar{x}} = 100 - (2)(2) = 100 - 4 = 96$

Decision rule: $\qquad\qquad$ Reject H_0, if $\bar{X} < 96$.

Remember, β is the probability of accepting H_0, $[P(\bar{X} \geq 96)]$ when H_0 is false ($\mu_T < 100$). We can find the levels of β for different assumed values of μ_T.

a. $\mu_T = 98$ $\quad$ **b.** $\mu_T = 96$ $\quad$ **c.** $\mu_T = 95$ $\quad$ **d.** $\mu_T = 94$ $\quad$ **e.** $\mu_T = 92$.

If μ_T is 98, what is the probability of accepting H_0? This can be written as if we were finding the probability in a normal distribution problem (see Chapter 6). It can be expressed thus: If the true mean of the population is 98, what is the probability that $\bar{X} \geq 96$ if a sample of 64 is taken and a standard deviation of 16 is found?

$$s = 16; \quad n = 64; \quad s_{\bar{x}} = s/\sqrt{n} = 16/\sqrt{64} = 2$$

a. Given $\mu_T = 98$

$$z = \frac{\bar{X} - \mu_T}{s_{\bar{x}}} = \frac{96 - 98}{2} = -1$$

$$P(\bar{X} \geq 96) = P(z \geq -1) = 0.8413$$

b. Given $\mu_T = 96$

$$z = \frac{\bar{X} - \mu_T}{s_{\bar{x}}} = \frac{96 - 96}{2} = 0$$

$$P(\bar{X} \geq 96) = P(z \geq 0) = 0.5000$$

c. Given $\mu_T = 95$

$$z = \frac{\bar{X} - \mu_T}{s_{\bar{x}}} = \frac{96 - 95}{2} = 0.5$$

$$P(\bar{X} \geq 96) = P(z \geq 0.5) = 0.3085$$

d. Given $\mu_T = 94$

$$z = \frac{\bar{X} - \mu_T}{s_{\bar{x}}} = \frac{96 - 94}{2} = 1$$

(handwritten: $\frac{.5}{2} = 1$ $2 = 1$ $2 = 1$)

$$P(\bar{X} \geq 96) = P(z \geq 1) = 0.1587$$

e. Given $\mu_T = 92$

$$z = \frac{\bar{X} - \mu_T}{s_{\bar{x}}} = \frac{96 - 92}{2} = 2$$

(handwritten: $.5 - 2 = 2$)

$$P(\bar{X} \geq 96) = P(z \geq 2) = 0.0228$$

The levels of β for the assumed means in Example 7 can be listed in a table.

μ_T	98	96	95	94	92
β	0.8413	0.5000	0.3085	0.1587	0.0228

We can see the various levels of β for different values of μ_T. This information can be used to determine the probability of accepting a bad shipment under different degrees of badness; if the population mean is actually 96, we have a 50% chance of accepting it. However, if the actual mean of population is 92, we have only a 2.28% chance of accepting it.

The β chart is used to determine if these probabilities of accepting a bad shipment are okay; if the levels are too high, adjustments can be made to decrease the levels of β.

For example, suppose we feel that the probability of accepting a bad shipment when the μ_T is 94 (and β is 0.1587) is too high. We can make adjustments to lower the levels of β by either increasing n or increasing α.

RELATIONSHIP BETWEEN α, β, AND n

There is an inverse relationship between α and β when n is held constant. If we want to decrease the level of β, we can increase the level of α. Conversely, if we decrease the level of α, the level of β will increase.

(handwritten left margin:
$\mu = 100$
$\alpha = .0668$
$m = 64 \} s_{\bar{x}} = 2$
$s = 16$
$z = 1.5$
$\bar{X} = \mu + z(s_{\bar{x}}) =$
$100 - 1.5(2) =$
$= 100 - 3 = 97$)

(handwritten table:

μ_T	98	96	95	94	92
β	.6915	.3085	.1587	.0668	.0062

)

Problem 3: Using the data in Example 7, find the level of β for the various true means if α is increased to 0.0668.

(handwritten work:
$\frac{97-98}{2} = -.5$ $P(\bar{X} \geq 97) = P(z \geq -.5) = .6915$

$\frac{97-96}{2} = .5 =$ $P(\bar{X} \geq 97) = P(z \geq .5) = .3085$

$\frac{97-95}{2} = 1$ $P(\bar{X} \geq 97) = P(z \geq 1) = .1587$

$\frac{97-94}{2} = 1.5$ $P(\bar{X} \geq 97) = P(z \geq 1.5) = .0668$

$\frac{97-92}{2} = 25$ $P(\bar{X} \geq 97) = P(z \geq 2.5) = .0062$)

Another way to decrease the level of β is to increase n while holding α constant. Conversely, if we decrease n while holding α constant, the level of β will increase.

(handwritten left margin:
$\mu = 100$
$\alpha = .0228$
$m = 256$ $z = 2$
$s = 16$
$s_{\bar{x}} = 1$
$\bar{X} = \mu + z(s_{\bar{x}})$
$= 100 - 2(1)$
$= 98$)

Problem 4: Using the data in Example 7, find the level of β for the various true means if n is increased to 256.

(handwritten table:

μ_T	98	96	95	94	92
β	.5	.0228	.00135	.00003	0.00+

)

(handwritten work:
$\frac{98-98}{1} = 0$ $P(\bar{X} \geq 98) = P(z \geq 0) = .5$

$\frac{98-96}{1} = 2$ $P(\bar{X} \geq 98) = P(z \geq 2) = .0228$

$\frac{98-95}{1} = 3$ $P(\bar{X} \geq 98) = P(z \geq 3) = .00135$

$\frac{98-94}{1} = 4$ $P(\bar{X} \geq 98) = P(z \geq 4) = .00003$

$\frac{98-92}{1} = 6$ $P(\bar{X} \geq 98) = P(z \geq 6) = .000$)

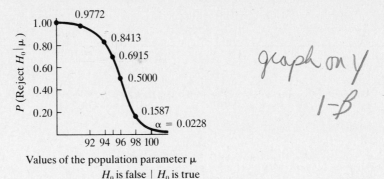

FIGURE 7-2
Power curve for the data in Example 7 (diet pizza example)

POWER CURVE

The power curve is a graphical presentation of the values of β for different assumed levels of the true mean. However, instead of the values of β (the probability of a Type II error) on the y-axis, the values of $1 - \beta$ (the probability of making a correct decision, that is rejecting H_0 when H_0 is false) are put on the y-axis for the assumed values of the true mean.

Example 8: Figure 7-2 shows the power curve for the data in Example 7.
The y axis is the probability of rejecting H_0 given a specific value of μ. The x axis is the values of the population parameter μ. Using the data from Example 7, we obtain:

μ_T	98	96	95	94	92
$1 - \beta$	0.1587	0.5000	0.6915	0.8413	0.9772

Problem 5: Construct the power curve for the results of Problem 3.

HYPOTHESIS TEST FOR A PROPORTION (LARGE SAMPLE)

Sometimes we are interested in testing hypotheses concerning a population proportion and not the mean of the population. If this is the case, we can do a hypothesis test concerning an assumed value of the population proportion.

Setup for Two-Tailed Test of One Proportion (Large Sample)

Step 1. $H_0: p = 0.25$

Step 2. $H_1: p \neq 0.25$

Step 3. Given a large sample we can use z.

Critical value:

$$z = k$$

$$p_c = \bar{p} \pm z\sigma_{\bar{p}}$$

where $\bar{p}_c = \bar{p}$ of the critical value

$$\sigma_{\bar{p}} = \text{standard error of proportion} = \sqrt{\frac{p(1-p)}{n}}$$

Decision rule: Reject H_0 if $z < -k$ or $z > k$; where $\bar{p} < Y$ or $\bar{p} > Z$.

Step 4. $z = \dfrac{\bar{p} - p}{\sigma_{\bar{p}}}$

Step 5. Make a decision and interpret the results.

Setup for One-Tailed Test

	For One-Tailed Lower	**For One-Tailed Higher**
Step 1.	$H_0: p \geq 0.25$	$H_0: p \leq 0.25$
Step 2.	$H_1: p < 0.25$	$H_1: p > 0.25$
Step 3. Critical value:	z or $\bar{p}_c = p - z\sigma_{\bar{p}} = Y$	z or $\bar{p}_c = p + z\sigma_{\bar{p}} = Z$
Decision Rule:	Reject H_0 if $z < -k$ or $\bar{p} < Y$.	Reject H_0 if $z > k$ or $\bar{p} > Z$.

Steps 4 and **5** are the same as in a two-tailed test.

In Step 3 we have a one-tailed test. Since the entire level of significance is in one tail, this changes the critical value and the decision rule.

Example 9: A production process is considered deficient if it produces more than 3% defective parts. A sample of 50 yields 3 defective parts. Test at $\alpha = .02$ to see if the production process is deficient.

$$n = 50; \quad x = 3; \quad \bar{p} = 0.06; \quad \alpha = .02; \quad z = 2.05$$
$$\sigma_{\bar{p}} = \sqrt{p(1-p)/n} = \sqrt{(0.03)(0.97)/50} = \sqrt{0.000582} = 0.024$$

Step 1. $H_0: p \leq 0.03$

Step 2. $H_1: p > 0.03$

Step 3. Critical value: $z = 2.05$

Decision rule: Reject H_0 if $z > 2.05$

Step 4. $z = \dfrac{\bar{p} - p}{\sigma_{\bar{p}}} = \dfrac{0.06 - 0.03}{0.024} = 1.25$

Step 5. $z = 1.25$; accept H_0. That is, $\bar{p} = 0.06$ is not significantly greater than $p = 0.03$.

The statistical evidence does not support the hypothesis that more than 3% of the products are defective at $\alpha = 0.02$.

Problem 6: A toothpaste company claims that at least 40% of the population likes its product. A sample of 500 people results in 180 liking the product. Test the company's claim at $\alpha = .05$.

(handwritten annotations):

$\bar{P} = \dfrac{180}{500} = .36$

$\sigma_{\bar{p}} = \sqrt{p(q)/n} = \sqrt{.24/500} = \sqrt{.00048} = .02191$

$P = .40$
$q = .60$
$m = 500$
$X = 180$
$\alpha = .05$

$\dfrac{.36 - .40}{.02191} = -1.826$

$z = 1.65$

$H_0: p \geq .40$
$H_1: p < .40$

$-1.826 - 1.65$

Reject H_0 in favor of H_1

HYPOTHESIS TESTS FOR TWO INDEPENDENT MEANS (LARGE SAMPLES)

So far, we have used hypothesis tests to infer something about the value of one population parameter, e.g. $\mu = 100$. However, in some cases we want to compare two unrelated (independent) populations and test the hypothesis concerning how their population parameters may differ.

Setup for Two-Tailed Hypothesis Test for 2 Independent Means (Large Samples),
σ_1 and σ_2 Unknown

Step 1. $H_0: \mu_1 = \mu_2$

Step 2. $H_1: \mu_1 \neq \mu_2$

Step 3. Critical value: $z = k$

Decision rule: Reject H_0 if $z < -k$ or $z > k$.

Step 4. $z = \dfrac{(\bar{X}_1 - \bar{X}_2) - (\mu_1 - \mu_2)}{s_{\bar{x}_1 - \bar{x}_2}}$ $\qquad s_{\bar{x}_1 - \bar{x}_2} = \sqrt{\dfrac{s_1^2}{n_1} + \dfrac{s_2^2}{n_2}}$

Step 5. Make a decision and interpret the results.

Setup for One-Tailed Test

	For One-Tailed Lower	For One-Tailed Higher
Step 1.	$H_0: \mu_1 \geq \mu_2$	$H_0: \mu_1 \leq \mu_2$
Step 2.	$H_1: \mu_1 < \mu_2$	$H_1: \mu_1 > \mu_2$
Step 3. Critical value:	$z = k$	$z = k$
Decision Rule:	Reject H_0 if $z < -k$.	Reject H_0 if $z > k$.

Steps 4 and **5** are the same as in a two-tailed test.

The z value changes because of the one-tailed test.

Example 10: Now let's look at a hypothesis test for 2 independent means (large sample), σ_1 and σ_2 unknown.

Big Bucks University claims that its graduates have a higher average income than its chief competitor, State University. A sample of 80 graduates from Big Bucks yields a mean salary of $35,000 and a standard deviation of 500. A sample of 100 graduates from State University yields a mean salary of $32,000 and a standard deviation of 400. Is the average salary of Big Bucks graduates greater than State? Test at $\alpha = .02$.

	Big Bucks (1)	State (2)
	$n_1 = 80$	$n_2 = 100$
	$\bar{X}_1 = \$35{,}000$	$\bar{X}_2 = \$32{,}000$
	$s_1 = \$500$	$s_2 = \$400$

$$s_{\bar{x}_1 - \bar{x}_2} = \sqrt{\frac{s_1^2}{n_1} + \frac{s_2^2}{n_2}} = \sqrt{\frac{500^2}{80} + \frac{400^2}{100}} = 68.7$$

$$S_{\bar{x}_1 - \bar{x}_2} = \sqrt{\frac{S_1^2}{m_1} + \frac{S_2^2}{m_2}}$$

$$= \sqrt{\frac{250{,}000}{80} + \frac{160{,}000}{100}}$$

$$= \sqrt{3125 + 1600}$$

$$= \sqrt{4725}$$

$$= 68.74$$

Step 1. $H_0: \mu_1 \leq \mu_2$

Step 2. $H_1: \mu_1 > \mu_2$

Step 3. Critical value: $z = 2.05$

Decision rule: Reject H_0 if $z > 2.05$.

Step 4. $z = \dfrac{(\bar{X}_1 - \bar{X}_2) - (\mu_1 - \mu_2)}{s_{\bar{x}_1 - \bar{x}_2}} = \dfrac{(35{,}000 - 32{,}000) - (0)}{68.7} = \dfrac{3{,}000}{68.7} = 43.7$

Step 5. $z = 43.7$; reject H_0

The statistical evidence supports the hypothesis that the average salary at Big Bucks is greater than that at State, at $\alpha = 0.02$.

$\alpha = .05$

Problem 7: A company wants to test if there is a difference in production between two shifts at its plant. A sample of 40 production days on shift 1 yields a mean of 100 units and a standard deviation of 20. A sample of 40 production days on shift 2 yields a mean of 90 and a standard deviation of 8. Test at $\alpha = .05$.

$m_1 = 40 \qquad m_2 = 40$
$\bar{X}_1 = 100 \qquad \bar{X}_2 = 90$
$s_1 = 20 \qquad s_2 = 8$

$z = \dfrac{100 - 90 - (0)}{3.41} = \dfrac{10}{3.41} = 2.93 \qquad \text{Reject } H_0$

$z = 1.96$

$s_{\bar{x}_1 - \bar{x}_2} = \sqrt{\dfrac{20^2}{40} + \dfrac{8^2}{40}}$

$= \sqrt{\dfrac{400}{40} + \dfrac{64}{40}} = \sqrt{10} \cdot 1.6 = 3.1$

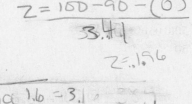

$H_0 = \mu_1 = \mu_2$
$H_1 = \mu_1 \neq \mu_2$

HYPOTHESIS TEST FOR TWO PROPORTIONS (LARGE SAMPLES)

Setup for Two-Tailed Test

Step 1. $H_0: p_1 = p_2$

Step 2. $H_1: p_1 \neq p_2$

Step 3. Critical value: $z = k$

Decision rule: Reject H_0, if $z < -k$ or $z > k$.

Step 4. $z = \dfrac{(\bar{p}_1 - \bar{p}_2) - (p_1 - p_2)}{s_{\bar{p}_1 - \bar{p}_2}}$

$s_{\bar{p}_1 - \bar{p}_2} = \sqrt{\hat{p}(1 - \hat{p})\left(\dfrac{1}{n_1} + \dfrac{1}{n_2}\right)}$

where $\hat{p} = \dfrac{n_1 \bar{p}_1 + n_2 \bar{p}_2}{n_1 + n_2}$

Step 5. Make a decision and interpret the results.

Setup for One-Tailed Test

	For One-Tailed Lower	For One-Tailed Higher
Step 1.	$H_0: p_1 \geq p_2$	$H_0: p_1 \leq p_2$
Step 2.	$H_1: p_1 < p_2$	$H_1: p_1 < p_2$
Step 3. Critical value:	$z = k$	$z = k.$
Decision Rule:	Reject H_0 if $z < -k.$	Reject H_0 if $z > k.$

Steps 4 and **5** are the same as in a two-tailed test.

The z value changes because of the one-tailed test.

Example 11: Now let's examine hypotheses for 2 proportions (large sample). Erwin the inventor has developed a new production process for widgets which he claims is better than the old process. He takes a sample of 50 using the new process and finds only one defective widget. He takes a sample of 50 using the old process and finds 3 defective widgets. Test Erwin's claim at $\alpha = 0.02$.

(handwritten: $\hat{p} = .04$ $q = .96$)

(handwritten: $\bar{p}_1 = \frac{1}{50} = .02$ $\bar{p}_2 = \frac{3}{50} = .06$)

	New Process (1)	Old Process (2)
	$x_1 = 1$	$x_2 = 3$
	$n_1 = 50$	$n_2 = 50$
	$\bar{p}_1 = 0.02$	$\bar{p}_2 = 0.06$

(handwritten: $\alpha = .02$)

$$\hat{p} = \frac{50(0.02) + 50(0.06)}{50 + 50} = 0.04$$

$$s_{\bar{p}_1 - \bar{p}_2} = \sqrt{(0.04)(0.96)\left(\frac{1}{50} + \frac{1}{50}\right)} = 0.039$$

(handwritten right side:
$$\hat{p} = \frac{m_1 \bar{p}_1 + m_2 \bar{p}_2}{m_1 + m_2}$$
$$\hat{p} = \frac{50(.02) + 50(.06)}{50 + 50} = \frac{1 + 3}{100} = .04$$
$$s_{\bar{p}_1 - \bar{p}_2} = \sqrt{\hat{p}\hat{q}\left(\frac{1}{m_1} + \frac{1}{m_2}\right)}$$
$$z = \frac{(\bar{p}_1 - \bar{p}_2) - (p_1 - p_2)}{s_{\bar{p}_1 - \bar{p}_2}}$$
$$= \frac{.02 - .06 - 0}{.039} = -1.03)$$

Step 1. $H_0: p_1 \geq p_2$

Step 2. $H_1: p_1 < p_2$

Step 3. Critical value: $z = 2.05$

(handwritten curve marked .02, .98, -2.05, -1.03)

Decision rule: Reject H_0 if $z < -2.05$.

Step 4. $z = \dfrac{(\bar{p}_1 - \bar{p}_2) - (p_1 - p_2)}{s_{\bar{p}_1 - \bar{p}_2}} = \dfrac{(0.02 - 0.06) - (0)}{0.039} = -\dfrac{0.04}{0.039} = -1.03$ *(handwritten: $z = 2.05$ table)*

Step 5. $z = -1.03$; accept H_0.

The statistical evidence does not support the hypothesis that the new production process is better at $\alpha = 0.02$.

(handwritten: $H_0: p_1 = p_2$ $H_1: p_1 \neq p_2$)

Problem 8: A political candidate takes a poll to see if there is any difference in his appeal to female versus male voters. A sample of 200 women is taken, and 120 prefer the candidate. A sample of 200 men is taken, and 100 men like the candidate. Test whether there is any difference in preference among the voters at *(handwritten circled: $\alpha = 0.5$.)*

(handwritten right margin: $m_1 = 200$ $m_2 = 200$ $x_1 = 120$ $x_2 = 100$ $\bar{p}_1 = .6$ $\bar{p}_2 = .5$ $z = 1.96$)

(handwritten work:
$$\hat{p} = \frac{m_1 \bar{p}_1 + m_2 \bar{p}_2}{m_1 + m_2}$$
$$= \frac{200(.6) + 200(.5)}{400} = \frac{120 + 100}{400} = .55$$
$$\hat{p} = .55 \quad \hat{q} = .45$$
$$s_{\bar{p}_1 - \bar{p}_2} = \sqrt{\hat{p}\hat{q}\left(\frac{1}{m_1} + \frac{1}{m_2}\right)}$$
$$= \sqrt{(.55)(.45)\left(\frac{1}{200} + \frac{1}{200}\right)}$$
$$= .05$$
$$= \frac{(.6 - .5) - 0}{.05} = \frac{.1}{.05} = 2$$
Reject H_0 in favor of H_1
(curve marked -1.92, 1.96, 2))

HYPOTHESIS TEST FOR A MEAN: UNKNOWN POPULATION STANDARD DEVIATION (SMALL SAMPLE)

Previously, we have looked at the hypothesis test for a mean when the sample is large ($n \geq 30$). Now we examine the setup for the hypothesis test for a mean when the sample is small ($n < 30$). Just as in confidence interval, we use t for small samples and the degrees of freedom are $n - 1$.

Setup for Two-Tailed Hypothesis Test of a Mean (Small Sample), σ Unknown

Step 1. $H_0: \mu = 50$

Step 2. $H_1: \mu \neq 50$

Step 3. Critical value: $t = w$

Decision rule: Reject H_0 if $t < -w$ or $t > w$.

Step 4. $t = \dfrac{\bar{X} - \mu}{s_{\bar{x}}}$ $s_{\bar{x}} = \dfrac{s}{\sqrt{n}}$

Step 5. Make a decision and interpret the results.

Setup of One-Tailed Test

	For One-Tailed Lower	For One-Tailed Higher
Step 1.	$H_0: \mu \geq 50$	$H_0: \mu \leq 50$
Step 2.	$H_1: \mu < 50$	$H_1: \mu > 50$
Step 3. Critical value:	$t = w$	$t = w$
Decision Rule:	Reject H_0 if $t < -w$.	Reject H_0 if $t > w$.

Steps **4** and **5** are the same as in a two-tailed test.

Remember, the t value changes because of the one-tailed test and the degrees of freedom are $n - 1$.

Example 12 (small sample): An automobile tire manufacturer claims that its tires last an average of at least 30,000 miles. A sample of 16 tires is taken and a mean of 29,500 and a standard deviation of 400 is found. Test the companies claim at $\alpha = 0.01$.

$$n = 16; \quad \bar{X} = 29{,}500; \quad s = 400; \quad t = 2.602$$

$$s_{\bar{x}} = \frac{s}{\sqrt{n}} = \frac{400}{\sqrt{16}} = 100$$

Step 1. $H_0: \mu \geq 30{,}000$

Step 2. $H_1: \mu < 30{,}000$

Step 3. Critical value: $t = 2.602$

Decision rule: Reject H_0 if $t < -2.602$.

Step 4. $t = \dfrac{\bar{X} - \mu}{s_{\bar{x}}} = \dfrac{29{,}500 - 30{,}000}{100} = -5$

Step 5. $t = -5$; Reject H_0.

The statistical evidence does not support the hypothesis that the tires last at least 30,000 miles at $\alpha = 0.01$.

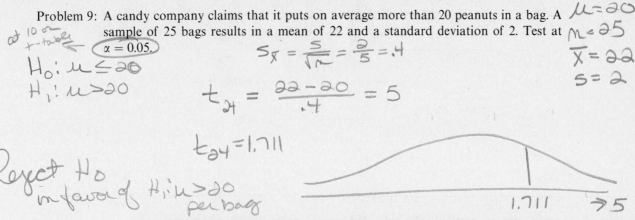

Problem 9: A candy company claims that it puts on average more than 20 peanuts in a bag. A sample of 25 bags results in a mean of 22 and a standard deviation of 2. Test at $\alpha = 0.05$.

HYPOTHESIS TEST FOR TWO MEANS WITH UNKNOWN POPULATION STANDARD DEVIATIONS (SMALL SAMPLES), $(n_1 + n_2 - 2 < 30)$

We also have a test for two means, σ_1 and σ_2 unknown, with degrees of freedom less than 30. In this case, we use t and the degrees of freedom are $n_1 + n_2 - 2$.

Setup for Two-Tailed Test

Step 1. $H_0: \mu_1 = \mu_2$

Step 2. $H_1: \mu_1 \neq \mu_2$

Step 3. Critical value: $t = k$

Decision rule: Reject H_0 if $t < -k$ or $t > k$.

Step 4. $t = \dfrac{(\bar{X}_1 - \bar{X}_2) - (\mu_1 - \mu_2)}{\hat{s}\sqrt{\dfrac{1}{n_1} + \dfrac{1}{n_2}}}$ where $\hat{s}^2 = \dfrac{(n_1 - 1)s_1^2 + (n_2 - 1)s_2^2}{n_1 + n_2 - 2}$

Step 5. Make a decision and interpret the results.

Setup for One-Tailed Test

	For One-Tailed Lower	For One-Tailed Higher
Step 1.	$H_0: \mu_1 \geq \mu_2$	$H_0: \mu_1 \leq \mu_2$
Step 2.	$H_1: \mu_1 < \mu_2$	$H_1: \mu_1 > \mu_2$
Step 3. Critical value:	$t = w$	$t = w$
Decision Rule:	Reject H_0 if $t < -w$.	Reject H_0 if $t > w$.

Steps **4** and **5** are the same as in a two-tailed test.

Remember, the t value changes because of the one-tailed test and the degrees of freedom are $n_1 + n_2 - 2$.

Example 13: Let's look at a hypothesis test for 2 means with unknown population standard deviations (small samples).

Farmer Brown claims that his tomato plants have a higher average yield than Farmer McDonald's. Farmer Brown takes a sample of 10 plants and finds a mean of 40 and a standard deviation of 8. Farmer McDonald takes a sample of 15 plants and finds a mean of 38 and a standard deviation of 7. Test Farmer Brown's claim at $\alpha = 0.05$.

	Farmer Brown (1)	Farmer McDonald (2)
	$n_1 = 10$	$n_2 = 15$
	$\bar{X}_1 = 40$	$\bar{X}_2 = 38$
	$s_1 = 8$	$s_2 = 7$

$$\hat{s}^2 = \frac{(n_1 - 1)s_1^2 + (n_2 - 1)s_2^2}{n_1 + n_2 - 2} = \frac{(9)64 + 14(49)}{23} = 54.87$$

$$\hat{s} = 7.41$$

$$\sqrt{\frac{1}{n_1} + \frac{1}{n_2}} = \sqrt{\frac{1}{10} + \frac{1}{15}} = \sqrt{0.167} = 0.408$$

Step 1. $H_0: \mu_1 \leq \mu_2$

Step 2. $H_1: \mu_1 > \mu_2$

Step 3. Critical Value: $t = 1.714$

Decision Rule: Reject H_0 if $t > 1.714$.

Step 4. $t = \dfrac{(\bar{X}_1 - \bar{X}_2) - (\mu_1 - \mu_2)}{\hat{s}\sqrt{\dfrac{1}{n_1} + \dfrac{1}{n_2}}} = \dfrac{(40 - 38) - (0)}{(7.41)(0.408)} = \dfrac{2}{3} = 0.667$

Step 5. $t = 0.667$; accept H_0.

The statistical evidence does not support Farmer Brown's Hypothesis that his tomato plants yield more than Farmer McDonald's at $\alpha = 0.05$.

Problem 10: A cereal company claims that it puts more raisins in its cereal than its top competitor. A sample of 15 boxes of the cereal yields a mean of 100 and a standard deviation of 5. A sample of 15 boxes of its competitors yields a mean of 98 and a standard deviation of 4. Test the cereal company's claim at $\alpha = 0.01$.

HYPOTHESIS TEST FOR PAIRED DIFFERENCES OR DEPENDENT MEANS

Previously we have compared two population parameters from independent or unrelated samples. However, in some cases the populations are related. When this is true, we can use the dependent means or paired difference approach; for example, for before and after evaluations of students in a class. The t distribution is used for dependent means and the degrees of freedom are $n - 1$.

Setup for Hypothesis Test for Paired Differences (Two-Tailed)

where $\bar{d} = \dfrac{\Sigma d}{n}$; $s_d = \sqrt{\dfrac{\Sigma(d - \bar{d})^2}{n - 1}}$; $s_{\bar{d}} = \dfrac{s_d}{\sqrt{n}}$

Step 1. $H_0: \mu_1 = \mu_2$

Step 2. $H_1: \mu_1 \neq \mu_2$

Step 3. Critical value: $t = w$

Decision rule: Reject H_0 if $t < -w$ or $t > w$.

Step 4. $t = \dfrac{\bar{d} - 0}{s_{\bar{d}}}$

Step 5. Make decision and interpret the results.

Setup for One-Tailed Test

	For One-Tailed Lower	For One-Tailed Higher
Step 1.	$H_0: \mu_1 \geq \mu_2$	$H_0: \mu_1 \leq \mu_2$
Step 2.	$H_1: \mu_1 < \mu_2$	$H_1: \mu_1 > \mu_2$
Step 3. Critical value:	$t = w$	$t = w$
Decision Rule:	Reject H_0 if $t < -w$.	Reject H_0 if $t > w$.

Steps 4 and **5** are the same as in a two-tailed test.

Remember, the t value changes because of the one-tailed test, and the degrees of freedom are $n - 1$.

Example 14: Absent-minded professor Bernie wants to test if there is a difference between his students' performance in the first two tests. He takes a sample of 10 and obtains the following results: Use $\alpha = 0.05$.

Student	First Test Grade	Second Test Grade	d_{2-1}	$\bar{d}$	$d - \bar{d}$	$(d - \bar{d})^2$
1	80	82	2	1	1	1
2	75	90	15		14	196
3	100	98	−2		−3	9
4	95	92	−3		−4	16
5	65	70	5		4	16
6	84	76	−8		−9	81
7	91	96	5		4	16
8	71	71	0		−1	1
9	77	75	−2		−3	9
10	81	79	−2		−3	9
			$\Sigma d = 10$			354

The first three columns are given. The first step is to find the values of d. It does not matter which column we subtract from the other. However, it is easier if we work with a positive Σd. So in this case, we subtract the first test grade from the second test grade. This gives us the fourth column d. Summing column 4, we obtain $\Sigma d = 10$.

$$\bar{d} = \frac{\Sigma d}{n} = \frac{10}{10} = 1$$

The next step is to obtain column 5, $(d - \bar{d})$, and then square these values to obtain column 6, $(d - \bar{d})^2$. Summing column 6, we obtain 354.

$$s_d = \sqrt{\frac{\Sigma(d - \bar{d})^2}{n - 1}} = \sqrt{\frac{354}{9}} = 6.27 \qquad s_{\bar{d}} = \frac{s_d}{\sqrt{n}} = \frac{6.27}{\sqrt{10}} = 1.98$$

Step 1. $H_0: \mu_1 = \mu_2$

Step 2. $H_1: \mu_1 \neq \mu_2$

Step 3. Critical value: $t = 2.262$

Decision rule: Reject H_0 if $t < -2.262$ or $t > 2.262$

Step 4. $t = \dfrac{1}{1.98} = 0.51$

Step 5. $t = 0.51$; accept H_0.

The statistical evidence supports the hypothesis that there is no difference in the test grades between the two exams at $\alpha = 0.05$.

Problem 11: Some workers were sent to a training school to increase their productivity. A sample of eight was taken to see if the program was effective. The following results were obtained. Test at $\alpha = 0.025$.

Worker	Productivity		d	$\bar{d}$	$d-\bar{d}$	$(d-\bar{d})^2$
	After Course	Before Course				
1	100	92	8	3	5	25
2	98	96	2	3	−1	1
3	95	94	1	3	−2	4
4	102	100	2	3	−1	1
5	115	113	2	3	−1	1
6	101	98	3	3	0	0
7	88	85	3	3	0	0
8	91	88	3	3	0	0

Handwritten annotations:

$dof = 8 - 1 = 7$

$t = 2.865$

$H_0: \mu_1 \leq \mu_2$
$H_1: \mu_1 > \mu_2$

$s_d = \sqrt{\dfrac{32}{7}} = 2.14$

$s_{\bar{d}} = \dfrac{2.14}{\sqrt{8}} = .76$

$t = \dfrac{\bar{d}}{s_{\bar{d}}} = \dfrac{3}{.76} = 3.95$

$\Sigma d \ \ 24 \qquad \Sigma = 32$

$2.365 \quad 3.95$

CHAPTER 7 REVIEW PROBLEMS

1. A college athlete wants to see if baseball players make more money, on average, than basketball players. A sample of 50 baseball players yields a mean of $300,000 and a variance of $10,000,000. A sample of 30 basketball players yields a mean of $270,000 and a variance of $5,000,000. Test at $\alpha = 0.02$.

2. A watch manufacturer claims that its product keeps time within one minute per year. A sample of 25 watches results in a mean of 1.2 minutes and a standard deviation of 0.8 minutes. Test this claim at $\alpha = 0.05$.

3. The production of a machine is claimed to be on average at least 2,000 units an hour. To test this claim, a sample of 100 is taken; a mean of 1,980 and a standard deviation of 150 is found. Test at $\alpha = 0.025$.

4. A state senator believes that more than 50% of his constituents favor a bill. He takes a sample of 250 people and finds 150 favor the bill. Test at $\alpha = 0.05$.

5. Given that the null hypothesis is $\mu \leq 500$ and the level of $\alpha = 0.0228$, what is the probability of accepting H_0 when H_0 is false if $\sigma = 50$ and $n = 100$? Solve for the following μ_T values: 505, 510, 515, 520 and 525.

6. Bill Board, an advertising consultant, wants to see if there is any difference in the proportion of men and women who smoke. A sample of 200 women finds that 60 women smoke, and a sample of 150 men finds that 40 men smoke. Test at $\alpha = 0.05$.

7. It is claimed that the average house in a community sells for less than $150,000. A sample of 64 houses in the community yield an average selling price of $147,000. Assume the standard deviation of the population is $8,000. Test at $\alpha = 0.02$.

8. A large oil company wants to test if a new brand of gasoline is better than its old brand in terms of miles per gallon. Two samples of 10 are taken, yielding the following results:

	1	2	3	4	5	6	7	8	9	10
New	30	41	42	18	29	28	37	26	29	33
Old	28	37	42	17	23	29	31	22	23	31

Test at $\alpha = 0.05$ that the new brand is better than the old brand.

9. The police commissioner claims that more than 90% of his policemen live in the city. A sample of 60 policemen shows that 56 live in the city. Test the police commissioner's claim at $\alpha = 0.05$.

10. The police commissioner in Review Problem 9 also claims that a greater percentage of policemen than firemen live in the city. A sample of 40 firemen shows that 32 live in the city. Using the data for policemen in Review Problem 9, test the police commissioner's claim at $\alpha = 0.05$.

11. A company claims that its new air freshener will last more than 20 days. A sample of 64 air fresheners is taken; a mean of 30 and a standard deviation of 12 are found. Test this claim at $\alpha = 0.10$.

12. A diamond firm claims that its employees have an average of 20 years' employment with the firm. A sample of 25 employees is taken. A mean of 18.2 and a standard deviation of 5 are found. Test at $\alpha = 0.10$ that the sample average does not differ significantly from 20 years.

13. Using the data in Review Problem 12, test at $\alpha = 0.02$.

14. Harry, a fast food restaurant owner, wants to see if there is any difference in the average sales between his two restaurants. A sample of 25 days is taken in each restaurant. The first

restaurant has average sales of $20,000 and a standard deviation of $1,000, whereas the second restaurant has average sales of $25,000 and a standard deviation of $2,000. Test at $\alpha = 0.05$.

15. A sample of 2 different types of lightbulbs yields the following results:

Lightbulb 1	Lightbulb 2
$\bar{X}_1 = 100$ hours	$\bar{X}_2 = 90$ hours
$s_1 = 10$	$s_2 = 8$
$n_1 = 12$	$n_2 = 15$

Test at $\alpha = 0.05$ that the average life is the same.

8

CHI-SQUARE TESTS AND ANALYSIS OF VARIANCE

Goodness of fit is a hypothesis test used to determine whether or not the sample data fits a specific probability distribution—for example, a binomial with a probability of success of 0.4. Goodness of fit can be used to test whether more than 2 proportions are equal (this is the same as testing for a uniform distribution). In testing goodness of fit, we use the χ^2 distribution.

Properties of the χ^2 distribution   Figure 8-1 shows graphically the χ^2 distribution

1. $\chi^2 \geq 0$
2. It is not symmetric
3. Critical value: $\chi^2(k - m - 1, \alpha)$

   $k - m - 1 = $ degrees of freedom

   $k = $ number of classes

   $m = $ number of parameters estimated by sample statistics

Use Table A-7 to find values for χ^2.

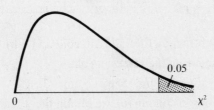

FIGURE 8-1

Example 1: Find the χ^2 value for $\alpha = 0.05$ when $k = 16$, $m = 1$.

$$\chi^2(k - m - 1, \alpha) = \chi^2(14, 0.05) = 23.685$$

Problem 1: Find the χ^2 value when

      a. $k = 20$, $m = 1$ $\alpha = 0.01$

      b. $k = 30$, $m = 1$ $\alpha = 0.02$

      c. $k = 15$, $m = 0$ $\alpha = 0.10$

a $(18, .01) = 34.805$

b. $(28, .02) = 45.419$

c. $(14, .10) = 21.064$

For our purposes, the hypothesis test using χ^2 is always a one-tailed upper test, so the decision rule is $\chi^2 > Q$ where $Q > 0$.

Setup of Hypothesis test for Goodness of Fit

1. H_0: We have a certain distribution (for example, Poisson with $\mu = 4$).
2. H_1: We don't have that distribution (not a Poisson with $\mu = 4$).
3. Critical value: $\chi^2(k - 1 - m, \;\; \alpha) = Q$

Decision rule: Reject H_0 if $\chi^2 > Q$.

4. $\chi^2 = \sum \dfrac{(f_o - f_t)^2}{f_t}$ where f_o = observed frequency

                                        f_t = theoretical frequency

5. Make decision and interpret the results.

    Example 2: A casino wants to test if the dice it buys are fair. It takes each die and rolls it 300 times. Given the following sample results for a die:

x	1	2	3	4	5	6
f_o	52	47	55	54	50	42

test at $\alpha = .02$ that the die is fair.

Table 8-1 shows the calculation of the χ^2 statistic.

- Columns (1) and (2) are given: x is the possible outcomes and f_o is the **observed frequencies**.
- Column (3) is the **theoretical frequencies**. If we roll a fair die, in theory $f(1) = f(2) = f(3) = f(4) = f(5) = f(6) = 1/6$ and we have a uniform distribution. If the rolls are independent, then $p_1 = p_2 = p_3 = p_4 = p_5 = p_6$. Thus, in theory each number should occur n/k times, which is $300/6 = 50$. So $f_t = 50$.
- Column (4) is obtained by subtracting the values in column (3) from column (2): $(f_o - f_t)$.
- Column (5) is obtained by squaring the values in column (4): $(f_o - f_t)^2$.
- Column 6 is obtained by dividing column (5) by column (3).
- When we sum the observations in column (6), we obtain the χ^2 statistic.

TABLE 8-1
Calculation of the χ^2 statistic

x	f_o	f_t	$f_o - f_t$	$(f_o - f_t)^2$	$\dfrac{(f_o - f_t)^2}{f_t}$
1	52	50	2	4	0.08
2	47	50	−3	9	0.18
3	55	50	5	25	0.50
4	54	50	4	16	0.32
5	50	50	0	0	0.0
6	42	50	−8	64	1.28
	300	300	0		2.36

The Hypothesis Test

1. H_0: The distribution is uniform.
2. H_1: The distribution is not uniform.
3. Critical value: $\chi^2(k - 1 - m, \quad \alpha)$
   There are 6 classes, so $k = 6$. In this test, $\alpha = 0.02$. No parameters are being estimated, so $m = 0$.

$$\chi^2(6 - 1 - 0, 0.02) = \chi^2(5, 0.02) = 13.388$$

Decision rule: Reject H_0 if $\chi^2 > 13.388$

4. $\chi^2 = \sum \dfrac{(f_o - f_t)^2}{f_t} = 2.36$

5. $\chi^2 = 2.36$, so we accept H_0. The statistical evidence supports the hypothesis that the die is fair at $\alpha = 0.02$.

Problem 2: A sample of 200 consumers is taken to determine if there is any difference in the consumer's preference among coffee brands. The following results were obtained:

$H_0: P_1 = P_2 = P_3 = P_4 = P_5$

$H_1:$ proportions are not equal (not a uniform dist)

Brand	Number of Consumers	f_t	$f_o - f_t$	$(f_o - f_t)^2$	$\dfrac{(f_o - f_t)^2}{f_t}$
A	30	40	−10	100	2.5
B	10	40	−30	900	22.5
C	50	40	−10	100	2.5
D	70	40	30	900	22.5
E	40	40	0	0	0
	200	200	0		50

Test at $\alpha = .01$ if there is any difference in preference among the consumers.

$5 - 1 - 0 = 4, .01 = 13.277$

Reject H_0

Example 3: The number of oil changes at Tommy's service station over the last 40 days are as follows:

(1) Number of Oil Changes Each Day x	(2) Observed Number of Days f_o	(3) col. (1) × col. (2) $x \cdot f_o$
0	5	0
1	10	10
2	15	30
3	4	12
4	3	12
5	2	10
6	1	6
	40	80

Test at $\alpha = 0.05$ that we have a Poisson distribution.

- Columns (1) and (2) are given: x is the possible number of oil changes each day, f_o is the observed number of days.

- The first step is to find the average number of oil changes per day. This is found by multiplying column (1) by column (2), which gives us column (3).

- If we sum column (3) and divide by the number of days, we can obtain the average $80/40 = 2$. We are testing for a Poisson distribution with a mean of 2.

Table 8-2 shows the computation of the theoretical frequencies.

We can find the Poisson distribution with a mean of 2 by going to Table A-3. This gives us the values for column (2), $f(x)$. Because this is a cumulative probability table, we subtract the value for $x \le 7$ from $x \le 8$ to obtain the probability of $x = 8$. We do this for each value of x, except for $x \le 0$. The probability that $x = 0$ can be read directly from Table A-3.

Column (3) is obtained by multiplying the number of days (40) by column (2), ($f(x)$) to obtain the theoretical number of days (f_t).

Next, we combine the two tables into one table (Table 8-3) to compute the χ^2 statistic.

Note that we have combined the values of 4, 5, and 6 units to read "4 or more" because when the f_t values are small (less than 5), using the approximation of a continuous χ^2 distribution for a

TABLE 8-2

Computation of theoretical frequencies

(1) x	(2) $f(x)$	(3) $f(x) \cdot 40$
0	0.135	5.4
1	0.271	10.84
2	0.271	10.84
3	0.180	7.20
4	0.090	3.60
5	0.036	1.44
6	0.012	0.48
7	0.004	0.16
8	0.001	0.04
	1.000	

TABLE 8-3
Calculation of the χ^2 statistic for demand for oil changes

(1) Number of Units per Day x	(2) Observed Number of Days f_o	(3) Theoretical Number of Days f_t	(4) $(f_o - f_t)$	(5) $(f_o - f_t)^2$	(6) $\dfrac{(f_o - f_t)^2}{f_t}$
0	5	5.4	−0.4	0.16	0.03
1	10	10.84	−0.84	0.71	0.07
2	15	10.84	4.16	17.31	1.60
3	4	7.20	−3.2	10.24	1.42
4 or more	6	5.72	0.28	0.08	0.01
	40	40.00	0		$\chi^2 = 3.13$

discrete distribution is inadequate. Thus, the probabilities of 4 through 6 units are combined to meet the criterion that values of $f_t \geq 5$.

- We can find column (4) by subtracting column (3) from column (2), which gives us $(f_o - f_t)$.
- Column (5) is obtained by squaring the observations in column (4).
- Column (6) is computed by dividing the values in column (5) by column (3).
- The χ^2 statistic is found by summing the values of the observations in column (6).

The Hypothesis Test

1. H_0: We have a Poisson distribution with $\mu = 2$.

2. H_1: We do not have a Poisson distribution with $\mu = 2$.

3. Critical value: $\chi^2(k - 1 - m, \quad \alpha)$
   There are five classes so, $k = 5$.

   We are estimating one parameter ($\mu = 2$), so $m = 1$, $\alpha = 0.05$.

   $$\chi^2(5 - 1 - 1, \quad 0.05) = \chi^2(3, 0.05) = 7.815$$

Decision rule: Reject H_0 if $(\chi^2 > 7.815)$.

4. $\chi^2 = \sum \dfrac{(f_o - f_t)^2}{f_t} = 3.13$

5. $\chi^2 = 3.13$; accept H_0. The statistical evidence supports the hypothesis that we have a Poisson distribution with $\mu = 2$ at $\alpha = 0.05$.

Problem 3: A salesman goes to five houses a night. The probability that he sells to any one person is 25%, and each person's decision is independent of all other decisions. A sample of 100 nights are reviewed. Given the following information, test at $\alpha = .02$ if this is a binomial process with $p = .25$.

Number of Sales	0	1	2	3	4	5	Total
Frequency of Occurrence	10	20	40	25	5	0	100

TEST OF INDEPENDENCE

The χ^2 distribution can also be used to test whether variables are independent. **Independent variables** mean that one event has no influence on the outcome of the other. We can use sample data to test whether population variables are independent.

Setup of Hypothesis for Test of Independence

1. H_0: The variables are independent.
2. H_1: The variables are not independent.
3. Critical value: $\chi^2[(r-1)(c-1), \alpha] = Q$ where r = the number of rows
c = the number of columns

Decision rule: Reject H_0 if $\chi^2 > Q$.

4. $\chi^2 = \sum \dfrac{(f_o - f_t)^2}{f_t}$

5. Make a decision and interpret results.

Example 4: A simple random sample of 1000 consumers is taken to test if age and purchase of a product are related. Test at $\alpha = 0.05$, if the variables are independent.

Table 8-4 contains the observed frequencies. We next construct the theoretical frequencies, assuming that the variables are independent.

If A and B are independent, then $P(A \text{ and } B) = P(A) \cdot P(B)$. We can obtain the probabilities of the A's and B's by finding the marginal probabilities from the joint probability table. (See Table 8-5.)

Next we find the joint probability, assuming the variables are independent, and we multiply this value by the size of the sample to obtain the theoretical frequencies.

$$P(A_1 \text{ and } B_1) = (.6)(.20) = .12 \quad .12 \times 1000 = 120$$
$$P(A_1 \text{ and } B_2) = (.6)(.65) = .39 \quad .39 \times 1000 = 390$$
$$P(A_1 \text{ and } B_3) = (.6)(.15) = .09 \quad .09 \times 1000 = \ 90$$
$$P(A_2 \text{ and } B_1) = (.4)(.20) = .08 \quad .08 \times 1000 = \ 80$$
$$P(A_2 \text{ and } B_2) = (.4)(.65) = .26 \quad .26 \times 1000 = 260$$
$$P(A_2 \text{ and } B_3) = (.4)(.15) = .06 \quad .06 \times 1000 = \ 60$$

TABLE 8-4

Observed frequencies on the relationship between age and purchase

	Buy A_1	Don't Buy A_2	Total
Under 21 B_1	100	100	200
21–40 B_2	400	250	650
Over 40 B_3	100	50	150
	600	400	1000

TABLE 8-5
Calculation of marginal probabilities

	Marginal Probabilities		
	A_1	A_2	Total
B_1			$\dfrac{200}{1000} = 0.20$
B_2			$\dfrac{650}{1000} = 0.65$
B_3			$\dfrac{150}{1000} = 0.15$
Total	$\dfrac{600}{1000} = 0.6$	$\dfrac{400}{1000} = 0.4$	

TABLE 8-6
Expected frequencies on the relationship between age and purchase

	A_1	A_2	Total
B_1	120	80	200
B_2	390	260	650
B_3	90	60	150
Total	600	400	1000

TABLE 8-7
Calculation of the χ^2 statistic

f_o	f_t	$f_o - f_t$	$(f_o - f_t)^2$	$\dfrac{(f_o - f_t)^2}{f_t}$
100	120	-20	400	3.33
400	390	10	100	0.26
100	90	10	100	1.11
100	80	20	400	5.00
250	260	-10	100	.38
50	60	-10	100	1.67
1000	1000	0		$\chi^2 = 11.75$

If A and B are independent, then the observations in theory would be as shown in Table 8-6. Table 8-7 combines data from Tables 8-4 and 8-6 to compute the χ^2 statistic.

The Hypothesis Test

1. H_0: Age and purchase are independent.
2. H_1: Age and purchase are not independent.

3. Critical value: $\chi^2[(r - 1)(c - 1), \alpha]$ $r = 3, \quad c = 2, \quad \alpha = 0.05$

$$\chi^2[(3 - 1)(2 - 1), 0.05]$$
$$\chi^2(2, 0.05) = 5.991$$

Decision rule: Reject H_0 if $(\chi^2 > 5.991)$.

4. $\chi^2 = \sum \dfrac{(f_o - f_t)^2}{f_t} = 11.75$

5. $\chi^2 = 11.75$; reject H_0. The statistical evidence supports the hypothesis that age and purchase are not independent at $\alpha = 0.05$.

Problem 4: Given the following information, test whether the variables are independent at $\alpha = 0.02$.

	A_1	A_2	A_3	Total
B_1	15	10	5	30
B_2	20	10	10	40
B_3	15	10	5	30
Total	50	30	20	100

ANALYSIS OF VARIANCE (ANOVA)

In Chapter 7, we learned how to test hypotheses for one mean and two means. We now analyze how to perform a hypothesis test for more than 2 means. We first examine the one-factor analysis of variance (ANOVA) test. This is called a **one-factor test** because we attempt to isolate one factor and hold everything else equal (for example, the *same* professor teaching the *same* course using a *different* book for each class—the one factor that is different is the textbook). An example of a **two-factor analysis** would be a different text and a different teacher for each section of a course—with two factors being different (the textbooks and the teachers).

The F distribution is used in all ANOVA tests.

Characteristics of the F distribution   Figure 8-2 shows graphically the F distribution

1. $F \geq 0$.

2. It is not symmetric

3. Critical value: $F_\alpha(v_1, v_2)$

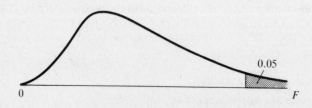

FIGURE 8-2

Example 5: Using Table A-8, find the F value for $\alpha = 0.01$ when $v_1 = 2$ and $v_2 = 12$.

$$F_{0.01}(2, 12) = 6.93$$

When using Table A-8, the first number (2) is the column value. The second number (12) is the row value.

Problem 5: Find the F value for

    a. $\alpha = 0.01$ $v_1 = 5$ $v_2 = 22$

    b. $\alpha = 0.05$ $v_1 = 7$ $v_2 = 26$

Setup of One-Factor ANOVA Test For More Than 2 Means

1. $H_0 : \mu_1 = \mu_2 = \mu_3 = \ldots = \mu_k$

2. H_1: The means are not equal.

3. Critical value: $F_\alpha(c - 1, n - c)$
    where c = the number of columns and n = the total number of observation

Decision rule: Reject H_0 if $F > Q$.

4. $F = \dfrac{MSA}{MSE}$ where MSA = treatment mean square
                              MSE = error mean squared

5. Make a decision and interpret results.

    Example 6: Given the following data for production of employees, test if the employees are equally productive at $\alpha = 0.05$.

workers

A	B	C	
83	94	56	233
96	81	79	256
72	68	73	213
87	79	97	263
62	88	85	235
400	410	390	

Machines

Calculation of Data to Test the Hypothesis

a. Between–treatment variation:

    Between–treatment sum of squares $(SSA) = \sum_j r(\bar{X}_j - \bar{\bar{X}})^2$

where r = the number of rows

    $\bar{X}_j$ = the mean of the jth column

    $\bar{\bar{X}}$ = grand mean

    $\sum_j$ = summation taken over all columns

$$r = 5$$
$$\bar{X}_a = 400/5 = 80$$
$$\bar{X}_b = 410/5 = 82$$
$$\bar{X}_c = 390/5 = 78$$
$$\bar{\bar{X}} = (80 + 82 + 78)/3 = 80$$
$$(\bar{X}_a - \bar{\bar{X}})^2 = (80 - 80)^2 = 0$$
$$(\bar{X}_b - \bar{\bar{X}})^2 = (82 - 80)^2 = 4$$
$$(\bar{X}_c - \bar{\bar{X}})^2 = (78 - 80)^2 = 4$$
$$SSA = \sum_j r(\bar{X}_j - \bar{\bar{X}})^2 = 5(0) + 5(4) + 5(4) = 40$$

b. Within-treatment variation:

$$\text{Within-treatment sum of squares } (SSE) = \sum_j \sum_i (X_{ij} - \bar{X}_j)^2$$

where X_{ij} = the value of the observation in the ith row, jth column

$\bar{X}_j$ = the mean of the jth column

$\sum_j \sum_i$ means that the squared deviations are first summed over all sample observations within a given column, then summed over all columns.

i	$(X_{i1} - \bar{X}_1)$	$(X_{i1} - \bar{X}_1)^2$	$(X_{i2} - \bar{X}_2)$	$(X_{i2} - \bar{X}_2)^2$	$(X_{i3} - \bar{X}_3)$	$(X_{i3} - \bar{X}_3)^2$
1	83–80	9	94–82	144	56–78	484
2	96–80	256	81–82	1	79–78	1
3	72–80	64	68–82	196	73–78	25
4	87–80	49	79–82	9	97–78	361
5	62–80	324	88–82	36	85–78	49
		702		386		920

$$SSE = \sum_j \sum_i (X_{ij} - \bar{X}_j)^2 = 702 + 386 + 920 = 2008$$

c. Total variation = Between-treatment + Within-treatment
variation   variation

SST	=	SSA	+	SSE
2,048	=	40	+	2,008

Table 8-8 gives the general format of a one-factor analysis of variance table. For data in Example 6, the analysis of variance table is:

(1) Source of Variation	(2) Sum of Squares	(3) Degree of Freedom	(4) Mean Square
Between treatments	40	2	20
Within treatments (error)	2,008	12	167.33
Total	2,048	14	

$$F = \frac{20}{167.33} = 0.12$$

TABLE 8-8
Analysis of variance table (ANOVA)

(1) Source of Variation	(2) Sum of Squares	(3) Degrees of Freedom	(4) Mean Square
Between treatment	SSA	$c - 1$	$MSA = \dfrac{SSA}{c - 1}$
Within treatment (error)	SSE	$n - c$	$MSE = \dfrac{SSE}{n - c}$
Total	SST		

$$F = \frac{MSA}{MSE}$$

Since we have the ANOVA table, we can do the hypothesis test.

Hypothesis Test

1. $H_0: \mu_1 = \mu_2 = \mu_3$: The production averages of the workers are equal.
2. H_1: The means are not equal; the production averages of the workers are not equal.
3. Critical value: $F_{0.05}(2, 12) = 3.88$

Decision rule: Reject H_0 if $F > 3.88$

4. $F = 20/167.33 = 0.12$
5. F is 0.12; accept H_0. The statistical evidence supports the hypothesis that the production averages of the workers are equal at $\alpha = 0.05$.

Problem 6: A statistics professor wants to test to see if there is any difference in the average quiz score of students depending on his method of testing. He has used three methods: (1) open-book, (2) closed book, and (3) formula sheets. The following sample results have been obtained for a quiz where a perfect score is 30.

	Testing Methods	
1	**2**	**3**
25	23	18
20	15	21
18	19	23
17	27	27
21	30	22

Test at $\alpha = 0.01$.

Two-Factor Analysis of Variance

In Example 6, we assumed that only one factor, the worker, influenced output. However, there may be other factors, such as the machines in the plant. Suppose we examine the data using a two-factor analysis of variance. In this case, we have two null hypotheses as shown in Example 7.

Example 7: Test at $\alpha = 0.05$ the following hypotheses, using the data in Example 6, where each row represents a different machine.

1. H_0: The production averages of the workers are equal.
2. H_0: The production averages of the machines are equal.

Using the short-cut rules, we have

$$SSA = \sum_j \frac{T_j^2}{r} - \frac{T^2}{rc} \qquad \text{(for the columns)}$$

$$SSB = \sum_i \frac{T_i^2}{c} - \frac{T^2}{rc} \qquad \text{(for the rows)}$$

$$SST = \sum_j \sum_i X_{ij}^2 - \frac{T^2}{rc} \qquad \text{(for the total)}$$

$$SSE = SST - SSA - SSB$$

where T_j = the total of the r observations in the jth column

T_i = the total of the c observations in the ith row

T = the grand total of all rc observations

All other terms are as previously defined.

$$T = 1,200$$

$$\sum_j \frac{T_j^2}{r} = \frac{(400)^2 + (410)^2 + (390)^2}{5} = 96,040$$

$$\sum_i \frac{T_i^2}{c} = \frac{(233)^2 + (256)^2 + (213)^2 + (263)^2 + (235)^2}{3} = 96,529.33$$

$$\sum_j \sum_i X_{ij}^2 = (83)^2 + (96)^2 + (72)^2 + \cdots + (85)^2 = 98,048$$

TABLE 8-9
2-Factor ANOVA table

(1) Source of Variation	(2) Sum of Squares	(3) Degrees of Freedom	(4) Mean Square
Treatment A	SSA	$c - 1$	$\dfrac{SSA}{c - 1} = MSA$
Treatment B	SSB	$r - 1$	$\dfrac{SSB}{r - 1} = MSB$
Error	SSE	$(r - 1)(c - 1)$	$\dfrac{SSE}{(r - 1)(c - 1)} = MSE$
Total	SST		

$$SSA = \sum_j \frac{T_j^2}{r} - \frac{T^2}{rc} = 96{,}040 - 96{,}000 = 40$$

$$SSB = \sum_i \frac{T_i^2}{c} - \frac{T^2}{rc} = 96{,}529.33 - 96{,}000 = 529.33$$

$$SST = \sum X_{ij}^2 - \frac{T^2}{rc} = 98{,}048 - 96{,}000 = 2{,}048$$

$$SSE = 2{,}048 - 40 - 529.33 = 1{,}478.67$$

Table 8-9 shows the general format of a two-factor analysis of variance table. For Example 7, the 2-factor ANOVA table would have the following values:

Source of Variation	Sum of Squares	Degrees of Freedom	Mean Square
Workers	40	2	20
Machines	529.33	4	132.33
Error	1478.67	8	184.83
Total	2048		

Since we have the ANOVA table, we can do the hypothesis test.

Hypothesis Test for Factor: Worker

1. $H_0: \mu_1 = \mu_2 = \mu_3$. The production averages of the workers are equal.
2. H_1: The means are not equal. The production averages of the workers are not equal.
3. Critical value: $F_{0.05}(2, 8) = 4.46$

Decision rule: Reject H_0 if $F > 4.46$.

4. $F = MSA/MSE = 20/184.83 = 0.108$
5. $F = 1.08$; accept H_0. The statistical evidence supports the hypothesis that the production averages of the workers are equal at $\alpha = 0.05$.

Hypothesis Test for Factor: Machine

1. $H_0: \mu_1 = \mu_2 = \mu_3 = \mu_4 = \mu_5$. The production averages of the machines are equal.
2. H_1: The means are not equal. The production averages of the machines are not equal.
3. Critical value: $F_{0.05}(4, 8) = 3.84$

Decision rule: Reject H_0 if $F > 3.84$.

4. $F = MSB/MSE = 132.34/184.83 = 0.72$
5. $F = 0.72$; accept H_0. The statistical evidence supports the hypothesis that the production averages of the machines are equal at $\alpha = 0.05$.

Problem 7: The statistics professor in Problem 6 also wants to test if different textbooks result in different average scores. Using the same data as in Problem 6 (see table on next page), test at $\alpha = 0.01$.

	Methods		
Text	1	2	3
A	25	23	18
B	20	15	21
C	18	19	23
D	17	27	27
E	21	30	22

CHAPTER 8 REVIEW PROBLEMS

1. A congressman wants to test if the area in which a person lives is independent of how they favor a proposed law. He obtained the following data:

	For	Against
Urban	60	40
Rural	50	50

Test at $\alpha = 0.05$.

2. A production manager wants to test if there is any difference in the average production of three separate shifts. The following sample data have been obtained:

1	2	3
52	45	40
62	62	56
74	68	58
62	61	54
50	54	42

Test at $\alpha = 0.01$ if there is any difference in the average production among shifts.

3. An advertising agency wants to test if there is any difference in consumer preference among brands of soap. The agency obtained the following sample results:

Brand	Number of Consumers
A	60
B	40
C	100
D	50
E	50

Test at $\alpha = 0.02$.

4. Two coins are tossed 100 times and the following results were obtained:

Number of Heads	Times Occurred
0	10
1	40
2	50

Test at $\alpha = 0.05$ if the coins are fair.

5. An apartment complex wants to test if its number of vacancies is a Poisson distribution. A sample provides the following information:

Vacancies	Number of Occurrences
0	3
1	7
2	12
3	57
4	10
5	8
6	3

Test at $\alpha = 0.01$.

6. A dietitian wants to test if there is any difference in the average weight loss of 3 diets. She obtained the following results in pounds:

1	2	3
10	19	16
22	21	37
18	30	12
30	27	21

Test at $\alpha = 0.05$.

7. A wheel of chance has 8 numbers. Before playing, Bob wants to check if the game is fair, so he observes 160 spins and obtains:

Outcome	Number of Times
A	20
B	17
C	24
D	19
E	25
F	17
G	18
H	20
	160

Test at $\alpha = 0.01$.

8. A high school guidance counselor is interested in determining if there is any difference in the average starting salary (in thousands of $) of recent graduates depending on major and school attended. He obtained the following:

School	Business	Major Liberal Arts	Computer
A	28	21	30
B	18	16	24
C	17	15	19
D	27	21	28
E	21	17	20

Test at $\alpha = 0.01$.

9. A sample of 1000 students was taken to determine if gender and major field of study are independent. The following was observed:

	Male	Female
Business	250	150
Liberal Arts	100	150
Engineering	100	40
Nursing	50	160

Test at $\alpha = 0.02$.

9

REGRESSION ANALYSIS AND CORRELATION ANALYSIS

Regression analysis is a method by which we use an equation to estimate the values of one variable from known or assumed values of one or more other variables. **Correlation analysis** measures the strength of the relationship among the variables.

THE REGRESSION EQUATION

We generally group variables into two categories: dependent and independent. Independent variables are designated by an X; dependent variables are designated by a Y. The value of the dependent variable depends on the values of the independent variable(s). The regression equation is used to estimate the values of the dependent variable Y from values of the independent variable(s) X. The regression equation estimates the average relationship that may exist among the variables. In this chapter we deal with simple regression, which has only one dependent and one independent variable. In Chapter 10 we will discuss multiple regression, which entails one dependent and more than one independent variable.

In regression analysis we deal with statistical relationships, which means that certain **average relationships** may exist among the variables. However, these average relationships do not allow us to make perfect predictions. There is some error involved with these estimations. In addition to estimating the regression equation, we obtain a measure of the error involved with the regression line. This is known as the **standard error of estimate**.

Objectives   There are three basic objectives to simple regression and correlation analysis. The first two deal with regression and the third with correlation analysis.

1. To estimate values of Y (the dependent variable) from known or assumed values of X (the independent variable).

2. To obtain a measure of the standard error of estimate (the error involved in using the regression equation).

3. To measure the strength of the relationship between X and Y.

Estimation Using the Regression Line

In this section, we deal with **simple linear regression**, *simple* in the sense that we have only one independent variable and *linear* in that we use a straight line for the purposes of estimating the Y values.

The true regression line is $\mu_{Y.X} = A + BX$; however, in order to obtain it, we would have to take the entire population. As in previous chapters, we can estimate population parameters by taking a sample. The rule for the sample regression line is $\hat{Y} = a + bX$ where a is the point estimator of A and b is the point estimator of B.

As we can see from the regression line, there is only one independent variable (X). Note that $\hat{Y}$ represents the estimated value of the dependent variable, a is the y intercept, and b is the slope of the line. Also, in a simple linear regression the sign of b determines the direction of the relationship.

- If $b > 0$, there is a direct relationship; that is, the values of X and Y tend to move in the same direction.

- If $b < 0$, there is an inverse relationship; that is, the values of X and Y tend to move in opposite directions.

- If $b = 0$, then there is no relationship.

$$\hat{Y} = a + bX = a + 0X = a$$

If changes in X do not change the value of Y, then X and Y are not related.

The values of a and b are estimated by the method of least squares. This gives us the best fitting line (that is, the one with the smallest error involved with the estimate).

Rule: The least squares rule used for computing a and b is

$$a = \bar{Y} - b\bar{X}$$

where $\bar{Y}$ is the average (arithmetic mean) of the Y observations: $\Sigma Y/n$

$\bar{X}$ is the average (arithmetic mean) of the X observations: $\Sigma X/n$

We can use the following rule for computing the value of a.

$$a = \frac{\Sigma Y}{n} - b\frac{\Sigma X}{n}$$

The rule for b is

$$b = \frac{\Sigma XY - n\bar{X}\bar{Y}}{\Sigma X^2 - n\bar{X}^2} \quad \text{or} \quad b = \frac{n\Sigma XY - \Sigma X\Sigma Y}{n\Sigma X^2 - (\Sigma X)^2}$$

Both rules for b are mathematically equivalent. Use the one that you find easier to compute.

Example 1: Suppose we estimate a to be 8 and b to be 12. Then the regression line is

$$\hat{Y} = a + bX = 8 + 12X$$

We can estimate values of Y for given values of X. Suppose $X = 7$, find $\hat{Y}$.

$$\hat{Y} = 8 + 12(7) = 8 + 84 = 92$$

However, if $X = 5$, then

$$\hat{Y} = 8 + 12X = 8 + 12(5) = 68$$

Example 2: A national pizza chain wants to examine the relationship between the price it charges for a large pizza and weekly sales. A sample of 10 restaurants reveals the following information:

Store	Sales in Units Y	Price in $ X
A	300	5.00
B	250	6.00
C	400	4.50
D	350	5.00
E	370	4.50
F	190	7.00
G	220	6.50
H	280	6.00
I	270	5.50
J	230	6.25

a. Find the regression line.

b. Find $\hat{Y}$ for price of $6.00.

a. From Table 9-1 we can find the values of a and b. The rule for

$$b = \frac{\Sigma XY - n\bar{X}\bar{Y}}{\Sigma X^2 - n\bar{X}^2} = \frac{15635 - 10(5.65)(286)}{326.25 - 10(5.65)^2} = -74.5907 = -74.6$$

$$a = 286 - (-74.5907)(5.65) = 707.4377 = 707.4$$

Substituting the computed values of a and b into the regression equation, we obtain

$$\hat{Y} = a + bX = 707.4 - 74.6X$$

b. Find $\hat{Y}$ when $X = $6.00

$$\hat{Y} = 707.4 - 74.6X = 707.4 - 74.6(6) = 259.8 = 260$$

Therefore, 260 is the estimated average weekly sales of a restaurant with a price of $6.00.

TABLE 9-1

Computation for regression and correlation analysis for pizza example

Restaurant	Y	X	XY	X^2	Y^2
A	300	5.00	1500	25.00	90000
B	250	6.00	1500	36.00	62500
C	400	4.50	1800	20.25	160000
D	350	5.00	1750	25.00	122500
E	370	4.50	1665	20.25	136900
F	190	7.00	1330	49.00	36100
G	220	6.50	1430	42.25	48400
H	280	6.00	1680	36.00	78400
I	270	5.50	1485	30.25	72900
J	230	6.50	1495	42.25	52900
	2860	56.50	15635	326.25	860600

Note: This does not mean that all pizza restaurants charging $6 for a large pizza will have weekly sales of 260; but it is the estimated average sales for all stores charging $6.

Some Thoughts Concerning the Regression Line

1. The regression line is valid only over a specific range of X values. For example, if $X = 0$ then $\hat{Y} = 707$. However, it is not feasible to discuss a price at or below zero or, conversely a $200 pizza.

2. Also, the regression line is valid only for pizza sales in this company. The relationship between price and pizza sales may be different for another company.

3. The regression line is valid only for the time period in which the sample was taken. If the sample was taken in 1985, the same relationship between price and pizza sales may not exist today.

4. We are measuring the statistical relationship between X and Y. It does not imply any cause or effect relationship. Thus, we cannot say the price (X, the independent variable) causes pizza sales (Y, the dependent variable).

Problem 1: The relationship between income and age is to be estimated. A sample of 10 yields the following:

$$\overline{Y} = \frac{369}{10} = 36.9$$

$$\overline{X} = \frac{303}{10} = 30.3$$

Person	Salary ($000) Y	Age (years) X	XY	Y^2	X^2
A	50	40	2000	2500	1600
B	30	27	810	900	729
C	28	25	700	784	625
D	40	34	1360	1600	1156
E	29	27	783	841	729
F	47	36	1692	2209	1296
G	46	32	1472	2116	1024
H	37	30	1110	1369	900
I	32	27	864	1024	729
J	30	25	750	900	625
	369	303	11,541	14,243	9413

a. Find the regression line.

b. Find $\hat{Y}$ for a person whose age is 30.

a) $b = \dfrac{\Sigma xy - \frac{1}{n}\Sigma x\,\Sigma y}{\Sigma x^2 - \frac{1}{n}(\Sigma x)^2} = \dfrac{11{,}541 - \frac{1}{10}(369)(303)}{9413 - \frac{1}{10}(303)^2} = \dfrac{11{,}541 - 11{,}180.7}{9413 - 9180.9} = \dfrac{360.3}{232.1} = 1.552$

$a = \overline{Y} - b\overline{X}$

$a = 36.9 - (1.552)(30.3)$

$a = 36.9 - 47.02 = -10.12$

$\hat{Y} = -10.12 + 1.552X$

b) $\hat{Y} = -10.12 + (1.552)(30)$

$\hat{Y} = 36.44$

or $36,440

STANDARD ERROR OF ESTIMATE
aka Std error of regression

The standard error of estimate measures the error involved in using the regression line (objective 2). It is a measure of dispersion. It measures the sum of the squared deviations about the regression line (that is, the difference between the actual Y values and the estimated Y values). We divide it by $n - 2$ degrees of freedom.

Rule for standard error of estimate:

$$s_{Y.X} = \sqrt{\frac{\Sigma(Y - \hat{Y})^2}{n - 2}} \quad \text{or} \quad s_{Y.X} = \sqrt{\frac{\Sigma Y^2 - a\Sigma Y - b\Sigma XY}{n - 2}} = S_e = S_{er} = S_{Y.X}$$

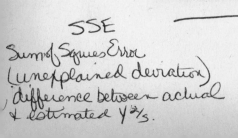

SSE
Sum of Squares Error
(unexplained deviation)
difference between actual
& estimated Y's.

Although either rule can be used (they are mathematically equivalent), the second is generally used. The subscript notation $Y.X$ denotes that the deviations are around the regression line.

Example 3: Using the data in Example 2, find the standard error of estimate.
From Table 9-1, we can find the values to compute the standard error of estimate

$$\Sigma Y^2 = 860{,}600 \qquad n = 10$$
$$\Sigma Y = 2860 \qquad a = 707.4$$
$$\Sigma XY = 15{,}635 \qquad b = 74.6$$

$$s_{Y.X} = \sqrt{\frac{\Sigma Y^2 - a\Sigma Y - b\Sigma XY}{n - 2}}$$

$$= \sqrt{\frac{860{,}600 - 707.4(2860) - (-74.6)(15{,}635)}{10 - 2}} = 21.8$$

Problem 2: Find the standard error of estimate, using the data in Problem 1.

$$Ser = \sqrt{\frac{\Sigma Y^2 - a\Sigma Y - b\Sigma XY}{m-2}} = \sqrt{\frac{14{,}243 - (-10.12)(369) - (1552)(11{,}541)}{8}}$$

$$= \sqrt{\frac{14{,}243 + 3734.28 - 17{,}911.632}{8}} = \sqrt{\frac{65.648}{8}} \doteq \sqrt{8.206} = 2.865$$

Standard Deviation of the Actual Y-Values

Besides finding an estimate of the error involved with our estimate, we can use the standard error of estimate to build confidence intervals and prediction intervals in regression analysis. Another measure that is used to build confidence intervals is the standard deviation of the actual Y-values (that is, the dispersion in the Y values).

The rule for the standard deviation of the Y values is:

$$s_Y = \sqrt{\frac{\Sigma(Y - \bar{Y})^2}{n - 1}} \quad \text{or} \quad s_Y = \sqrt{\frac{n\Sigma Y^2 - (\Sigma Y)^2}{n(n - 1)}}$$

$$= Ser \quad \frac{1}{\sqrt{\Sigma x^2 - \frac{1}{n}(\Sigma x)^2}} = \frac{2.865}{\sqrt{2321}} = \frac{2.865}{15.234} = .188$$

The two rules are mathematically equivalent.

Example 4: Find the standard deviation of the Y values for the data in Example 2.
The second rule is easier to compute because from Table 9-1 we already have $\Sigma Y^2 = 860{,}600$, $\Sigma Y = 2{,}860$, and $n = 10$. So

$$s_Y = \sqrt{\frac{n\Sigma Y^2 - (\Sigma Y)^2}{n(n - 1)}}$$

$$= \sqrt{\frac{10(860{,}600) - (2860)^2}{10(9)}} = \sqrt{4737.78} = 68.83$$

Problem 3: Using the data in Problem 2, find the standard deviation of the Y values.

$$s_Y = \sqrt{\frac{10(14{,}243) - (369)^2}{10(9)}} = \sqrt{\frac{142{,}430 - 136{,}161}{90}} = \sqrt{\frac{6269}{90}} = 8.345$$

Confidence Intervals in Regression Analysis

Similar to the construction of the confidence interval for the population mean using $\bar{X}$ (Chapter 6), we can construct the confidence interval for the population mean using $\bar{Y}$.

Confidence Interval for the Population Mean First we look at the confidence interval for the population mean. The rule is

$$\bar{Y} \pm ts_{\bar{Y}}$$

where $s_{\bar{Y}} = s_{ind}$ [handwritten]

where $\bar{Y}$ is the sample mean

t is the t distribution value

$n - 1$ is the degrees of freedom

$s_{\bar{Y}}$ is the estimated standard error of the mean and is equal to $s_Y/\sqrt{n}$

n is the sample size

Example 5: Using the data in Examples 2 and 4, find the 95% confidence interval for the population mean.

$$\bar{Y} = 286 \quad n = 10 \quad n - 1 = 9 \quad s_Y = 68.83 \quad \alpha = 0.05 \quad t = 2.262$$

$$s_{\bar{Y}} = \frac{s_Y}{\sqrt{n}} = \frac{68.83}{\sqrt{10}} = 21.77$$

$$\bar{Y} \pm ts_{\bar{Y}} = 286 \pm 2.262(21.77) = 286 \pm 49.24 \quad \text{or} \quad 236.76 \text{ to } 335.24$$

Problem 4: Using the data in Problems 1 and 3, find the 90% confidence interval for the population mean.

Confidence Interval for the Conditional Mean

A confidence interval using regression analysis is the confidence interval for the conditional mean or the regression line. It is called the conditional mean because we are finding the confidence interval for $\mu_{Y.X}$ given a specific X value. The value of $\hat{Y}$, the point estimator of $\mu_{Y.X}$, is a function of the value of X (for example, $\hat{Y} = 2 + 10X$, $\hat{Y} = 22$ when $X = 2$, but $\hat{Y} = 42$ when $X = 4$). The rule for the confidence interval for the regression line ($\mu_{Y.X}$) is

$$\hat{Y} \pm ts_{\hat{Y}}$$

where $\hat{Y}$ is the estimated Y value for a given value of X.

t is the t distribution value

$n - 2$ is the degrees of freedom

$s_{\hat{Y}}$ is the estimated standard error of the conditional mean

The rule for $s_{\hat{Y}}$ is

$$s_{\hat{Y}} = s_{Y.X}\sqrt{\frac{1}{n} + \frac{(X_0 - \bar{X})^2}{\Sigma(X - \bar{X})^2}} \quad \text{or} \quad s_{\hat{Y}} = s_{Y.X}\sqrt{\frac{1}{n} + \frac{(X_0 - \bar{X})^2}{\Sigma X^2 - \frac{(\Sigma X)^2}{n}}}$$

where X_0 is the given value of X.

Example 6: Using the data in Examples 2 and 3, find the 95% confidence interval for $\mu_{Y.X}$ given $X_0 = \$6.00$.

$$\hat{Y} = 260 \quad n = 10 \quad n - 2 = 8 \quad s_{Y.X} = 21.8 \quad \alpha = 0.05 \quad t = 2.306$$

$$s_{\hat{Y}} = s_{Y.X} \sqrt{\frac{1}{n} + \frac{(X_0 - \bar{X})^2}{\Sigma X^2 - \frac{(\Sigma X)^2}{n}}}$$

$$= 21.8 \sqrt{\frac{1}{10} + \frac{(6.00 - 5.65)^2}{326.25 - \frac{(56.50)^2}{10}}} = 21.8(0.34) = 7.4$$

$$\hat{Y} \pm ts_{\hat{Y}} = 260 \pm 2.306(7.4) = 260 \pm 17.1 \quad \text{or} \quad 242.9 \text{ to } 277.1$$

Problem 5: Using the data in Problems 1 and 2, find the 90% confidence interval for $\mu_{Y.X}$ when $X_0 = 30$.

[handwritten annotations:]

$t_8 = 1.860$

$S_{MEAN} = Se\sqrt{\frac{1}{n} + \frac{(X_0 - \bar{X})^2}{\Sigma X^2 - \frac{1}{n}(\Sigma X)^2}} = Se\sqrt{\frac{1}{10} + \frac{(30-30.3)^2}{9413 - \frac{1}{10}(303)^2}} = Se\sqrt{.01 + \frac{.09}{232.1}} = Se\sqrt{.01 + .000388}$

$= Se\sqrt{1.00388} = 2.865 \times .3168 \approx .91$

$\hat{Y} = 10.12 + 1.552 X$

$\hat{Y} = 36.44$

Prediction Interval for an Individual Value of Y

In this case, we predict an individual value of Y for a given X value. This is similar to the confidence interval for the conditional mean except that Y is used to predict an individual Y. This adds an additional measure of dispersion—that is, the dispersion of the individual Y's about the regression line. The rule for the prediction interval is:

$$\hat{Y} \pm ts_{IND}$$

where s_{IND} is the standard error of forecast.

   t is the t distribution value

   $n - 2$ is the degrees of freedom

The rule for s_{IND} is

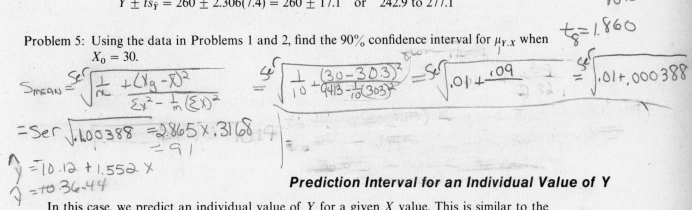

$$s_{IND} = s_{Y.X} \sqrt{1 + \frac{1}{n} + \frac{(X_0 - \bar{X})^2}{\Sigma X^2 - \frac{(\Sigma X)^2}{n}}}$$

Example 7: Using the data from Example 6, find the prediction interval for an individual value of Y when $X_0 = \$6.00$.

$$s_{IND} = s_{Y.X} \sqrt{1 + \frac{1}{n} + \frac{(X_0 - \bar{X})^2}{\Sigma X^2 - \frac{(\Sigma X)^2}{n}}}$$

$$= 21.8 \sqrt{1 + \frac{1}{10} + \frac{(6.00 - 5.65)^2}{326.25 - \frac{(56.50)^2}{10}}}$$

$$= 21.8\sqrt{1.12} = 21.8(1.06) = 23.1$$

$$\hat{Y} \pm ts_{IND} = 260 \pm (2.306)(23.1) = 260 \pm 53.3 \quad \text{or} \quad 206.7 \text{ to } 313.3$$

Problem 6: Using the data from Problem 5, find the prediction interval for an individual value of Y when $X_0 = 30$.

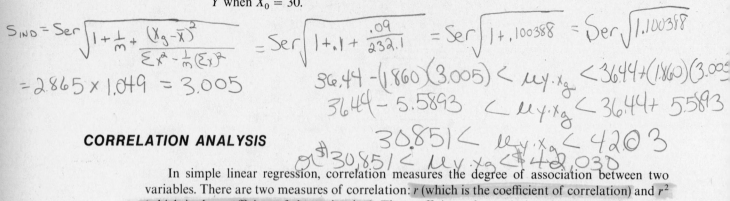

$$S_{IND} = S_{er}\sqrt{1 + \frac{1}{m} + \frac{(X_g - \bar{X})^2}{\Sigma X^2 - \frac{1}{m}(\Sigma X)^2}} = S_{er}\sqrt{1 + .1 + \frac{.09}{232.1}} = S_{er}\sqrt{1 + .100388} = S_{er}\sqrt{1.100388}$$

$$= 2.865 \times 1.049 = 3.005$$

$$36.44 - (1.860)(3.005) < \mu_{Y \cdot X_g} < 36.44 + (1.860)(3.005)$$
$$36.44 - 5.5893 < \mu_{Y \cdot X_g} < 36.44 + 5.5893$$
$$30.851 < \mu_{Y \cdot X_g} < 42.03$$
$$\$30,851 < \mu_{Y \cdot X_g} < \$42,030$$

CORRELATION ANALYSIS

In simple linear regression, correlation measures the degree of association between two variables. There are two measures of correlation: r (which is the coefficient of correlation) and r^2 (which is the coefficient of determination). The coefficient of correlation, (r) can take on values between -1 and 1. A negative value indicates a negative correlation and a positive value indicates a positive correlation. In a simple linear regression if $b > 0$ then $r > 0$, and if $b < 0$ then $r < 0$. Also, r^2 is the proportion of the variation in Y that can be explained by the regression line. Some of the variation in the Y values can be explained by the variation in the X values. This is known as the **explained variation**. However, there are other independent variables that can explain some of the variation in Y that we have not included in this regression equation. This portion is known as the **unexplained variation in Y**. The coefficient of determination (r^2) is the ratio of the explained variation to total variation.

Note that r^2 does not measure cause and effect relationship. We cannot state that X causes Y. Statistical relationships do not measure cause and effect.

Although r^2 can be expressed as either

$$r^2 = \frac{\text{Explained variation}}{\text{Unexplained variation}} \quad \text{or} \quad r^2 = 1 - \frac{\text{Unexplained variation}}{\text{Total variation}}$$

r^2 is usually expressed in the latter form because it is easier to compute. The total variation is $\Sigma(Y - \bar{Y})^2$ and the unexplained variation is $\Sigma(Y - \hat{Y})^2$. Thus r^2 can be expressed as

$$r^2 = 1 - \frac{\Sigma(Y - \hat{Y})^2}{\Sigma(Y - \bar{Y})^2} \quad \frac{SSE}{SST}$$

The $\Sigma(Y - \hat{Y})^2$ can be obtained by multiplying $(n - 2)s_{Y \cdot X}^2$. The $\Sigma(Y - \bar{Y})^2$ can be obtained by multiplying $(n - 1)s_{Y \cdot X}^2$. Thus, $r^2 = 1 - \dfrac{(n - 2)s_{Y \cdot X}^2}{(n - 1)s_Y^2}$.

Example 8: Using the data in Examples 3 and 4, find r^2.

$$r^2 = 1 - \frac{\Sigma(Y - \hat{Y})^2}{\Sigma(Y - \bar{Y})^2} = 1 - \frac{3,802}{42,638} = 1 - 0.089 = 0.911$$

$$\Sigma(Y - \hat{Y})^2 = (n - 2)s_{Y \cdot X}^2 = (10 - 2)(475.24) = 3802$$
$$\Sigma(Y - \bar{Y})^2 = (n - 1)s_Y^2 = (10 - 1)(4737.6) = 42,638$$

Problem 7: Using the data in Problems 2 and 3, find r^2.

$$1 - \quad 65.648$$

It is also possible to compute r^2 using the following rule:

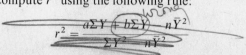

$$r^2 = \frac{a\Sigma Y + b\Sigma XY - n\bar{Y}^2}{\Sigma Y^2 - n\bar{Y}^2}$$

Example 9: Using the data in Example 2, find r^2.

$a = 707.4 \quad b = -74.6 \quad \Sigma Y = 2860 \quad \Sigma XY = 15,635 \quad \Sigma Y^2 = 860,600 \quad \bar{Y} = 286 \quad n = 10$

Substituting the values into the rule, we obtain

$$r^2 = \frac{a\Sigma Y + b\Sigma XY - n\bar{Y}^2}{\Sigma Y^2 - n\bar{Y}^2}$$

$$= \frac{707.4(2860) + (-74.6)(15,635) - 10(286)^2}{860,600 - 10(286)^2} = \frac{38,833}{42,640} = .911$$

Problem 8: Using the data in Problem 1, find r^2.

(handwritten) $r^2 = \dfrac{-10.12(369) + (1.552)(11.541) - 10(36.9)^2}{14,243 - 10(36.9)^2} = \dfrac{-3734.28 + 17911.632 - 13616.1}{14,243 - 13616.1}$

$= \dfrac{561.252}{626.9} = .895$ *approx 90% of variation is explained by the regression*

The coefficient of correlation r is the square root of r^2, so from Example 8, $r^2 = 0.911$ and $r = -0.95$. The sign of r in a simple linear regression is determined by the sign of b in the regression equation. If $b > 0$, then $r > 0$ and if $b < 0$, then $r < 0$. In this case $b < 0$ ($b = -74.6$), so r is negative.

We can also find r_c^2. This is the corrected r^2, corrected for degrees of freedom. The rule for

$$r_c^2 = 1 - \frac{s_{Y \cdot X}^2}{s_Y^2}.$$

HYPOTHESIS TESTING IN REGRESSION AND CORRELATION ANALYSIS

In this section, we use the sample information to make inferences concerning the population parameters. First, we do a hypothesis test concerning the population correlation coefficient ρ. Later, we deal with the hypothesis test for the population regression coefficient β.

Inference about the Population Correlation Coefficient

We want to determine, using the sample information, whether or not a relationship exists between the variables. If $\rho = 0$, then there is no relationship between the variables. If $\rho \neq 0$, then there is a relationship between the variables.

As with the hypothesis test in Chapter 7, there are 5 basic steps to the hypothesis test for ρ. The t distribution is used for the critical value and the degrees of freedom are $n - 2$.

Hypothesis Test for ρ

1. $H_0: \rho = 0$
2. $H_1: \rho \neq 0$
3. Critical value: $t = w$

Decision rule: Reject H_0 if $t < -w$ or $t > w$

4. $t = \dfrac{r - \rho}{s_r}$ where $s_r = \sqrt{\dfrac{1 - r^2}{n - 2}}$

5. Make a decision and interpret the results.

The hypothesis test for ρ is a two-tailed test.

Example 10: Using the data in Example 9, do the hypothesis test for ρ using $\alpha = 0.05$.

$$n = 10 \quad r^2 = 0.911$$

$$s_r = \sqrt{\frac{1 - r^2}{n - 2}} = \sqrt{\frac{1 - 0.911}{8}} = \sqrt{0.0111} = 0.105$$

1. $H_0: \rho = 0$
2. $H_1: \rho \neq 0$
3. Critical value: $t = 2.306$

Decision rule: Reject H_0 if $t < -2.306$ or $t > 2.306$.

4. $t = \dfrac{r - \rho}{s_r} = \dfrac{-0.95 - 0}{0.105} = -9.05$

5. $t = -9.05$, reject H_0. The statistical evidence supports the hypothesis that price and pizza sales are related at $\alpha = 0.05$.

Problem 9: Using the data in Problem 8, do the hypothesis test for ρ using $\alpha = 0.10$

[handwritten notes:]

no relationship

$H_0: \rho \neq 0$ relationship
$H_1: \rho \neq 0$

$r^2 = .895$

$r = .946$

$s_r = \sqrt{\dfrac{1-r^2}{n-2}}$

$= \sqrt{\dfrac{.105}{8}} = .114$

$t = \dfrac{.946 - 0}{.114} = \dfrac{.946}{.115} = 8.226$

Reject H_0 in favor of
$H_1: \rho \neq 0$ that there is
a relationship

1.860   1.860

Inferences about the Population Regression Coefficient, $\overline{B}$

The b value in a regression line describes how a change in X will change $\hat{Y}$. For example, if $\hat{Y} = 12 + 2X$, then a unit increase in X will increase $\hat{Y}$ by 2. Remember, the true regression line is $\mu_{Y.X} = A + BX$. We can test the value of the population parameter B by using sample data.

Setup for the Two-Tailed Hypothesis Test for the Value of B

1. $H_0: B = 0$
2. $H_1: B \neq 0$
3. Critical value: $t = w$

Decision rule: Reject H_0 if $t < -w$ or $t > w$; degrees of freedom are $n - 2$.

4. $t = \dfrac{b - B}{s_b}$ where $s_b = \dfrac{s_{Y.X}}{\sqrt{\dfrac{n\Sigma X^2 - (\Sigma X)^2}{n}}}$

5. Make a decision and interpret the results.

A one-sided hypothesis test can be done for the value of B. Remember the critical value changes with a one-tailed test.

Example 11: Using the data in Examples 2 and 3 test the hypothesis that B is equal to -80 at $\alpha = 0.05$.

$$s_b = \dfrac{s_{Y.X}}{\sqrt{\dfrac{n\Sigma X^2 - (\Sigma X)^2}{n}}} = \dfrac{21.8}{\sqrt{\dfrac{10(326.25) - (56.5)^2}{10}}} = \dfrac{21.8}{2.65} = 8.23$$

1. $H_0: B = -80$
2. $H_1: B \neq -80$
3. Critical value: $t = 2.306$

Decision rule: Reject H_0 if $t < -2.306$ or $t > 2.306$.

4. $t = \dfrac{b - B}{s_b} = \dfrac{-74.6 - (-80)}{8.23} = \dfrac{5.4}{8.23} = 0.66$

5. $t = 0.66$, accept H_0. The statistical evidence supports the hypothesis that $B = -80$ at $\alpha = 0.05$.

Problem 10: Using the data in Problems 1 and 2, test the hypothesis that B is equal to 2 at $\alpha = 0.10$.

[handwritten:]
$H_0: B = 2$
$H_1: B \neq 2$

$t = \dfrac{1.552 - 2}{.1880} = \dfrac{-.448}{.1880} = -2.383$

Reject H_0 in favor H_1
the $B \neq 2$

$S_b = \dfrac{Ser}{\sqrt{\Sigma x^2 - \frac{1}{n}(\Sigma x)^2}}$
$= \dfrac{2.865}{\sqrt{232.1}}$
$= \dfrac{2.865}{15.235} = .1880$

$-1.860 \qquad -1.860$

Hypothesis Test to Determine Statistical Relationships   We can also use the hypothesis test of the level of B to determine whether there is a statistical relationship between the X and Y variables. The true regression line is $\mu_{Y.X} = A + BX$. If $B = 0$ then the regression line would be $\mu_{Y.X} = A + 0X$ or $\mu_{Y.X} = A$. Thus, as X changes, it would not influence the $\mu_{Y.X}$ value. To test if there is a relationship between X and Y, we test the null hypothesis that $B = 0$. If we reject H_0, then $B \neq 0$ and there is a relationship between the variables. However, if we accept H_0, then $B = 0$ and there is no relationship between the variables. When testing for the relationship between two variables, a two-tailed test is always used. Also, in a simple linear regression, the hypothesis test for $\rho = 0$ and $B = 0$ test the same thing and only one of these tests is needed. They will always yield the same result.

Example 12: Using the data in Example 11, test whether there is a statistical relationship between price and sales at $\alpha = 0.05$.

1. $H_0: B = 0$
2. $H_1: B \neq 0$
3. Critical value: $t = 2.306$

Decision rule: Reject H_0 if $t < -2.306$ or $t > 2.306$.

4. $t = \dfrac{b - B}{s_b} = \dfrac{-74.6 - 0}{8.23} = -9.06$

5. $t = -9.06$; reject H_0. The statistical evidence supports the hypothesis that there is a statistical relationship between price and sales at $\alpha = 0.05$.

In Example 10, the test of $\rho = 0$, and in Example 12, the test of $B = 0$, we obtain the same results. This is consistent with the above discussion. The t values in each differ (4.15 and 4.19) due to rounding error.

Problem 11: Using the data in Problem 10, test whether there is a statistical relationship between age and income at $\alpha = 0.10$.

[handwritten:]
$H_0: B = 0 \qquad H_1: B \neq 0$

$t = \dfrac{1.552 - 0}{.1880} = \dfrac{1.552}{.1880} = 8.2553$

CHAPTER 9 REVIEW PROBLEMS

1. Given $\hat{Y} = 18 - 20X$ and $r^2 = .25$, determine the value of r.

2. Given $n = 10$ $\Sigma X = 50$ $\Sigma Y = 30$ $\Sigma XY = 200$ $\Sigma X^2 = 350$ $\Sigma Y^2 = 420$

   a. Find the regression line.

   b. Find the standard error of the estimate.

   c. If $s_b = 2$, test at $\alpha = 0.05$ if X and Y are related.

   d. Estimate Y when $X = 4$.

3. Given the following regression equation for 20 cars:

$$\hat{Y} = 40 - 0.2X \qquad s_b = 0.05 \qquad r^2 = 0.64$$

   a. Test at $\alpha = 0.05$ that miles per gallon and weight are related.

   b. Interpret r^2.

   c. Find the value of r.

4. Given the following data concerning weekly sales of large pizzas (Y) and weekly advertising expenditures (X):

					Store					
	A	B	C	D	E	F	G	H	I	J
X	150	100	250	180	210	100	120	180	170	160
Y	300	250	400	350	370	190	220	280	270	230

   a. Find the regression equation.

   b. Find the standard error.

   c. Find r^2.

5. Using the data in Review Problem 4, test at $\alpha = 0.02$ if there is a relationship between sales and advertising.

6. Using the data in Review Problem 4, find

   a. $\hat{Y}$ when $X = 150$.

   b. 98% confidence interval for $\mu_{Y \cdot X}$ when $X_0 = 150$.

   c. 98% prediction interval when $X_0 = 150$.

7. An advertising firm claims that for every dollar spent on advertising, holding everything else constant, sales will increase by $10. A sample of 42 is taken and the following regression line was estimated: $\hat{Y} = 1000 + 9.8X$ and $s_b = 2$. Test at $\alpha = 0.01$.

8. A production manager wants to estimate the relationship between number of years (X) on the job and number of mistakes (Y) in a year. A sample of 10 is taken and the following was observed:

X	3	4	6	8	2	1	9	11	7	5
Y	26	20	15	12	25	30	10	7	14	18

   a. Find the regression equation.

   b. Find the standard error of estimate.

    c. Find r^2 and r.

    d. Test at $\alpha = 0.05$, if there is a relationship between mistakes and number of years on the job.

9. Using the data in Review Problem 8, find the 95% confidence interval for the population mean of the Y variable.

10. Given the following regression analysis for a sample of 122 salesmen:

$$\hat{Y} = -10 + X \qquad X = \text{Age in years}$$

                               Age Range between 30 and 50

             $Y = \text{Annual Commission in thousands of \$}$

$$s_Y = 5 \quad s_{Y.X} = 3 \quad s_b = .2$$

    a. The sales manager objected to the results of the equation because the value $a = -10$ did not seem reasonable to him. Explain briefly how you would reply to the sales manager.

    b. Would you conclude there is any correlation between age and annual commissions at $\alpha = .05$?

    c. Estimate the commission of a 45-year-old salesperson.

11. A statistician compiled the following data concerning salary (Y) in \$1,000s and shoe size (X).

X	10	8	7	9	11	13	10	9	12	10
Y	30	25	20	40	20	25	35	30	55	40

    a. Find the regression equation.

    b. Find the standard error of estimate.

    c. Find r^2.

    d. Test at $\alpha = 0.02$ if shoe size and salary are related.

10
MULTIPLE REGRESSION AND CORRELATION ANALYSIS

Multiple regression and correlation analysis have the same three objectives as simple regression.

Objectives

1. To estimate the value of the dependent variable from known or assumed values of the independent variables.

2. To obtain a measure of the error involved in using the regression equation.

3. To measure the strength of the relationship between the independent and dependent variables.

Multiple regression differs from simple regression in that **multiple regression** has more than one independent variable. The multiple regression equation is

$$\hat{Y} = a + b_1 X_1 + b_2 X_2 + \cdots + b_{k-1} X_{k-1}$$

where a is the constant term

b's are the net regression coefficients

X's are the independent variables

$k - 1$ is the number of independent variables

$\hat{Y}$ is the estimated value of Y, the dependent variable

For the above regression equation, the value of a and the values of b's are obtained from sample information, so we are estimating the true regression equation.

a is the y-intercept

b's are the net regression coefficient(s)

Each individual b measures the change in Y per unit change in the individual X holding all the other X values constant.

Example 1: Given the following multiple regression equation

$$\hat{Y} = 2,000 + 0.7X_1 - 80X_2 + 0.6X_3$$

where X_1 = income in dollars

X_2 = price in dollars

X_3 = wealth in dollars

Y = consumption in dollars

a. Find $\hat{Y}$ when $X_1 = 30,000$, $X_2 = 40$, $X_3 = 10,000$.

b. If income increases by \$1,000 ($X_1 = 31,000$), holding all the other X's constant, how much will consumption change?

a. $\hat{Y} = 2,000 + 0.7X_1 - 80X_2 + 0.6X_3$

$= 2,000 + 0.7(30,000) - 80(40) + 0.6(10,000)$

$= 2,000 + 21,000 - 3,200 + 6,000 = 25,800$

So \$25,800 is the estimated average consumption of a family with income of \$30,000, when the price level is 40 and wealth of \$10,000.

b. As stated above, the net regression coefficient b_1 measures that change in $\hat{Y}$ per unit change in X_1 holding all the other X's constant. In this case, $b_1 = 0.7$ and the change in $X_1 = 1,000$, so change in $\hat{Y}$ is

$$\Delta\hat{Y} = b_1 \cdot \Delta X_1 = 0.7(1,000) = 700$$

This can also be shown by using the multiple regression equation.

$$\hat{Y} = 2,000 + 0.7X_1 - 80X_2 + 0.6X_3$$

$$= 2,000 + 0.7(31,000) - 80(40) + 0.6(10,000)$$

$$= 2,000 + 21,700 - 3,200 + 6,000 = 26,500$$

Either way, the same \$700 increase in consumption is obtained.

THE MULTIPLE REGRESSION EQUATION

Just like simple regression, we can use the least squares equations for obtaining the values of a and the b's in multiple regression analysis. The rules for a multiple regression with two independent variables are

$$\Sigma Y = na + b_1\Sigma X_1 + b_2\Sigma X_2$$

$$\Sigma X_1 Y = a\Sigma X_1 + b_1\Sigma X_1^2 + b_2\Sigma X_1 X_2$$

$$\Sigma X_2 Y = a\Sigma X_2 + b_1\Sigma X_1 X_2 + b_2\Sigma X_2^2$$

We now have three equations and three unknowns, so the equations must be solved simultaneously to obtain the values of a, b_1, and b_2.

Example 2: Given the following data from a sample of 10 pizza stores, answer parts (a), (b), and (c).

a. Find the linear multiple regression equation.

b. Find $\hat{Y}$ when $X_1 = \$5$ and $X_2 = 150$

c. Interpret the net regression coefficients b_1 and b_2.

a. The basic data for salary, years of work experience, and years of post-secondary education are shown in the first three columns of Table 10-1. The necessary computation to obtain a, b_1, and b_2 are shown in the other columns of Table 10-1.

The least square equations are:

$$\Sigma Y = na + b_1\Sigma X_1 + b_2\Sigma X_2$$

$$\Sigma X_1 Y = a\Sigma X_1 + b_1\Sigma X_1^2 + b_2\Sigma X_1 X_2$$

$$\Sigma X_2 Y = a\Sigma X_2 + b_1\Sigma X_1 X_2 + b_2\Sigma X_2^2$$

TABLE 10-1
Computation for multiple regression analysis: sales (Y), price (X_1), and advertising expenditures (X_2)

Y	X_1	X_2	X_1Y	X_2Y	X_1X_2	Y^2	X_1^2	X_2^2
300	5.00	150	1,500	45,000	750	90,000	25.00	22,500
250	6.00	100	1,500	25,000	600	62,500	36.00	10,000
400	4.50	250	1,800	100,000	1,125	160,000	20.25	62,500
350	5.00	180	1,750	63,000	900	122,500	25.00	32,400
370	4.50	210	1,665	77,700	945	136,900	20.25	44,100
190	7.00	100	1,330	19,000	700	36,100	49.00	10,000
220	6.50	120	1,430	26,400	780	48,400	42.25	14,400
280	6.00	180	1,680	50,400	1,080	78,400	36.00	32,400
270	5.50	170	1,485	45,900	935	72,900	30.25	28,900
230	6.50	160	1,495	36,800	1,040	52,900	42.25	25,600
2,860	56.50	1,620	15,635	489,200	8,855	860,600	326.25	282,800

Substituting these values into the least squares equations, we obtain:

$$2,860 = 10a + 56.5b_1 + 1,620b_2$$
$$15,635 = 56.5a + 326.25b_1 + 8,855b_2$$
$$489,200 = 1,620a + 8,855b_1 + 282,800b_2$$

Solving simultaneously for a, b_1, and b_2, we obtain:

$$a = 517.399 \qquad b_1 = -54.5211 \qquad b_2 = 0.473119$$

Rounding off, we have: $a = 517.4$, $b_1 = -54.52$, $b_2 = 0.473$. The regression equation is

$$\hat{Y} = 517.4 - 54.52X_1 + 0.473X_2$$

b. We can estimate $\hat{Y}$ when $X_1 = 5$ and $X_2 = 150$.

$$\hat{Y} = 517.4 - 54.52(5) + 0.473(150) = 315.75 = 316$$

So, 316 is the estimated weekly average sales of large pizzas for a store charging $5 and spending $150 on advertising.

c. We can interpret the net regression coefficients:

b_1 measures the change in sales $\hat{Y}$ per unit change in price X_1 holding advertising X_2 constant. Given $b_1 = -54.52$, then estimated sales will decrease by 54.52 per unit increase in X_1, holding X_2 constant. In this case, if we increase X_1 by 1, holding X_2 constant, $\hat{Y}$ will decrease by 54.52.

b_2 measures the change in sales $\hat{Y}$ per unit change in advertising X_2 holding price X_1 constant. Given $b_2 = 0.473$, then estimated sales will increase by 0.473 per unit change in X_2 holding X_1 constant. In this case, if we increase X_2 by 1, holding X_1 constant, $\hat{Y}$ will increase by 0.473.

Note: For multiple regression, the computations are often tedious, therefore the computations are usually done by computer. There are numerous regression packages available.

Problem 1: Given the following multiple regression equation

$$\hat{Y} = -2000 + 0.12X_1 + 210X_2 + 50X_3$$

where Y = savings

X_1 = income

X_2 = interest rate in percentage

X_3 = age

a. Estimate Y when X_1 = \$30,000, X_2 = 8, X_3 = 40.

b. If the interest rate increases by one percentage point, holding all other X's constant, how will that change $\hat{Y}$?

c. Interpret the net regression coefficient b_2.

ⓐ $\hat{Y} = 2000 + .12(30,000) + 210(8) + 50(40)$
$= 2000 + 3600 + 1680 = 2000$
$= 9280$

ⓑ $\Delta \hat{Y} = b_2 \cdot \Delta X$
$= 210(1)$
$= 210$
Y will increase by 210

STANDARD ERROR OF ESTIMATE

Just as in simple regression, we can compute the standard error of estimate in multiple regression analysis. The general rule for the standard error of estimate is:

$$S_{Y.12\ldots(k-1)} = \sqrt{\frac{\Sigma(Y - \hat{Y})^2}{n - k}}$$

where k = the number of constants being estimated. The rule for two independent variables is:

$$S_{Y.12} = \sqrt{\frac{\Sigma(Y - \hat{Y})^2}{n - 3}} \quad \text{or} \quad S_{Y.12} = \sqrt{\frac{\Sigma Y^2 - a\Sigma Y - b_1\Sigma X_1 Y - b_2\Sigma X_2 Y}{n - 3}}$$

Both of these rules are mathematically equivalent.

Example 3: Using the data in Example 2, find the standard error of estimate.

$$S_{Y.12} = \sqrt{\frac{860,600 - 517.4(2860) - (-54.52)(15,635) - (0.473)(489,200)}{10 - 3}}$$

$$= 16.32$$

COEFFICIENT OF MULTIPLE DETERMINATION

As in simple linear regression, the degree of association between the dependent and independent variables can be measured for multiple regressions. The coefficient of multiple determination is used to measure the proportion of the variation in the dependent variable Y that can be explained by the independent variables (Xs). The general rule for the corrected r^2 in simple regression is

$$r_c^2 = 1 - \frac{s_{Y.X}^2}{s_Y^2}$$

The rule for the corrected R^2 for the two independent variable case is:

$$R_{Y.12}^2 = 1 - \frac{S_{Y.12}^2}{s_Y^2}$$

TABLE 10-2

Correlation coefficients for each pair of the three variables: Sales (Y), price (X_1), and advertising (X_2)

	Y	X_1	X_2
Y	1.00		
X_1	-0.957	1.00	
X_2	0.878	-0.788	1.00

where

$$S^2_{Y.12} = \frac{\Sigma(Y - \hat{Y})^2}{n - 3}$$

$$s^2_Y = \frac{\Sigma(Y - \bar{Y})^2}{n - 1} \quad \text{or} \quad s^2_Y = \frac{\Sigma Y^2 - n\bar{Y}^2}{n - 1}$$

Example 4: Using the data in Examples 2 and 3, find the coefficient of multiple determination. From Example 3, $S_{Y.12} = 16.32$ so $S^2_{Y.12} = (16.32)^2 = 266.34$

$$s^2_Y = \frac{\Sigma Y^2 - n\bar{Y}^2}{n - 1} = \frac{860,600 - 10(286)^2}{10 - 1} = 4737.78$$

Thus, $R^2_c = 1 - 266.34/4737.78 = 1 - 0.056 = 0.944$. We can also compute the uncorrected R^2.

$$R^2_{Y.12} = 1 - \frac{(n - k)S^2_{Y.12}}{(n - 1)s^2_Y} = 1 - \frac{7(266.34)}{9(4737.78)} = 0.956$$

Besides measuring the degree of association between the independent variables considered collectively and the dependent variable ($R^2_{Y.12}$), it is often important to know the degree of association between the individual independent variables and the dependent variable as well as the degree of association between each pair of independent variables. This can be accomplished through the use of a correlation coefficient. Table 10-2 gives the correlation coefficients for the data in Example 2.

From Table 10-2, we see that $r_{Y.1} = -0.957$, $r_{Y.2} = 0.878$ and $r_{1.2} = -0.788$. The first two terms measure the association between Y and the individual X variables. This is the r value that would be obtained if a simple linear regression was run against the individual X value. The third term, $r_{1.2}$, is the r that would be obtained if we ran a regression between X_1 and X_2. This value is used in helping to determine whether multicollinearity exists.

COMPARISON OF SIMPLE AND MULTIPLE REGRESSION

In Problem 1 of Chapter 9, we looked at the data for the simple regression relationship between sales and price. In this chapter, we ran a multiple regression using two independent varables price, (X_1) and advertising (X_2).

In Table 10-3, we compare the simple (X_1) and multiple (X_1 and X_2) regression results.

The addition of an independent variable changes the values of a and b. For example, in the pizza sales example, the inclusion of advertising (X_2) changed the value of a from 707.44 to 517.4 and changed the value of b_1 from -74.6 to -54.3. The inclusion of another independent variable has an influence on the other independent variable. If this influence or association between the independent variables is strong, we may have the problem of multicollinearity. (This concept is discussed later in the chapter.) The addition of X_2 in the pizza example decreases a and increases b_1.

TABLE 10-3

Comparison of simple and multiple regression analysis for pizza stores problem

	Simple	Multiple
Regression equation	$\hat{Y} = 707.4 - 74.6X_1$	$\hat{Y} = 517.4 - 54.52X_1 + 0.473X_2$
Standard error of estimate	$s_{Y.X} = 21.8$	$S_{Y.12} = 16.32$
Coefficient of determination*	$r^2 = 0.911$	$R^2_{Y.12} = 0.956$

* r^2 and $R^2_{Y.12}$ are not corrected.

However, the addition of an independent variable may increase, decrease, or have no effect on the y-intercept and the net regression coefficient values.

The addition of an independent variable usually changes the value of the standard error of estimate and the correlation coefficient. The standard error of estimate generally decreases because some of the unexplained variation is explained by the additional independent variable. Also, the addition of an independent variable usually increases the coefficient of determination, because the proportion of the explained variation to the total variation increases.

However, even though the addition of another independent variable may decrease the standard error of estimate and increase the coefficient of determination, it should only be added if there is a significant relationship between the additional independent variable and the dependent variable. This can be determined by doing a hypothesis test concerning the net regression coefficients. A problem that often arises as more independent variables are included in the equation is that of multicollinearity.

INFERENCES ABOUT POPULATION NET REGRESSION COEFFICIENTS

In Chapter 9, we tested whether $B = 0$ to determine if there was any relationship between X and Y. In this chapter, we can test $B_i = 0$ to see if there is any relationship between X_i and Y. We are testing whether the individual B's are equal to zero. We use t. The degrees of freedom are $n - k$, where $k =$ the number of constants being estimated.

Setup for Hypothesis Test of B_i for a Regression Equation with Two Independent Variables

1. $H_0: B_i = 0$
2. $H_1: B_i \neq 0$
3. Critical value: $t = w$

Decision rule: Reject H_0 if $t_i < -w$ or $t_i > w$

4. $t_i = (b_i - B_i)/s_{b_i}$

$$s_{b_i} = \frac{S_{Y.12}}{\sqrt{(\Sigma(X_i - \bar{X}_i)^2)(1 - r_{12}^2)}} \quad \text{or} \quad s_{b_i} = \frac{S_{Y.12}}{\sqrt{\left(n\Sigma X_i - \frac{(\Sigma X_i)^2}{n}\right)(1 - r_{12}^2)}}$$

5. Make a decision and interpret the results.

Example 5: Using data in Examples 2 and 3, test at $\alpha = 0.05$, if

a. sales (Y) and price are related (X_1)

b. sales (Y) and advertising are related (X_2)

a. Setup for test of B_1

$$n = 10 \quad k = 3 \quad n - k = 7 \quad r_{12} = -0.787 \text{ (from Table 10-2)} \quad \alpha = 0.05$$

$$s_{b_1} = \frac{S_{Y.12}}{\sqrt{\left(\dfrac{n\Sigma X_1^2 - (\Sigma X_1)^2}{n}\right)(1 - r_{12}^2)}} = \frac{16.32}{\sqrt{\dfrac{10(326.25) - (56.5)^2}{10}[1 - (-0.787)^2]}}$$

$$= \frac{16.32}{1.635} = 9.98$$

1. $H_0: B_1 = 0$

2. $H_1: B_1 \neq 0$

3. Critical value: $t = 2.365$

Decision rule: Reject H_0 if $t < -2.365$ or $t > 2.365$.

4. $t_1 = (b_1 - B_1)/s_{b_1} = (-54.52 - 0)/9.98 = -5.46$

5. $t_1 = -5.46$; reject H_0.

The statistical evidence supports the hypothesis $(H_1: B_1 \neq 0)$ that sales and price are related at $\alpha = 0.05$.

b. Setup for test of B_2

$$n = 10 \quad k = 3 \quad \alpha = 0.05$$

$$s_{b_2} = \frac{S_{Y.12}}{\sqrt{\left(\dfrac{n\Sigma X_2^2 - (\Sigma X_2)^2}{n}\right)(1 - r_{12}^2)}} = \frac{16.32}{\sqrt{\dfrac{10(282,800) - (1620)^2}{10}[1 - (-0.787)^2]}}$$

$$= \frac{16.32}{88.03} = 0.185$$

1. $H_0: B_2 = 0$

2. $H_1: B_2 \neq 0$

3. Critical value: $t = 2.365$

Decision rule: Reject H_0 if $t < -2.365$ or $t > 2.365$.

4. $t_2 = (b_2 - B_2)/s_{b_2} = (0.473 - 0)/0.185 = 2.56$

5. $t_2 = 2.56$; reject H_0.

The statistical evidence supports the hypothesis that sales and advertising are related at $\alpha = 0.05$.

Problem 2: Given the following regression equation for 20 cars

$$\hat{Y} = 54 - 4X_1 - 16X_2 \quad s_{b_1} = 1 \quad s_{b_2} = 5$$

where Y = miles per gallon

X_1 = engine size in hundred − cubic − inch

X_2 = weight in tons

Test at $\alpha = .05$ that the dependent variable is related to the individual independent variables.

TABLE 10-4

General format of analysis of variance in regression analysis

(1) Source of Variation	(2) Sum of Square	(3) Degrees of Freedom	(4) Mean Square
Regression	$\Sigma(\hat{Y} - \bar{Y})^2$	$v_1 = k - 1$	$\Sigma(\hat{Y} - \bar{Y})^2/(k-1)$
Error	$\Sigma(Y - \hat{Y})^2$	$v_2 = n - k$	$\Sigma(Y - \hat{Y})^2/(n-k)$
Total	$\Sigma(Y - \bar{Y})^2$	$n - 1$	

$$F = \frac{\Sigma(\hat{Y} - \bar{Y})^2/(k-1)}{\Sigma(Y - \hat{Y})^2/(n-k)}$$

THE ANALYSIS OF VARIANCE

In the previous section, we tested whether the individual independent variables were related to the dependent variable. In this section we use the analysis of variance procedure to test the overall significance of the regression equation. The null hypothesis which we test is that all of the B values are equal to zero. As was done for the ANOVA test in Chapter 8 an F test is used.

Setup for the ANOVA Test for Regression

1. H_0: All of the B_i values are equal to zero.
2. H_1: Not all of the B_i values are equal to zero.
3. Critical value: $F_\alpha(v_1, v_2) = w$ where $v_1 = k - 1$ and $v_2 = n - k$

Decision rule: Reject H_0 if $F > w$.

4. $F = \dfrac{\text{MSS Regression}}{\text{MSS Error}}$

5. Make a decision and interpret the results.

The rule for the error sum of squares is

$$\Sigma(Y - \hat{Y})^2 = (n - k)S^2_{Y.12,\dots,k-1}$$

The rule for the sum of squares total is

$$\Sigma(Y - \bar{Y})^2 = (n - 1)s^2_Y$$

Also, the F test for ANOVA is always a one-tailed test in which the critical region is in the upper tail of the F distribution.

Example 6: Using the data in Examples 3 and 4, test whether all of the B_i values equal zero at $\alpha = 0.05$.

$$\Sigma(Y - \hat{Y})^2 = (n - k)S^2_{Y.X} = (10 - 3)266.34 = 1864.4$$
$$\Sigma(Y - \bar{Y})^2 = (n - 1)s^2_Y = (10 - 1)4737.78 = 42640.2$$

To find the regression sum of squares, we subtract the error sum of squares from the total sum of squares.

Regression sum of squares = Total sum of squares − Error sum of squares

$$= 42{,}640.2 - 1{,}864.4$$
$$= 40{,}775.8$$

We can use this data to fill in the values for Table 10-5.

TABLE 10-5

Format of the analysis of variance in the multiple regression with income (Y), experience (X_1), and years of post-secondary education (X_2)

(1) Source of Variation	(2) Sum of Squares	(3) Degrees of Freedom	(4) Mean Square
Regression	40,775.8	$v_1 = 2$	20,387.9
Error	1,864.4	$v_2 = 7$	266.34
Total	42,640.2		

$$F = 20,387.9/266.34 = 76.55$$

Given the above information we can do the hypothesis test.

1. H_0: All of the B_i values are equal to zero.

2. H_1: Not all of the B_i values are equal to zero.

3. Critical value: $F_\alpha(v_1, v_2) = F_{0.05}(2, 7) = 4.74$ (From Table A-8).

Decision rule: Reject H_0 if $F > 4.74$.

4. $F = \dfrac{\text{MSS Regression}}{\text{MSS Error}} = 76.55$

5. $F = 76.55$; reject H_0.

The statistical evidence supports the hypothesis that not all of the B_i values are equal to zero at $\alpha = 0.05$.

Generally, these computations are done by computer and the computer will give us the F value on the printout.

Problem 3: Given the following ANOVA table.

(1) Source of Variation	(2) Sum of Square	(3) Degrees of Freedom	(4) Mean Square
Regression	300	4	75
Error	1,000	20	50
Total	1,300		

$$F = 75/50 = 1.5$$

Test at $\alpha = 0.01$, if all the B_i values are equal to zero.

DUMMY VARIABLE TECHNIQUES

So far we have used only quantitative data for our regression analysis. The dummy variable technique allows us to convert qualitative data into quantitative data and enables us to use qualitative data in regression analysis. We use as an example, a dummy variable, which is an independent variable, that has the values zero or one. For example, suppose we want to consider the variable of male or female as our second independent variable, then we can define variable X_2 as $X_2 = 0$ (if male) or $X_2 = 1$ (if female).

The regression line with one dummy variable and one other independent variable can be expressed as

$$\hat{Y} = a + b_1 X_1 + b_2 X_2$$

where $X_2 = 0$ for male

$X_2 = 1$ for female

The regression line for males ($X_2 = 0$) would be:

$$\hat{Y} = a + b_1 X_1 + b_2 X_2 = a + b_1 X_1 + b_2 \cdot 0 = a + b_1 X_1 \quad \text{for } X_2 = 0 \text{ male}$$

The regression line for females ($X_2 = 1$) would be:

$$\hat{Y} = a + b_1 X_1 + b_2 \cdot 1 = a + b_1 X_1 + b_2 = (a + b_2) + b_1 X_1 \quad \text{for } X_2 = 1 \text{ female}$$

We now have two different equations for male and female. Using ordinary least squares methods we can obtain the values for a, b_1, and b_2.

Example 7: For the following data,

a. Find the regression equation using the dummy variable technique.

b. Estimate the income ($\hat{Y}$) of a 30-year-old male.

c. Estimate the income ($\hat{Y}$) of a 30-year-old female.

d. Compare your answers in parts (b) and (c).

Let the dummy variable $X_2 = 0$ for male and $X_2 = 1$ for female.

Income ($000)	Y	50	30	60	25	40	75	40	50	65	42	37	29
Age	X_1	29	23	34	21	36	40	35	37	41	35	40	23
Sex	X_2	0	1	1	0	0	1	1	0	0	1	1	0

a. Using a computer, we obtain the following regression equation:

$$\hat{Y} = a + b_1 X_1 + b_2 X_2 = -4.98 + 1.55 X_1 - 0.98 X_2$$

The regression line for males ($X_2 = 0$) is

$$\hat{Y} = -4.98 + 1.55 X_1$$

The regression line for females ($X_2 = 1$) is

$$\hat{Y} = -4.98 + 1.55 X_1 - 0.98(1) = -5.96 + 1.55 X_1$$

b. $\hat{Y} = -4.98 + 1.55 X_1 = -4.98 + 1.55(30) = 41.52$
So, \$41,520 is the estimated average income of a 30-year-old male.

c. $\hat{Y} = -5.96 + 1.55 X_1 = -5.96 + 1.55(30) = 40.54$
So, \$40,540 is the estimated average income of a 30-year-old female.

d. It is estimated that a 30-year-old male on average makes \$980 more than a 30-year-old female.

Problem 4: Given the following regression equation for 20 cars:

$$\hat{Y} = 10,000 - 1000X_1 + 450X_2 \quad (s_{b_1} = 200 \quad s_{b_2} = 200)$$

X_1 = Age in years

X_2 = Air conditioning

X_2 = 0 for no air conditioning in car

X_2 = 1 for air conditioning in car

Y = Price of used car.

a. Estimate $\hat{Y}$ for a 5-year-old car without air conditioning.

b. Estimate $\hat{Y}$ for a 5-year-old car with air conditioning.

c. Compare your answers in **a** and **b**.

Multicollinearity

We have assumed that the independent variables are not related to each other. However, this is not always true. If two independent variables have a high degree of association, then the problem of multicollinearity exists and odd results may occur. If this is the case then the net regression coefficients may not accurately reflect the individual influences of each independent variable.

When a model is being built, we expect certain signs for each net regression coefficient. For example, suppose we are estimating a demand equation and one of the independent variables is price, we would expect a negative b value. If we obtain a positive b value, we are fairly certain that something is wrong with the equation. Also, even if the right sign occurs, the b value may not be significantly different from zero. If this occurs with a variable that we expect to be very important, then multicollinearity may exist.

There is no rule that states that a certain level of association is high. However, a fairly high correlation coefficient with the wrong sign for b or an insignificant b value for a variable which you expect is important is a signal that multicollinearity may exist and that one of the highly correlated independent variables should be omitted.

A COMPUTER APPLICATION

The computer is often used to compute the multiple regression equation, and there are many canned programs available. Different programs vary in the way they report the data, but they all give essentially the same information.

Example 8: Figure 10-1 is a computer printout of the data used in Example 2. The number of independent variables is 3 because this particular computer program counts the constant term as an independent variable. The number of observations is the sample size which is 10.

The variables are

$$C = \text{constant term} \quad 1 = X_1 \quad 2 = X_2 \quad 3 = Y$$

```
NUMBER OF INDEPENDENT VARIABLES - 3
NUMBER OF OBSERVATIONS        - 10
VARIABLE      AVERAGE        VARIANCE

   C             1          1.578984E-14
   1           5.65          .7805556
   2           162          2262.222
   3           286          4737.778

            CORRELATION COEFFICIENTS

 VAR.I        VAR.J         CORRELATION

   1             2           -.7879602
   1             3           -.9574134
   2             3            .8783484

VARIABLE     COEFFICIENT    ST.ERROR

   C           517.399       81.64705
   1          -54.52111       9.898416
   2            .4731194       .1838653

STANDARD ERROR OF THE ESTIMATE - 16.15385
COEFFICIENT OF MULTIPLE DETERMINATION - .9571628
F-VALUE - 78.20251
DURBIN-WATSON STATISTIC - 1.605206

  T          Y(T)          YEST(T)        ERROR

  1           300          315.7613     -15.76129
  2           250          237.5842      12.41579
  3           400          390.3338       9.666199
  4           350          329.9549      20.04511
  5           370          371.409       -1.409027
  6           190          183.0631       6.936875
  7           220          219.7861        .2139588
  8           280          275.4338       4.566223
  9           270          297.9631     -27.96314
 10           230          238.7108      -8.710816
```

FIGURE 10-1

Note: The values on the printout may differ from those computed in the chapter because of rounding error.

The average and variance for each variable is given: for example, $\bar{X}_1 = 5.65$, and $s_1^2 = 0.78056$. Next, the correlation coefficients are given. We can construct a correlation coefficient table from this information (see Table 10-2). Again, the correlation coefficients can be used in helping to determine if multicollinearity may exist.

The next set of numbers is the coefficients and standard errors of the variables

$$a = 517.399 \qquad s_a = 81.64705$$
$$b_1 = -54.5211 \qquad s_{b_1} = 9.898416$$
$$b_2 = 0.473119 \qquad s_{b_2} = 0.1838653$$

Thus, $\hat{Y} = 517.4 - 54.52X_1 + 0.473X_2$ (rounding off). The standard error of estimate is $S_{Y.12} = 16.15$. The coefficient of multiple determination is the uncorrected $R^2 = 0.9571628$. The F-value is computed by using the ANOVA table (see Table 10-4). In the last set of numbers, $Y(T)$ is the actual Y values, YEST(T) is the estimated Y values ($\hat{Y}$), "Error" is the difference between Y and $\hat{Y}(Y - \hat{Y})$. For example, in the first observation of the sample: $Y = 300$, $X_1 = 5$, and $X_2 = 150$. The actual value was $Y(T) = 300$. The estimated value ($\hat{Y}$) when $X_1 = 5$ and $X_2 = 150$ would be

$$\hat{Y} = 517.4 - 54.52(5) + 0.473(150) = 315.76$$

CHAPTER 10 REVIEW PROBLEMS

1. Given the following regression equation for a sample of 20:

$$\hat{Y} = -40 + 2X_1 + 10X_2 \quad (s_{b_1} = 0.5 \quad s_{b_2} = 2)$$

   Y = Income in \$1000s X_1 = ranges from 30 to 50
   X_1 = Age X_2 = 0 when No College Degree
   X_2 = College Degree X_2 = 1 when Having a College Degree

   a. Test at $\alpha = .02$ if the individual independent variables are related to the dependent variable.
   b. Estimate Y for a 40 year old with a college degree.
   c. Interpret the b_2 coefficient.

2. Given the following regression equation for a sample of 32:

$$\hat{Y} = 600 + 0.5X_1 - 0.8X_2 + 6X_3 \quad (s_{b_1} = 0.5 \quad s_{b_2} = 0.2 \quad s_{b_3} = 2)$$

   a. Test at $\alpha = .10$ if there is a relationship between each independent variable and the dependent variable.
   b. Estimate Y when $X_1 = 10$, $X_2 = 100$, $X_3 = 5$

3. Given the following ANOVA table for Y = cost of painting a house, X_1 = number of linear feet, X_2 = number of workers, X_3 = use of scaffold.

(1) Source of Variation	(2) Sum of Squares	(3) Degrees of Freedom	(4) Mean Square
Regression	300	3	100
Error	55	21	2.62
Total	355		

$$F = 100/2.62 = 38.2$$

   Test at $\alpha = 0.01$ if all the B's are equal to zero.

4. Given the following regression equation for a sample of 25 fast-food restaurants:

$$\hat{Y} = 10 + 50X_1 + 10X_2 \quad (s_{b_1} = .10 \quad s_{b_2} = 2)$$

   X_1 = number of households in thousands within 3 mile radius of the store
   X_2 = Location of restaurant   ($X_2 = 0$ for Mall $X_2 = 1$ for Highway)
   Y = Sales in thousands of \$

   a. Test at $\alpha = .02$ if there is a relationship between the independent and the dependent variables.
   b. Find the regression equation for a restaurant located on the highway.

5. An automobile firm estimated the following valid regression equation for the demand for automobiles in its dealership:

$$\hat{Y} = 2,000 - 100X_1 - 25X_2$$

where Y = number of automobiles sold

   X_1 = price of automobiles in thousands

   X_2 = interest rate in percentages

a. Estimate Y when $X_1 = 10$, $X_2 = 10$

b. Suppose the car dealership offered a $500 rebate. What effect would this have on sales, holding interest rates constant?

c. Suppose the car dealership offered an 8% interest rate, holding the price constant; what effect would this have on sales?

6. Given the following regression equation for a sample of 25:

$$\hat{Y} = -30 + 2.2X_1 + 1.4X_2$$

$$\text{Income} = Y(\$1,000) \quad (S_{b_1} = 0.5) \quad (S_{b_2} = 0.3)$$

$$\text{Age} = X_1$$

$$\text{Marital Status} = X_2 \quad \begin{aligned} X_2 &= 0 \text{ (Unmarried)} \\ X_2 &= 1 \text{ (Married)} \end{aligned}$$

a. Test at $\alpha = .05$ if the independent variables are related to the dependent variable.

b. Estimate the income of a 30 year old unmarried man.

7. Using the data in Example 7,

a. Find the standard error of estimate.

b. Find R^2.

c. Test at $\alpha = 0.05$ whether the individual independent variables are related to the dependent variable.

8. Given the following data:

Graduate GPA Y	Undergraduate GPA X_1	X_1^2	GMAT Score X_2	X_2^2	X_1Y	X_2Y	X_1X_2
3.4	3.0	9	600	360,000	10.2	2040	1800
3.6	2.8	7.84	700	490,000	10.08	2520	1960
3.1	2.9	8.41	400	160,000	8.99	1240	1160
3.2	3.2	10.24	500	250,000	10.24	1600	1600
4.0	4.0	16.00	750	562,500	16.00	3000	3000
2.8	2.6	6.76	450	202,500	7.28	1260	1170
3.6	3.0	9.00	600	360,000	10.8	2160	1800
3.5	2.9	8.41	700	490,000	10.15	2450	2030
3.2	2.7	7.29	450	202,500	8.64	1440	1215
3.9	3.6	12.96	650	422,500	14.04	2535	2340
	34.3	30.7 95.91	5800		106.42	20245	18075

Handwritten left margin: 11.56, 12.96, 9.61, 10.24, 16.00, 7.84, 12.96, 12.25, 10.24, 15.21, 118.87

10

3,500,000

a. Find the regression equation.

b. Find the standard error of estimate.

c. Find R^2.

d. Test at $\alpha = 0.10$, whether the individual independent variables are related to the dependent variable.

e. Find $\hat{Y}$ when $X_1 = 600$ and $X_2 = 3.2$.

9. The following data concerns height in inches (Y), age (X_1), and sex (X_2). $X_2 = 0$ for girls and $X_1 = 1$ for boys.

Y	X_1	X_2
46	6	1
38	5	0
48	7	0
55	8	1
52	9	0
39	5	1
40	6	0
51	8	0
47	7	0
56	9	1
37	6	0
40	5	1
41	6	0
53	7	1

a. Find the regression equation.

b. Find the standard error of estimate.

c. Find R^2.

d. Test at $\alpha = 0.01$ whether all the individual independent variables are related to the dependent variable.

e. Test at $\alpha = 0.01$ whether all the B_i values are equal to zero.

11

TIME SERIES

In this chapter, we examine data over a period of time (for example, annual sales of a firm over a 15-year time period or quarterly sales over a 5-year time period). **Time series** uses historic data to forecast future values. The classical time series consists of four components: trend, cyclical fluctuations, seasonal variations, and irregular movements. **Trend** (T) is the long-term pattern of the data, generally represented by a smooth upward or downward movement. **Cyclical fluctuations** (C) are recurrent, but temporary, movements above or below the trend line due to the business cycle. **Seasonal variations** (S) are a recurrent pattern within a given year. For example sales may be higher in certain months or quarters than in other time periods during the year. Ice cream sales every year will be highest in the summer months. There is no seasonal variation when the data are stated annually or longer. **Irregular movements** (I) follow no regular pattern and are difficult to predict—for example, a fire in the plant, a strike, or a flood.

The time series model that we examine is multiplicative—that is, $Y = T \cdot C \cdot S \cdot I$. However, it can also be expressed as an additive model, $Y = T + C + S + I$.

FITTING TREND LINES

The major purpose of the trend is to forecast future trend values. However, it can also be used to describe historic data as well as study the other components of the time series by eliminating the trend value.

If trend is linear, the trend line can be estimated using the method of least squares. The trend line is expressed as

$$Y_t = a + bx$$

where Y_t represents the trend value for a specific time period

   a is the y-intercept

   b is the slope of the line

   x is the value of the time period

The least square rules for obtaining a and b are:

$$a = \frac{\Sigma Y}{n} \qquad b = \frac{\Sigma xY}{\Sigma x^2}$$

TABLE 11-1
Straight-line trend fitted by the method of least squares for the annual data of gasoline sales, 1970–1988

(1)	(2)	(3) Sales	(4)	(5)	(6)	(7) Percentage of Trend
Year	x	Y	xY	x^2	Y_t	$Y/Y_t \cdot 100$
1970	−9	18	−162	81	17.398	103.5
1971	−8	22	−176	64	21.231	103.6
1972	−7	25	−175	49	25.064	99.7
1973	−6	30	−180	36	28.897	103.8
1974	−5	31	−155	25	32.730	94.7
1975	−4	37	−148	16	36.563	101.2
1976	−3	42	−126	9	40.396	104.0
1977	−2	47	−94	4	44.229	106.3
1978	−1	45	−45	1	48.062	93.6
1979	0	50	0	0	51.895	96.3
1980	1	53	53	1	55.728	95.1
1981	2	58	116	4	59.561	97.4
1982	3	62	186	9	63.394	97.8
1983	4	67	268	16	67.227	99.7
1984	5	74	370	25	71.060	104.1
1985	6	76	456	36	74.893	101.5
1986	7	82	574	49	78.726	104.2
1987	8	80	640	64	82.559	96.9
1988	9	87	783	81	86.392	100.7
~~1989~~	~~10~~	~~95~~	~~950~~	~~100~~	~~90.225~~	~~105.3~~
		986	2185	570		

Example 1: Refer to Table 11-1 for the annual data of sales for a gas station. Find the trend line.

$$a = \Sigma Y/n = 986/19 = 51.89473 = 51.895$$

$$b = \Sigma xY/\Sigma x^2 = 2,185/570 = 3.833$$

$$Y_t = 51.895 + 3.833x \quad (x = 0 \text{ in } 1979)$$

The first step is to determine the x values. This is done by finding the median year and letting $x = 0$ for that year. In Example 1, the median year is $(19 + 1)/2 = 10$th year, which is 1979. For each year after the median year, we use a positive value to denote the number of years away from the median year (for example, 1982 is 3 years from the median, so $x = 3$). For each year before the median year, we use a negative value to represent the number of years away from the median (for example, 1975 is 4 years from the median, so $x = -4$). By doing this for every year, we obtain the x values.

• Column (4) is obtained by multiplying column (2) by column (3).

• Column (5) is obtained by squaring the observations in column (2).

• Column (6) Y_t is obtained by substituting the x values into the trend line (for example, $Y_t = 51.895 + 3.833x$, when $x = -9$, $Y_t = 17.398$) or by adding the b value to each successive Y_t value

$$Y_{1966} = 17.398$$

$$Y_{1967} = Y_{1966} + 3.833 = 17.398 + 3.833 = 21.231$$

• Column (7) is obtained by dividing column (3) by column (6) and multiplying by 100

$$\frac{18}{17.398} \times 100 = 103.5$$

We can also project future trend values by substituting in the x-value of the future year. The x-value of the future years can be obtained by determining how far from the median year the future year is (for example, the x-value for 1989 is $x = 10$, for 1990, $x = 11$).

A Technical Point

The procedure described above for obtaining the x-values is valid only when n is odd. When n is even, a slightly different procedure is used. Assume we have the data for 1989 and we have an actual value of 95, n is now equal to 20. The median year $(n + 1)/2 = (20 + 1)/2 = 10.5$th year. In this case $x = 0$, in the middle of 1979, which is on July 1, 1979. The year 1980 is $+\frac{1}{2}$ year away from July 1979. To avoid the use of fractions, we designate the x-values of the number of half-years away from the median year. Thus, $x = 1$ for the year 1980, $x = 3$ for 1981, and $x = -11$ for 1974. The computation of a and b is the same. However, a is the y-intercept for the mid-year of 1979 and b measures the change per half year.

Problem 1: Use the data in Example 1 and add the 1989 sales of 95.

    a. Find the trend line.

    b. Find the trend values for each observation.

    c. Find the percentage of trend for each observation.

Example 2: Use the data in Example 1 to forecast the trend value for 1990.

$$Y_t = 51.895 + 3.833x \quad \text{(for 1990, } x = 11)$$
$$= 51.895 + 3.833(11) = 94.058$$

This forecasts the trend value and not the actual sales figures for 1990. In order to predict the actual sales in 1990, the other components of the time series must be taken into account. When using annual data, there is no seasonal variable component of the time series. The other components of the time series for annual data are cyclical fluctuations and irregular movements.

Problem 2: Using the data in problem 1 forecast the trend value for 1990.

CYCLICAL FLUCTUATIONS

Cyclical fluctuations measure the effect of the business cycle in a time series. The cyclical fluctuations and irregular movements can be measured by dividing the original data Y by the trend values Y_t and multiplying by 100 to obtain the percentage of trend. The rule for percentage of trend is:

$$\text{Percentage of trend} = \frac{Y}{Y_t} \cdot 100$$

This percentage of trend contains only cyclical and irregular movements.

$$\frac{Y}{Y_t} = \frac{T \times C \times I}{T} = C \times I$$

We can measure the **relative cyclical residual** by using the following rule:

$$\frac{Y - Y_t}{Y_t} \cdot 100 \quad \text{or} \quad \% \text{ of trend} - 100\%$$

Example 3: Using the data in Example 2, find the relative cyclical residual.

a. for 1973   **b.** for 1982

a. Relative cyclical residual $= \%$ of trend $- 100\%$

$$= 103.8\% - 100\% = 3.8\%$$

In 1973, the actual value is 3.8% above the trend value due to cyclical fluctuations and irregular movements.

b. Relative cyclical residual $= \%$ of trend $- 100\%$

$$= 97.8\% - 100\% = -2.2\%$$

In 1982, the actual value is 2.2% below the trend value due to cyclical fluctuations and irregular movements.

Problem 3: Using the data in Problem 1, find the relative cyclical residual.

a. for 1970   **b.** for 1983

Second-Degree Trend Lines

The straight line trend that we have estimated assumes that the change is constant over time (that is, in Example 1, it was assumed that sales were increasing by constant amounts). This is not always true. Sometimes sales may increase by increasing amounts or increase by decreasing amounts. Sales may also decrease by increasing or decreasing amounts. We can estimate trend lines that take this into account.

Using a second-degree trend line, the amounts of change may increase or decrease over time. The second-degree trend line can be expressed as:

$$Y_t = a + bx + cx^2$$

The least squares rules for finding a, b, and c are:

$$\Sigma Y = na + c\Sigma x^2$$
$$\Sigma x^2 Y = a\Sigma x^2 + c\Sigma x^4$$
$$b = \Sigma x Y / \Sigma x^2$$

The computation for a second-degree line is sufficiently complex that it is usually done by computer. The procedure for finding the x values is the same as in the straight line trend example.

Fitting Logarithmic Trend Lines

The logarithmic trend line measures the percentage rate of change in the trend.
The rule for logarithmic trend lines is

$$\log Y_t = a + bx$$

The rules for obtaining a and b are

$$a = \frac{\Sigma \log Y}{n} \qquad b = \frac{\Sigma x \log Y}{\Sigma x^2}$$

These computations are generally done by a computer.

MEASUREMENT OF SEASONAL VARIATIONS

As stated, when time series data are expressed in time periods shorter than a year (that is, monthly or quarterly), then some seasonal variation may exist. For example, sales of Christmas trees are higher in December than any other month of the year. In order to take these seasonal variations into account, we use the following procedure.

Example 4: Table 11-2 lists the quarterly data of retail toy sales. Compute the seasonal indices and deseasonalize the original data. **Columns (1) and (2)** are given. **Column (3)** is obtained by summing the first 4 observations in column (2)—$100 + 105 + 112 + 140 = 457$—and putting the sum in the third slot of column (3). The second observation in column (3) is obtained by dropping the first observation in column (2)—100—and adding the fifth observation in column (2) to the second, third, and fourth observation in column (2)—$105 + 112 + 140 + 107 = 464$. The rest of the values for column (3) are obtained by using the same procedure—that is, drop the first observation in the sum and add in the next observation. For example

100			
105	105		
112	112	112	
140	140	140	140
457	107	107	107
	464	112	112
		471	125
			484

This gives us the four-quarter moving total.

Column (4) is obtained by summing two successive values in column (3). The first value in column (4) is obtained by adding $457 + 464 = 921$. The next value for column (4) is obtained by dropping the first observation in the sum (457) and adding the next observation (471). Thus, the second value in column (4) is 935(464 + 471). The other values in column (4) are obtained by using the same procedure. For example

457			
464	464		
921	471	471	
	935	484	484
		955	514
			998

This gives us the two-of-a-four-quarter moving total.

Column (5) is obtained by multiplying column (4) by 1/8. The rationale for this is that column (4) is made up of 8 observations, so in dividing column (4) by 8, we obtain the moving average.

Column (6) is obtained by dividing column (2) by column (5) and then multiplying by 100.

TABLE 11-2

Sales of a toy store by quarters, 1982–1987: Computations for seasonal indices and deseasonalizing of original data

(1) Quarter	(2) Sales ($000)	(3) Four-Quarter Moving Total	(4) Two-of a-Four-Quarter Moving Total	(5) Moving Average Col 4 · $\frac{1}{8}$	(6) Original Data as a % of Moving Average $\frac{\text{Col 2}}{\text{Col 5}} \cdot 100$	(7) Seasonal Index	(8) Deseasonalized Sales $\frac{\text{Col 2}}{\text{Col 7}} \cdot 100$
1982							
1	100					87.9	113.8
2	105					91.1	115.3
3	112	457	921	115.125	97.3	95.3	117.5
4	140	464	935	116.875	119.8	125.7	111.4
1983							
1	107	471	955	119.375	89.6	87.9	121.7
2	112	484	998	124.750	89.8	91.1	122.9
3	125	514	1041	130.125	96.1	95.3	131.2
4	170	527	1069	133.625	127.2	125.7	135.2
1984							
1	120	542	1097	137.125	87.5	87.9	136.5
2	127	555	1145	143.125	88.7	91.1	139.4
3	138	590	1195	149.375	92.4	95.3	144.8
4	205	605	1228	153.500	133.6	125.7	163.1
1985							
1	135	623	1249	156.125	86.5	87.9	153.6
2	145	626	1247	155.875	93.0	91.1	159.2
3	141	621	1257	157.125	89.7	95.3	148.0
4	200	636	1289	161.125	124.1	125.7	159.1
1986							
1	150	653	1340	167.500	89.6	87.9	170.6
2	162	687	1399	174.875	92.6	91.1	177.8
3	175	712	1426	178.250	98.2	95.3	183.6
4	225	714	1433	179.125	125.6	125.7	179.0
1987							
1	152	719	1445	180.625	84.2	87.9	172.9
2	167	726	1474	184.250	90.6	91.1	183.3
3	182	748				95.3	191.0
4	247					125.7	196.5

Column (7), the seasonal index, is computed by setting up the data in column (6) as shown in Table 11-3.

Once we have set up the table, the first step is to eliminate the lowest and highest value in each quarter (for example, in quarter I, 84.2 is the lowest and 89.6 is the highest value). This is done for the other quarters as shown in Table 11-3. We remove the lowest and highest values in each column to eliminate the irregular movement.

TABLE 11-3

Sales of a toy store: Calculation of quarterly seasonal indices from percentage of moving average figures

| | **Percentage of Moving Averages** Quarters | | | |
	I	**II**	**III**	**IV**
Year				
1982			97.3	~~119.8~~
1983	~~89.6~~	89.8	96.1	127.2
1984	87.5	~~88.7~~	92.4	~~133.6~~
1985	86.5	~~93.0~~	~~89.7~~	124.1
1986	89.6	92.6	~~98.2~~	125.6
1987	~~84.2~~	90.6		
Modified means	87.9	91.0	95.3	125.6

Total of modified means = 399.8

Adjustment factor = 400/399.8 = 1.0005

| | **Seasonal Indices** | | | |
	I	**II**	**III**	**IV**
Modified mean	87.9	91.0	95.3	125.6
Adjustment factor	× 1.0005	× 1.0005	× 1.0005	× 1.0005
	87.9	91.1	95.3	125.7

After we remove the irregular movement from each column, we sum the remaining values in the column and divide by the number of values. For example, for the first quarter 263.6/3 = 87.9 (87.5 + 86.5 + 89.6 = 263.6). This gives us the modified means for each quarter. Next, we sum the values of the modified means (87.9 + 91.0 + 95.3 + 125.6 = 399.8) to obtain the total of modified means. We then use the total of modified means, to determine the adjustment factor. For quarterly data, the sum of the seasonal indices should equal 400 (for monthly, the sum is 1,200). If the total of modified means does not equal 400, an adjustment must be made to the modified means to obtain the seasonal indices. The rule for the adjustment factor for quarterly data is:

$$\text{Adjustment factor} = \frac{400}{\text{Total of modified means}}$$

For monthly data the rule is:

$$\text{Adjustment factor} = \frac{1{,}200}{\text{Total of modified means}}$$

In this case the adjustment factor is 400/399.8 = 1.0005. Multiplying each quarter's modified mean by the adjustment factor, we obtain the seasonal index for each quarter, as shown in Table 11-3.

The values for **column (7)** of Table 11-2 are obtained by filling in the respective seasonal index for each quarter. Thus, 87.9 is the seasonal index value for each first quarter. **Column (8)** is obtained by dividing column (2) by column (7) and then multiplying by 100.

The deseasonalized values represent what sales would have been if there had been no seasonal variation.

Problem 4: For the listed data concerning gasoline sold at a gas station, compute the seasonal indices and deseasonalize the original data.

Data for Problem 4

Quarter	Sales (1,000 gal)	Quarter	Sales (1,000 gal)	Quarter	Sales (1,000 gal)
1980		1982		1984	
I	40	I	55	I	77
II	42	II	57	II	82
III	60	III	82	III	110
IV	45	IV	60	IV	86
1981		1983			
I	47	I	64		
II	50	II	70		
III	70	III	95		
IV	52	IV	73		

Exponential Smoothing

Exponential smoothing is a method of forecasting that takes into account the most recent actual data and the current forecast to obtain new forecast values.
The rule is

$$F_t = wA_{t-1} + (1 - w)F_{t-1}$$

where F_t is the forecast for time period t

  A_{t-1} is the actual figure for time period t − 1

  F_{t-1} is the forecast for time period t − 1

    w is a constant whose value is between 0 and 1

  t − 1 is the current time period

We can express the preceding equation as

  New forecast = w(current actual) + (1 − w)(current forecast)

The higher the value of w, the more influence the later values have.

Example 5: Using the data from Example 1, use the exponential smoothing procedure to prepare next year's forecast, with weighting factors of w = 0.4 and w = 0.9.

Data for Example 5

Year	Actual Sales	Estimate $w = 0.4$	Estimate $w = 0.9$
1970	$18 = a_1$	$18 = F_2$	$18 = F_2$
1971	22	18	18
1972	25	19.6	21.6
1973	30	21.76	24.66
1974	31	25.06	29.47
1975	37	27.43	30.85
1976	42	31.26	36.38
1977	47	35.56	41.44
1978	45	40.13	46.44
1979	50	42.08	45.14
1980	53	45.25	49.51
1981	58	48.35	52.65
1982	62	52.21	57.47
1983	67	56.13	61.55
1984	74	60.48	66.45
1985	76	65.89	73.25
1986	82	69.93	75.72
1987	80	74.76	81.37
1988	87	76.86	80.14

For example $F_{1973} = 0.4(25) + 0.6(19.6) = 21.76$.

Problem 5: Using the data from Example 1 and Problem 1, employ the exponential smoothing procedure to prepare next year's forecast, with weighing factors of $w = 0.5$ and $w = 0.8$.

CHAPTER 11 REVIEW PROBLEMS

1. The following table is annual data for shoe sales in hundreds of thousands.

Year	1975	1976	1977	1978	1979	1980	1981	1982	1983	1984	1985	1986	1987	1988	1989
Y	20	25	37	33	45	52	61	73	82	101	97	105	111	123	131

    a. Find the least squares straight line trend.

    b. Find the trend values.

    c. Find the percentage of trend.

2. Use the data in Review Problem 1.

    a. Estimate the trend value for 1984.

    b. Estimate the trend value for 1990.

3. Using the data in Review Problem 1, employ the exponential smoothing procedure to prepare next year's forecast with weighting factors of $w = 0.3$ and $w = 0.7$.

4. For the listed data concerning beer sales at a local store, compute the seasonal indices and deseasonalize the original data.

Data for Review Problem 4

Quarter	Sales ($000)	Quarter	Sales ($000)	Quarter	Sales ($000)
1980		1982		1984	
I	20	I	29	I	42
II	27	II	37	II	54
III	40	III	62	III	90
IV	22	IV	33	IV	49
1981		1983		1985	
I	24	I	35	I	50
II	32	II	45	II	60
III	50	III	75	III	110
IV	27	IV	40	IV	60

5. Given the listed percentage of moving averages, find the seasonal indices.

Data for Review Problem 5

	Quarters			
Year	I	II	III	IV
1978			95.0	97.2
1979	104.1	101.2	99.3	91.7
1980	110.2	95.6	97.1	94.2
1981	107.4	102.1	96.2	96.5
1982	103.2	106.7	103.1	98.1
1983	105.4	102.4	98.1	97.3
1984	103.5	103.1	97.0	96.0

6. The following data was compiled for monthly turkey sales.

Month	Actual Turkey Sales (1,000)	Seasonal Index
October	60	80
November	120	150
December	90	105

Find the deseasonalized values for these months.

7. Use the data in Review Problem 1 and add the 1990 observation value of 140 to find the following:

a. the trend line

    b. the trend values

    c. the percentage of trend values

8. Use the data in Review Problem 7.

    a. Estimate the trend value for 1984.

    b. Estimate the trend value for 1991.

9. Using the data in Review Problem 7, employ the exponential smoothing procedure to prepare next year's forecast with weighting factors of $w = 0.25$ and $w = 0.50$.

10. Find the level of actual sales by referring to the following deseasonalized data on sales of bathing suits.

Month	Deseasonalized Sales	Seasonal Index
March	25,000	85.0
April	26,000	88.2
May	27,500	98.3
June	28,000	126.2
July	28,750	158.4

11. Using the data in Review Problem 1, find the relative cyclical residual.

    a. for 1980

    b. for 1984

12
INDEX NUMBERS

An **index number** is a relative measure that represents the relationship between two numbers when one of the numbers is used as the base. Index numbers are used to measure average changes over time—for example, the Consumer Price Index (CPI), which is an attempt to measure changes in consumer prices over time.

Four Basic Steps to the Construction of Index Numbers

1. Determine the items to be included in the index: In the case of the CPI, this includes the determination of the market basket.
2. Choose a base period: Select one that is not too far from the present and that represents a normal period.
3. Choose a mathematical technique: There are two basic techniques—aggregate and average of relatives.
4. Determine weights to be used: These weights represent the importance or significance of the item.

Suppose we want to determine how food prices have changed from 1980 to 1985. The first step is to determine which food items to include in our market basket; we might pick 4 items: milk, tea, butter, and chicken. The second step is to determine the base year. The third step is to choose a mathematical technique. Of the two basic techniques, aggregate and average of relatives, we first look at aggregates and then examine the average of relatives. Finally, we look at unweighted and weighted averages.

AGGREGATIVE PRICE INDICES

Unweighted

Rule: $$\frac{\Sigma P_n}{\Sigma P_0} \cdot 100$$ where P_n = price in non-base period

P_0 = price in base period

Example 1: Let 1980 be the base year. Find the unweighted aggregative price index. Suppose the unit prices are as follows:

Item	1980 P_0	1985 P_n
Milk (gal)	$1.60	$1.85
Tea (box of 100)	1.49	1.98
Butter (lb)	1.70	2.10
Chicken (lb)	0.79	0.95
	$\Sigma P_0 = \$5.58$	$\Sigma P_n = \$6.88$

$$\text{Index} = \frac{\Sigma P_n}{\Sigma P_0} \cdot 100 = \frac{\$6.88}{\$5.58} \cdot 100 = 117.01$$

In 1985 it cost 17% more than in 1980 to purchase the same market basket.

Unfortunately the unweighted aggregative price index does not take into account the amount of each item purchased. It assumes that all items are purchased in the same quantities. This is usually not the case. We would expect in Example 1 that more units of chicken would be purchased than tea. To take into account the different quantities purchased, a weighted aggregative price index can be used.

Weighted

When weighting by quantities purchased, it is necessary to determine which quantities should be used (that is, quantities in the base or non-base period). The Laspeyres index uses base year quantities.

Rule for weighted aggregative price index   (quantities base year)

$$\frac{\Sigma P_n Q_0}{\Sigma P_0 Q_0} \cdot 100 \quad \text{(Laspeyres)}$$

The Paasche index uses non-base year quantities as weights.

Rule for weighted aggregative price index   (quantities non-base year)

$$\frac{\Sigma P_n Q_n}{\Sigma P_0 Q_n} \cdot 100 \quad \text{(Paasche)}$$

Example 2: In this example we show the computation of a Laspeyres Index (weighted aggregative price index, quantities base year).

Using data from Example 1 and adding base year quantities, we obtain the following:

Item	Q_{80}	P_{80}	P_{85}	$P_{80}Q_{80}$	$P_{85}Q_{80}$
Milk (gal)	3	$1.60	$1.85	$4.80	$5.55
Tea (box of 100)	1	1.49	1.98	1.49	1.98
Butter (lb)	2	1.70	2.10	3.40	4.20
Chicken (lb)	5	0.79	0.95	3.95	4.75
				$13.64	$16.48

$$\text{Laspeyres} = \frac{\Sigma P_n Q_0}{\Sigma P_0 Q_0} \cdot 100 = \frac{\$16.48}{\$13.64} \cdot 100 = 120.82$$

In 1985 it cost 20.82% more to purchase the same market basket of quantities purchased in 1980.

Sometimes, we are interested in how much prices have changed from some base period using our present market basket (non-base). In this case, we use non-base quantities.

Example 3: In this example we show the computation of a Paasche Index (weighted aggregative price index, quantities non-base). Using data from Example 1 and adding non-base year quantities, we obtain the following:

Item	Q_{1985}	P_{80}	P_{85}	$P_{80}Q_{85}$	$P_{85}Q_{85}$
Milk (gal)	2	$1.60	$1.85	$ 3.20	$ 3.70
Tea (box of 100)	1	1.49	1.98	1.49	1.98
Butter (lb)	1	1.70	2.10	1.70	2.10
Chicken (lb)	6	0.79	0.95	4.74	5.70
				11.13	13.48

$$\text{Paasche} = \frac{\Sigma P_n Q_n}{\Sigma P_0 Q_n} \cdot 100 = \frac{\$13.48}{\$11.13} \cdot 100 = 121.11$$

In 1985 it cost 21.11% more than in 1980 to purchase the present market basket (quantities purchased in 1985).

Problem 1: Using 1982 as a base year, find the unweighted aggregative price index for the following market basket.

Item	1982 P_0	1985 P_n
Shoes (pair)	$25.00	$27.00
Shirt (dress)	18.00	22.00
Pants (pair)	22.00	25.00

Problem 2: Using the data in Problem 1 and adding the following base year quantities, find the Laspeyres index.

Item	Q_{82}	P_{82}	P_{85}
Shoes (pair)	1	$25.00	$27.00
Shirt (dress)	3	18.00	22.00
Pants (pair)	2	22.00	25.00

Problem 3: Using the data in Problem 1 and adding the following non-base year quantities, find the Paasche index.

Item	Q_{85}	P_{82}	P_{85}
Shoes (pair)	2	$25.00	$27.00
Shirt (dress)	4	18.00	22.00
Pants (pair)	3	22.00	25.00

An advantage of the Laspeyres index over the Paasche index is that we can compare changes for more than two time periods because the quantities (base period) are constant in the Laspeyres. With the Paasche, these comparisons cannot be made because the quantities (non-base) are changing in each time period. A change in the Paasche index could result from either a change in prices or a change in quantities, whereas a change in the Laspeyres index can result only from a change in prices.

AVERAGE OF RELATIVES

Unweighted

Rule:

$$\frac{\sum\left(\frac{P_n}{P_0} \cdot 100\right)}{n}$$

where P_n = prices in non-base year

P_0 = prices in base year

n = number of items in market basket

Example 4: Unweighted arithmetic mean of relatives, using data in Example 1

Item	P_{80}	P_{85}	$\dfrac{P_{85}}{P_{80}} \cdot 100$
Milk (gal)	$1.60	$1.85	115.6
Tea (box of 100)	1.49	1.98	132.9
Butter (lb)	1.70	2.10	123.5
Chicken (lb)	0.79	0.95	120.3
			492.3

Rule:

$$\frac{\sum\left(\frac{P_n}{P_0} \cdot 100\right)}{n} = \frac{\sum\left(\frac{P_{85}}{P_{80}} \cdot 100\right)}{n} = \frac{492.3}{4}$$

$$\text{Index} = 123.08$$

1983, on the average, it cost 23.08% more per item than in 1980 to purchase this market basket.

A problem with the unweighted arithmetic mean of relative index is that it doesn't take into account the amount of each item purchased. To take into account the different quantities purchased, a weighted arithmetic mean of relatives can be used.

Weighted

The general rule for the weighted arithmetic mean of relative index is:

Rule:
$$\frac{\sum\left(\frac{P_n}{P_0} \cdot 100\right) w}{\sum w}$$

where P_n = price in non-base year

P_0 = prices in base year

Q_0 = quantities in base year

$w = \sum P_0 Q_0$

This equation is mathematically equivalent to the Laspeyres index when base quantities are used as the weights and to the Paasche index when non-base quantities are used as the weights.

Example 5: Using the data in Example 2, find the weighted arithmetic mean of relative index. (Use 1980 quantities.)

	Q_{1980}	P_{80}	P_{85}	$\frac{P_{85}}{P_{80}} \cdot 100$	$P_{80}Q_{80}$	$\frac{P_{85}}{P_{80}} \cdot 100\, P_{80}Q_{80}$
Milk (gal)	3	$1.60	$1.85	115.6	$ 4.80	$ 554.88
Tea (box of 100)	1	1.49	1.98	132.9	1.49	198.02
Butter (lb)	2	1.70	2.10	123.5	3.40	419.90
Chicken (lb)	5	0.79	0.95	120.3	3.95	475.19
					$13.64	$1,647.99

$$\text{Index} = \frac{\sum\left(\frac{P_n}{P_0} \cdot 100\right)(P_0 Q_0)}{\sum P_0 Q_0} = \frac{\sum\left(\frac{P_{85}}{P_{80}} \cdot 100\right) P_{80}Q_{80}}{\sum P_{80}Q_{80}} = \frac{\$1647.99}{\$13.64}$$

$$= 120.82$$

In 1985 it cost 20.82% more to purchase the market basket of quantities purchased in 1980.

This example shows that the same results will be obtained using either the weighted aggregative price index or the weighted arithmetic mean of relatives if base period weights are used.

Problem 4: Using the data in Example 3, show that the same results will be obtained using the average of relative index as was obtained using the aggregate index.

Problem 5: Using the data in Problem 1, find the unweighted average of relatives index.

Problem 6: Using the data in Problem 2, find the weighted average of relatives index.

Problem 7: Using the data in Problem 3, find the weighted average of relatives index.

QUANTITY INDICES

So far we have measured the change in prices, holding quantities constant. A **quantity index** measures the change in value of a market basket from the base period to the non-base period that results from changes in quantities, holding price constant.

The rules for the weighted relative of aggregates quantity index and the weighted arithmetic mean of relatives quantity index are the same. The Laspeyres quantity index uses base period prices, whereas the Paasche quantity index uses non-base period prices.

Rule for Laspeyres quantity index (prices base year).

$$\text{Laspeyres} = \frac{\Sigma Q_n P_0}{\Sigma Q_0 P_0} \cdot 100$$

Example 6: Using the data in Examples 2 and 3 and 1980 as the base year, find the Laspeyres quantity index.

	P_{80}	Q_{80}	Q_{85}	$Q_{80}P_{80}$	$Q_{85}P_{80}$
Milk (gal)	$1.60	3	2	$4.80	$3.20
Tea (box of 100)	1.49	1	1	1.49	1.49
Butter (lb)	1.70	2	1	3.40	1.70
Chicken (lb)	0.79	5	6	3.95	4.74
				$13.64	$11.13

$$\text{Laspeyres index} = \frac{\Sigma Q_n P_0}{\Sigma Q_0 P_0} \cdot 100 = \frac{\Sigma Q_{85} P_{80}}{\Sigma Q_{80} P_{80}} \cdot 100 = \frac{\$11.13}{\$13.64} \cdot 100 = 81.6$$

In 1985 consumption level decreased by 18.4% from what it was in 1980.

Rule for Paasche quantity index (prices non-base year).

$$\text{Paasche index} = \frac{\Sigma Q_n P_n}{\Sigma Q_0 P_n} \cdot 100$$

Problem 8: Using the data in Examples 2 and 3 and 1980 as the base year, find the Paasche quantity index.

Problem 9: Using the data in Problems 2 and 3 and 1982 as the base year, find the Laspeyres quantity index.

Problem 10: Using the data in Problems 2 and 3 and 1982 as the base year, find the Paasche quantity index.

DEFLATION BY PRICE INDICES

Suppose we want to compare some dollar figures over a period of time—for example, a time series on someone's income. However, not only has your income increased but also prices may have changed. So, we want to know how much has income changed in real terms—that is, how much will your income buy, or how has your purchasing power changed.

Example 7: Suppose your income from 1980 to 1985 increased from $30,000 to $50,000. Does this mean that you are $20,000 richer? Not necessarily, because prices probably increased over this time period. Suppose the price index, using 1980 as the base, was 150 in 1985. This means the prices increased by 50% during the period 1980 to 1985. Thus, how much better off are you in real terms? We can adjust for price changes and deflate the value of your income by using the following rule:

$$\text{Real value} = \frac{\text{Nominal value}}{\text{Price index}} \cdot 100$$

Using the data from above

$$\text{Real value} = \frac{50,000}{150} \cdot 100 = 33,333.33$$

Thus, $50,000 in 1985 dollars is worth only $33,333 in 1980 dollars. So, of your $20,000 increase, $16,667 was taken away by inflation and your real income or purchasing power was increased by only $3,333.

Also, we can adjust any value series for changes in prices by choosing a base period and comparing the other values in terms of the base period dollars.

Example 8: Using 1980 as a base, deflate the following sales figures.

Year	Sales in Dollars	Price Index
1980	100,000	100
1981	200,000	105
1982	400,000	108
1983	600,000	110
1984	700,000	115
1985	1,000,000	118

	Deflated Sales (1980 base)
1980	$100,000/100 \cdot 100 = 100,000$
1981	$200,000/105 \cdot 100 = 190,476$
1982	$400,000/108 \cdot 100 = 370,370$
1983	$600,000/110 \cdot 100 = 545,455$
1984	$700,000/115 \cdot 100 = 608,696$
1985	$1,000,000/118 \cdot 100 = 847,458$

Problem 11: Deflate nominal income for the following data, using 1980 as a base.

Year	Income	Price Index
1979	25,000	97
1980	30,000	100
1981	32,000	105
1982	34,000	108
1983	35,000	110

SHIFTING THE BASE

Previously, we stated that the base period should not be too far from the present. Thus, it is often necessary to shift the base to bring it closer to the present. This can be accomplished by finding the shift value. The rule for the shift value is:

Rule:
$$\frac{\text{Old base index}}{\text{New base index}} \cdot 100$$

Once we have the shift value, we divide each price index by that value to obtain the new price index.

Example 9: Using the data in Example 8, shift the base to 1985.

Year	(1) Original Data	(2) Price Index (1980 base)	(3) Price Index (1985 base)
1980	100,000	100	84.75
1981	200,000	105	88.98
1982	400,000	108	91.53
1983	600,000	110	93.22
1984	700,000	115	97.46
1985	1,000,000	118	100

The rule for the shift value is (Old base index)/(New base index), which in this case is $100/118 = 0.8475$. Multiplying column (2) by the shift value, we obtain column (3).

Problem 12: Using the data in Problem 11, shift the base period to 1983 and revise the price indices.

CHAPTER 12 REVIEW PROBLEMS

Use the following data for Review Problems 1 through 6. Use 1984 as the base period.

Item	P_{84}	P_{86}	Q_{84}	Q_{86}
Flounder (lb)	3.98	4.50	4	5
Shrimp (lb)	7.50	8.00	2	3
Lobster (lb)	9.00	10.00	2	1

1. Find the unweighted aggregative price index.
2. Find the Laspeyres price index.
3. Find the Paasche price index.
4. Find the unweighted average of relatives price index.
5. Find the Laspeyres quantity index.
6. Find the Paasche quantity index.
7. In the past 5 years, your nominal income has increased from $25,000 to $35,000. However, prices during that time period have increased by 40%. What has happened to your real income?
8. Given the following revenue and price indices, compute the real revenue of the firm during this time period.

Year	Revenue	Price Index
1979	100,000	112
1980	110,000	116
1981	125,000	120
1982	137,000	126
1983	160,000	135
1984	175,000	137
1985	200,000	140

9. The following are sales of a tire company in nominal dollars:

Year	Sales	Price Index
1977	$ 91,000	100
1978	99,000	110
1979	128,000	117
1980	137,000	121
1981	158,000	125
1982	170,000	129
1983	190,000	133
1984	198,000	135
1985	210,000	138

a. Shift the base to 1985.

b. Convert the nominal dollars to real dollars, using the 1985 base.

Use the following data for Review Problems 10 through 13. Use 1984 as the base year.

Item	P_{84}	P_{86}	Q_{84}	Q_{86}
Beef	3.10	3.50	10	8
Chicken	1.05	1.20	6	8
Pork	1.75	1.89	4	5
Lamb	2.28	2.50	2	3

10. Find the unweighted aggregative price index.

11. Find the unweighted average of relative price index.

12. Find the Laspeyres price index.

13. Find the Paasche price index.

13
NONPARAMETRIC STATISTICS

For most hypothesis tests that we have covered, we have assumed that the probability distribution of the population is known. However, we don't always know the probability distribution of the population. When the probability distribution is unknown or when no valid assumption can be made concerning the distribution, we can use a nonparametric hypothesis test. We have not yet developed a test for ordinal or qualitative data; nonparametrics allows us to test such data. The major disadvantage of the nonparametric tests is that, for a given level of α, the levels of β are higher than in parametric tests.

THE SIGN TEST

The sign test is used for paired differences or when comparing sample values against some benchmark. However, instead of using the actual values, we examine whether the value is greater than, equal to, or less than the value of its paired observation or the benchmark.

- If the value is greater than, a $(+)$ is used.
- If the value is equal to, a (0) is used.
- If the value is less than, a $(-)$ is used.

The sign test is used to determine whether the number of plus signs is significantly different from the number of minus signs. The zero observations are omitted from the test. Thus, the null hypothesis is $p = 0.50$.

An advantage of the sign test is that it doesn't make any assumptions concerning the population distribution. One of the steps of a hypothesis test is to determine the test statistic. In this case, the criteria meets that of binomial distribution. We can use the normal approximation of the binomial and use z as our test statistic.

Setup for Sign Test (Two-Tailed)

1. $H_0: p = 0.50$
2. $H_1: p \neq 0.50$
3. Critical value: $z = k$

Decision rule: Reject H_0 if $z < -k$ or $z > k$.

4. $z = \dfrac{\bar{p} - p}{\sigma_{\bar{p}}}$ where $\bar{p}$ = percentage of plus signs in the sample $\sigma_{\bar{p}} = \sqrt{\dfrac{p(1 - p)}{n}}$

5. Make a decision and interpret the results.

The sign test can also be one-tailed. The only differences from the two-tailed would be in the statement of the null hypothesis and alternative hypothesis and in the third step, where the critical value z would have the entire level of α on one tail.

Example 1: A sample of 200 consumers was taken: 100 preferred Cola A, 70 preferred Cola B, and 30 had no preference. Test at $\alpha = 0.05$ that Cola A is preferred to Cola B by the population.

Let A being preferred be a $(+)$, then $(+) = 100, (-) = 70$, and $(0) = 30$. The (0) are omitted so, $n = 170$.

$$\bar{p} = 100/170 = 0.588$$

$$\sigma_{\bar{p}} = \sqrt{\frac{p(1 - p)}{n}} = \sqrt{\frac{(0.5)(0.5)}{170}} = 0.038$$

1. $H_0: p \le 0.50$

2. $H_1: p > 0.50$

3. Critical value: $z = 1.65$

Decision Rule: Reject H_0 if $z > 1.65$.

4. $z = \dfrac{\bar{p} - p}{\sigma_{\bar{p}}} = \dfrac{0.588 - 0.50}{0.038} = \dfrac{0.088}{0.038} = 2.32$

5. $z = 2.32$; reject H_0. The statistical evidence supports the hypothesis that Cola A is preferred by the population at $\alpha = 0.05$.

Problem 1: Tony, the pizza man, claims his pizza is equal to the national brand. He takes a sample of 25 people and has them eat both pizzas. The consumers rank the pizza from 1 to 5. The results are shown in the table. Test Tony's claim at $\alpha = 0.02$, using the sign test.

Data for Problem 1

Person	Tony's Pizza	National Brand	Person	Tony's Pizza	National Brand
1	4	3	14	2	3
2	5	2	15	4	2
3	1	3	16	5	1
4	2	2	17	5	5
5	3	4	18	4	2
6	1	2	19	3	5
7	1	5	20	2	4
8	4	2	21	1	2
9	3	3	22	2	4
10	4	4	23	4	4
11	5	2	24	5	3
12	1	4	25	3	5
13	1	5			

WILCOXON MATCHED PAIR SIGNED RANK TEST

The major difference between the Wilcoxon and the sign test is that the Wilcoxon takes into account the magnitude of the difference between the matched pairs. Also, like the sign test, when the difference between the matched pairs is zero, the observation is omitted from the sample.

The Wilcoxon is similar to the parametric matched paired test discussed in Chapter 7; however, unlike the matched paired, where the differences were summed, in the Wilcoxon the differences are ranked and the ($+$) and ($-$) ranks are summed separately. We are testing whether there is a significant difference between the sum of the ($+$) ranks and the sum of the ($-$) ranks. The normal distribution can be used for the test statistic when $n \geq 25$.

Setup for Wilcoxon Test

1. H_0: Σ rank $(+)$ = Σ rank $(-)$
2. H_1: Σ rank $(+)$ $\neq$ Σ rank $(-)$
3. Critical value: $T = w$

Decision rule: Reject H_0 if $T \leq w$.

4. T = smaller of ranked sums
5. Make decision and interpret the results.

Reading the Wilcoxon (T), Table A-9
If $n = 20$, $\alpha = 0.05$, and we have a two-tailed test, then $T = 52$.

Decision rule: Reject H_0 if $T \leq 52$.

Also, if $n \geq 25$, the normal distribution can be used as the test statistic. This changes steps 3, 4 and 5 above.

3. Critical value: $z = k$

Decision rule: Reject H_0 if $z < -k$ or $z > k$.

4. $z = \dfrac{T - \mu_T}{\sigma_T}$ where $\mu_T = \dfrac{n(n + 1)}{4}$

$$\sigma_T = \sqrt{\dfrac{n(n + 1)(2n + 1)}{24}}$$

5. Make a decision and interpret the results.

The Wilcoxon test can also be one-tailed. The only difference from the two-tailed test is in the statement of the hypotheses and in the third step, the critical value would be one-tailed.

Example 2: A sample of 10 people who were following a new seafood diet was taken to see if the diet was effective. Using the sample results shown in the table and the Wilcoxon matched-paired signed rank test, test if the diet is effective at $\alpha = 0.01$.

The first three columns are given. Column (4) is obtained by subtracting column (3) from column (2). Column (5) is obtained by ranking the absolute values of the data in column (4). Zeroes are omitted and when ties occur the average ranking is used. Column (6) contains the positive ranks, and the negative ranks, separately. These ranks are summed and the lower sum is the T value. Also, since there are two zeroes, the sample size is now $10 - 2 = 8$. We can now do the hypothesis test. In order for the diet to be effective, the Σ rank $(+)$ should be greater than the Σ rank $(-)$, which is the alternative hypothesis.

Data for Example 2

(1)	(2)	(3)	(4)	(5)	(6) Signed Rank	
Person	Weight Before	Weight After	Difference $d = (B - A)$	Rank of $\lvert d \rvert$	Rank (+)	Rank (−)
1	200	180	20	8	8	
2	190	185	5	5.5	5.5	
3	185	185	0			
4	191	192	−1	1		1
5	220	205	15	7	7	
6	185	180	5	5.5	5.5	
7	197	195	2	2.5	2.5	
8	190	190	0			
9	182	184	−2	2.5		2.5
10	193	189	4	4	4	
					32.5	$T = 3.5$

$n = 8, \alpha = 0.01$ $T_{0.01} = 1$ (Table A-9). $T = 3.5$ which is the lower of the signed rank sums.

1. $H_0: \Sigma$ rank $(+) \leq \Sigma$ rank $(-)$
2. $H_1: \Sigma$ rank $(+) > \Sigma$ rank $(-)$
3. Critical value: $T_{0.01} = 1$

Decision rule: Reject H_0 if $T \leq 1$.

4. $T = 3.5$
5. $T = 3.5$; accept H_0. The statistical evidence does not support the hypothesis that the diet is effective at $\alpha = 0.01$.

Problem 2: A sample of 25 students is taken before and after a course to see if they have learned

Data for Problem 2

Student	After Course	Before Course	Student	After Course	Before Course
1	40	35	14	48	30
2	42	30	15	32	18
3	50	45	16	31	17
4	41	30	17	26	15
5	25	10	18	28	10
6	18	17	19	32	30
7	22	23	20	33	18
8	31	30	21	41	21
9	25	18	22	38	19
10	40	12	23	25	20
11	35	21	24	18	22
12	20	17	25	41	30
13	45	20			

anything in the course. They were given a multiple choice test of 50 questions before and after the course. Test at $\alpha = 0.05$ the results that are listed in the table.

MANN-WHITNEY U TEST

In this test, we deal with two independent samples and use ranking to test whether the two populations from which they were drawn have the same mean.

The first step is to assign a letter value to each sample (say A for sample 1 and B for sample 2). Next, we rank all the observations from lowest to highest. In cases where ties occur, an average rank is given to the test values. We then sum the ranks of sample 1 (R_1) and sum the ranks of sample 2 (R_2). If n_1 and n_2 are both greater than 10, we can use the normal distribution for the test statistic.

Setup for Two-Tailed Mann-Whitney U Test ($n_1 \geq 10$ and $n_2 \geq 10$).

1. H_0: The samples were drawn from populations with equal means.
2. H_1: The samples were drawn from populations with unequal means.
3. Critical value: $z = k$

Decision rule: Reject H_0 if $z < -k$ or $z > k$.

4. $z = \dfrac{U - \mu_U}{\sigma_U}$ where $U = n_1 n_2 + \dfrac{n_1(n_1 + 1)}{2} - R_1$

$$\mu_U = \frac{n_1 n_2}{2}$$

$$\sigma_U = \sqrt{\frac{n_1 n_2 (n_1 + n_2 + 1)}{12}}$$

5. Make a decision and interpret the results.

Note: The rule for U can also be $U = n_1 n_2 + [n_2(n_2 + 1)]/2 - R_2$ and the same z value would occur.

The Mann-Whitney test can also be done as a one-tailed test. This would change the null and alternative hypotheses. Remember that the equal sign has to be in the null hypothesis. Also the critical value will change. Again the entire α would be in one tail.

Example 3: A sample of 12 right-handed shot-putters and 12 left-handed shot-putters is taken to determine if there is any difference between right-handed and left-handed shot putters. Using the Mann-Whitney U test and the following data, determine whether there is any difference in the population at $\alpha = 0.05$.

Hand	Length of Throw											
Right	50	52	53	56	58	60	62	62	65	68	71	73
Left	53	54	55	56	57	59	62	62	67	68	70	74

Rank of throws by hand (left and right) for shotputters.

Rank	Throw	Hand	Rank	Throw	Hand
1	50	R	14.5	62	R
2	52	R	14.5	62	R
3.5	53	L	14.5	62	L
3.5	53	R	14.5	62	L
5	54	L	17	65	R
6	55	L	18	67	L
7.5	56	L	19.5	68	R
7.5	56	R	19.5	68	L
9	57	L	21	70	L
10	58	R	22	71	R
11	59	L	23	73	R
12	60	R	24	74	L

The sum of the ranks of right-handed shotputters is 146.5 so $R_1 = 146.5$. We can now do the hypothesis test. Since we are testing that they are equal, we have a two-tailed test.

$$U = n_1 n_2 + \frac{n_1(n_1 + 1)}{2} - R_1 = 12(12) + \frac{12(13)}{2} - 146.5 = 75.5$$

$$\sigma_U = \sqrt{\frac{n_1 n_2 (n_1 + n_2 + 1)}{12}} = \sqrt{\frac{12(12)(12 + 12 + 1)}{12}} = 17.3$$

$$\mu_U = \frac{n_1 n_2}{2} = \frac{12(12)}{2} = 72$$

1. H_0: The samples are drawn from populations with equal means.
2. H_1: The samples were drawn from populations with unequal means.
3. Critical value: $z = 1.96$

Decision rule: Reject H_0 if $z < -1.96$ or $z > 1.96$.

4. $z = \dfrac{U - \mu_U}{\sigma_U} = \dfrac{75.5 - 72}{17.3} = 0.202$

5. $z = 0.202$; accept H_0. The statistical evidence supports the hypothesis that the samples were drawn from populations with equal means at $\alpha = 0.05$.

Problem 3: A researcher is interested in testing if there is any difference between the scores of males and females on the math portion of the SAT test. A sample of 15 males and 15 females reveals the following results:

SAT Math Score

Male	Female	Male	Female
250	280	505	510
275	300	525	520
325	305	535	540
355	320	605	570
405	400	660	600
430	450	720	725
455	475	790	740
470	495		

Test using the Mann-Whitney U whether there is any difference in the means of the male and female population at $\alpha = 0.02$.

ONE-SAMPLE TEST OF RUNS

We have generally assumed that the samples are random. The one-sample test of runs gives us a procedure to test this assumption when there are only two possible outcomes to each trial. A **run** r is a continuous chain of like outcomes in a sample where there are only two possible outcomes to each trial.

Example 4: We toss a coin 10 times and obtain the following:

$$HHTTTHTTHH$$

How many runs are there?

$$\begin{array}{ccccc} HH & TTT & H & TT & HH \\ 1 & 2 & 3 & 4 & 5 \end{array}$$

There are 5 runs. So, $r = 5$, $n_1 = 5$ (the number of H's), $n_2 = 5$ (the number of T's).

Problem 4: Given the following sequence, determine the number of runs.

$$AABBABBABBAABBA$$

If a sample has too few runs or too many runs relative to its size, we would expect that the sample is not random. If either n_1 or n_2 is greater than 20, we can use the normal distribution as the test statistic. A two-tailed test is used for randomness. We can also test for randomness of numerical values for runs above and below a certain value or odd and even results.

Setup for the Test of Runs (Randomness)

1. H_0: The sample is random.
2. H_1: The sample is not random.
3. Critical value: $z = k$

Decision rule: Reject H_0 if $z < -k$ or $z > k$.

4. $z = \dfrac{r - \mu_r}{\sigma_r}$ where $r =$ the number of runs

$$\mu_r = \frac{2n_1 n_2}{n_1 + n_2} + 1$$

$$\sigma_r = \sqrt{\frac{2n_1 n_2 (2n_1 n_2 - n_1 - n_2)}{(n_1 + n_2)^2 (n_1 + n_2 - 1)}}$$

5. Make a decision and interpret the results.

Example 5: An economics professor gives 50 true-false questions on an exam and wants to test at $\alpha = 0.05$ if the correct answers are random. The sequence of answers are:

$$TT/FF/T/FF/TTT/FF/T/FF/TT/FF/TTT/FFF/T/FF/TTTT/FF/$$
$$T/F/TT/F/T/F/TT/FFFF/T/F/T/$$

The first step is to determine the number of runs, $r = 27$. Next we find the number of true (n_1) and the number of false (n_2) answers; $n_1 = 25$, $n_2 = 25$.

Given that n_1 or n_2 is greater than 20, we can use the normal distribution for the test statistic.

$$\alpha = 0.05 \quad n_1 = 25 \quad n_2 = 25 \quad r = 27$$

$$\mu_r = \frac{2n_1 n_2}{n_1 + n_2} + 1 = \frac{2(25)(25)}{25 + 25} + 1 = 26$$

$$\sigma_r = \sqrt{\frac{2n_1 n_2 (2n_1 n_2 - n_1 - n_2)}{(n_1 + n_2)^2 (n_1 + n_2 - 1)}} = \sqrt{\frac{2(25)(25)[(2)(25)(25) - 25 - 25]}{(25 + 25)^2 (25 + 25 - 1)}} = 3.5$$

1. H_0: The sample is random.

2. H_1: The sample is not random.

3. Critical value: $z = 1.96$

Decision rule: Reject H_0 if $z < -1.96$ or $z > 1.96$.

4. $z = \dfrac{r - \mu_r}{\sigma_r}$

$$z = \frac{27 - 26}{3.5} = \frac{1}{3.5} = 0.29$$

5. $z = 0.29$; accept H_0. The statistical evidence supports the hypothesis that the test answers are random at $\alpha = 0.05$.

Problem 5: A die is rolled 40 times to see if the results of obtaining an odd or even are random. The sample data are

$$6351164251135244613354261352145312643215$$

Test at $\alpha = 0.05$ if the sample is random.

KRUSKAL-WALLIS TEST

The Kruskal-Wallis test expands the Mann-Whitney test so that we can test whether more than 2 means are equal. This is a nonparametric test analogous to the parametric F for the ANOVA test in Chapter 8. However, it makes no assumption concerning the population distribution. Just like the Mann-Whitney, the Kruskal-Wallis test uses ranks instead of actual differences in the values. The hypothesis to be tested is whether all the means are equal. The χ^2 statistic can be used when all the samples sizes are greater than 5.

Setup of Kruskal-Wallis Test

1. H_0: The samples were drawn from populations having the same mean.

2. H_1: The samples were drawn from populations having different means.

3. Critical value: $\chi^2(c - 1, \alpha) = Q$

Decision rule: Reject H_0 if $\chi^2 > Q$, where c = number of samples.

4. $\chi^2 = K = \dfrac{12}{n(n + 1)}\left(\sum \dfrac{R_j^2}{n_j}\right) - 3(n + 1)$

    where n = total number of observations in all the samples combined

            R_j = the sum of the ranks of the jth sample

            n_j = number of observations in the jth sample

5. Make a decision and interpret the results.

Note: In case of ties, the observations are assigned the average of the tied ranks and a corrected K_c is used.

$$K_c = \dfrac{K}{1 - \left[\dfrac{\Sigma(t_j^3 - t_j)}{(n^3 - n)}\right]}$$ where t_j is the number of tied scores in the jth sample

Example 6: A fisherman has tried three different techniques of fishing; in a boat, on a pier and on the beach. He takes a sample of 6 days using each technique and obtains the results shown in the table. Test at $\alpha = 0.05$ if the means of the population are the same.

Data for Example 6

Boat		Pier		Beach	
Number Caught	**Rank**	**Number Caught**	**Rank**	**Number Caught**	**Rank**
25	12	20	9	10	3
15	6	18	7	5	1
31	15	14	5	7	2
29	14	21	10	12	4
27	13	19	8	22	11
42	18	40	17	35	16
$n_1 = 6$		$n_2 = 6$		$n_3 = 6$	
$R_1 = 78$		$R_2 = 56$		$R_3 = 37$	

We can find the rank for each catch by ranking the values from lowest to highest.

Number caught	Rank	Number caught	Rank
5	1	21	10
7	2	22	11
10	3	25	12
12	4	27	13
14	5	29	14
15	6	31	15
18	7	35	16
19	8	40	17
20	9	42	18

We place the rank values next to the observation. Next we sum the ranks, $R_1 = 78$, $R_2 = 56$, and $R_3 = 37$. We can now do the hypothesis test.

$$c = 3; \quad n = n_1 + n_2 + n_3 = 6 + 6 + 6 = 18$$

$$\sum \frac{R_j^2}{n_j} = 78^2/6 + 56^2/6 + 37^2/6 = 1{,}014 + 522.7 + 228.2 = 1{,}764.9$$

1. H_0: The samples were drawn from populations having the same mean.
2. H_1: The samples were drawn from populations having different means.
3. Critical value: $\chi^2(c - 1, \alpha) = \chi^2(2, 0.05) = 5.991$

Decision rule: Reject H_0 if $(\chi^2 > 5.991)$

4. $\chi^2 = K = \dfrac{12}{n(n + 1)}\left(\sum \dfrac{R_j^2}{n_j}\right) - 3(n + 1)$

$\chi^2 = K = \dfrac{12}{18(18 + 1)}(1764.9) - 3(18 + 1) = 4.93$

5. $\chi^2 = 4.93$; accept H_0. The statistical evidence supports the hypothesis that the populations have equal means at $\alpha = 0.05$.

Problem 6: Three farmers use different fertilizers for growing tomatoes. Each takes a sample of 6 plants and obtains the following results (in lbs.):

Plants	Farmer A	Farmer B	Farmer C
1	20	19	27
2	16	32	36
3	14	27	18
4	18	15	19
5	21	20	26
6	37	38	39

Using the Kruskal-Wallis analysis of variance by rank, test that there is no difference between fertilizer at $\alpha = 0.02$.

RANK CORRELATION

The nonparametric correlation analysis allows us to test if there is any relationship between ranked or ordinal data. In Chapters 9 and 10, we used the parametric test to see if there was any relationship between cardinal (numerical) values. We are testing if the variables are related. The t distribution can be used as the test statistic. The degrees of freedom are $n - 2$. If ranks are tied, the average rank value is used. Always use the two-tailed test when testing whether a relationship exists.

Setup of Rank Correlation Test

1. H_0: The variables are not related.
2. H_1: The variables are related.
3. Critical value: $t = w$

Decision rule: Reject H_0 if $t < -w$ or $t > w$.

4. $t = \dfrac{r_r}{\sqrt{\dfrac{1 - r_r}{n - 2}}}$ where $r_r = 1 - \dfrac{6\Sigma d^2}{n(n^2 - 1)}$

$\Sigma d^2 =$ sum of the squared difference in rank

5. Make a decision and interpret the results.

Example 7: Fourteen employees were ranked on manual and mental skills (see table). Test at $\alpha = 0.05$ if there is any relationship between manual and mental skills.

	(1)	(2) Manual X	(3) Mental Y	(4) Difference in rank $d = (X - Y)$	(5) d^2
	A	1	2	-1	1
	B	2	4	-2	4
	C	3	1	2	4
	D	4	5	-1	1
	E	5	7	-2	4
	F	6	9	-3	9
	G	7	6	1	1
	H	8	8	0	0
	I	9	10	-1	1
	J	10	3	7	49
	K	11	14	-3	9
	L	12	12	0	0
	M	13	11	2	4
	N	14	13	1	1

Data for Example 7

$$\Sigma d^2 = 88$$

The first three columns are given. Column (4) is obtained by subtracting column (3) from column (2). Column (5) is obtained by squaring the observations in column (4). Next, we sum column (5) to obtain Σd^2.

The Hypothesis Test

1. H_0: The variables are not related.
2. H_1: The variables are related.
3. Critical value: $t = 2.179$

Decision rule: Reject H_0 if $t < -2.179$ or $t > 2.179$ for $n - 2 = 14 - 2 = 12$ degrees of freedom.

$$r_r = 1 - \frac{6\Sigma d^2}{n(n^2 - 1)} = 1 - \frac{6(88)}{14(14^2 - 1)} = 0.81 \qquad r_r^2 = 0.66$$

4. $t = \dfrac{r_r}{\sqrt{\dfrac{1 - r_r^2}{n - 2}}} = \dfrac{0.81}{\sqrt{\dfrac{1 - 0.66}{14 - 2}}} = \dfrac{0.81}{0.17} = 4.8$

5. $t = 4.8$; reject H_0. The statistical evidence supports the hypothesis that the variables are related at $\alpha = 0.05$.

Problem 7: Ten fraternities at Mid-East University were ranked by academic and athletic ability (see table). Test at $\alpha = 0.05$ if there is any relationship between the two variables, academic and athletic ability.

Data for Problem 7		
	Ability	
Fraternity	Athletic X	Academic Y
A	1	5
B	2	7
C	3	4
D	4	2
E	5	1
F	6	8
G	7	9
H	8	3
I	9	10
J	10	6

CHAPTER 13 REVIEW PROBLEMS

1. A statistics teacher wants to test if there is any correlation between students' grades and how long it takes them to finish an exam. A sample of 15 students reveals the following results:

Student	A	B	C	D	E	F	G	H	I	J	K	L	M	N	O
Grade	1	2	3	4	5	6	7	8	9	10	11	12	13	14	15
Time Done	12	2	7	5	15	6	11	3	13	10	4	14	8	9	1

Test at $\alpha = 0.05$ if there is a rank correlation between the variables.

2. A stockbroker has examined the daily movement of a stock over the past 60 days. Given the following information, test if the changes in the price of the stock are random at $\alpha = 0.05$. ($U = $ Up, $D = $ Down)

$$UUDUDDUUUUDDDUUDDDDDUUDUDDUUU$$
$$DDDDDDDUDDUUUUDDDUUUUDUDDUUUDD$$

3. An economics professor who has students for two sequential courses, takes a sample of their grades in the two courses. The following data are obtained:

Student	1st Course Grade	2nd Course Grade
A	78	82
B	81	87
C	94	98
D	96	93
E	87	89
F	75	73
G	65	72
H	71	77
I	62	70
J	75	82
K	84	92
L	80	82

Use the Wilcoxon matched-pairs sign rank test to determine if students do better in the second course at $\alpha = 0.01$.

4. The vice-president of a bank takes a survey to see how his bank compares to two other banks in terms of service. He takes a sample of 6 customers from each bank and obtains the following ratings:

Bank A	Bank B	Bank C
70	74	95
80	83	87
65	71	67
90	94	81
50	68	75
97	98	100

Use the Kruskal-Wallis analysis of variance by ranks test to determine whether the banks have equal ratings at $\alpha = 0.05$.

5. A sample of 100 people was taken to see if they preferred Bleach A over Bleach B. Forty-five preferred Bleach A, 40 preferred Bleach B, and 15 had no preference. Use the sign test to determine if A is preferred to B at $\alpha = 0.02$.

6. A personnel director wants to see if there is any correlation between a job applicant's test score and that applicant's personnel interview rating. A sample of 10 applicants yields the following:

Applicant	Test Score X	Personnel Interview-Rating
A	1	2
B	2	1
C	3	4
D	4	3
E	5	8
F	6	9
G	7	5
H	8	7
I	9	6
J	10	10

Test at $\alpha = 0.02$ if there is a rank correlation between the variables.

7. A production manager wants to determine if there is any difference in average output of two machines. A sample of 15 outputs from each machine was taken and the following was obtained:

Machine A	Machine B
102	100
97	98
95	95
115	99
112	96
94	102
100	95
97	97
103	89
110	109
121	89
104	86
88	95
93	99
97	103

Using the Mann-Whitney U test, determine whether there is a difference in the average output of the machines. Use $\alpha = 0.05$.

8. A manager who wants to determine if there is any difference between 3 production workers obtains the following sample results:

	Worker A	Worker B	Worker C
1	50	45	35
2	48	40	38
3	46	47	41
4	51	42	44
5	49	43	37
6	52	39	36

Use the Kruskal-Wallis analysis of variance by ranks test to determine whether the production workers are equal at $\alpha = 0.01$.

9. An admissions officer at University A, who wants to see if the graduates of University A earn equal starting salaries on average as graduates of University B, takes a sample of 12 from each university. The following results were obtained:

	Salary ($000)				
	University A	University B		University A	University B
A	22	21	G	26	19
B	20	20	H	18	24
C	16	18	I	16	19
D	15	16	J	27	23
E	24	15	K	18	26
F	19	23	L	14	19

Using the Mann-Whitney U test, determine whether the average starting salaries for students graduating from University A are the same as those of students graduating from University B. Test at $\alpha = 0.01$.

10. Two brands of bread are rated by 30 people from 1 to 5, with 5 being the best. The following were the results:

Brand A	Brand B	Brand A	Brand B	Brand A	Brand B
5	4	4	3	2	2
2	5	5	2	1	4
3	2	1	5	2	4
3	3	5	5	2	2
4	1	5	1	4	5
2	5	4	4	3	3
2	4	4	5	5	4
3	4	4	4	5	2
3	4	3	3	3	2
4	3	3	2	2	1

Use the sign test to determine if there is any difference in the preference for the brands at $\alpha = 0.02$.

11. A soda company decides to change the formula for its soda. It takes a sample of 25 stores' sales to see if the new formula has increased sales. It obtained the following data:

Data for Review Problem 11

Sales (Bottles of Soda)

Store	New Formula	Old Formula	Store	New Formula	Old Formula
A	500	600	N	721	730
B	350	400	O	800	820
C	100	125	P	650	670
D	98	90	Q	400	410
E	1000	950	R	250	270
F	500	640	S	200	190
G	600	610	T	190	200
H	450	410	U	125	150
I	650	620	V	650	700
J	100	120	W	480	500
K	150	130	X	460	440
L	179	159	Y	325	330
M	205	220			

Use the Wilcoxon matched-pairs sign rank test to determine if the new formula has increased sales at $\alpha = 0.02$.

12. A sample of 25 bags of potato chips were tested to see if the overfilling or underfilling of the bags was random. Test the following results at $\alpha = 0.05$. (U = underfilled, O = overfilled)

UUOOOUOOUUOOOUUOOOOUUOUUO

14
DECISION MAKING USING PRIOR INFORMATION

Business decisions are generally made by choosing the best of many alternatives. However, deciding which is the best alternative is difficult in a world of uncertainty and lack of perfect information. In this chapter, we develop techniques that will enable us to make decisions based on the information available. Some of the techniques involve the use of probability, whereas others do not. However, they all involve the payoff table. The payoff table shows the various alternatives that you can choose and the payoff (or value) of the possible outcomes.

Example 1: A payoff table with three possible outcomes (O) and three possible alternatives (A).

Payoff Table (profits in $000s)

	A_1	A_2	A_3
O_1	200	100	50
O_2	125	300	100
O_3	20	250	500

where A_1 = build a small plant

A_2 = build a medium plant

A_3 = build a large plant

O_1 = little demand for product

O_2 = medium demand for product

O_3 = great demand for product

If there is little demand and you build a small plant, then your profits (payoff) will be $200,000. However, if a large plant is built and there is little demand for your product, you will receive a profit (payoff) of only $50,000. The problem involves selecting the best alternative. We examine some methods that have been developed to help us answer this question. The first step is to determine if one alternative is superior to another alternative. That is, if you choose a certain alternative, will it give you a higher payoff under all possible outcomes? For example, look at the following payoff table.

Payoff Table

	A_1	A_2	A_3	A_4
O_1	10	20	5	10
O_2	25	40	60	55
O_3	30	60	70	80

Note that A_2 is superior to A_1 because no matter which outcome prevails, A_2 yields a higher payoff than A_1 ($20 > 10, 40 > 25, 60 > 30$). In Example 1, no alternative is superior.

MAXIMIN CRITERION

This decision process involves a pessimistic or risk-aversion strategy. The person makes a decision by picking the alternative that is the "best of the worst."

Example 2: Using the payoff table in Example 1, find the maximin solution.

Data for Example 2

Payoff Table (profits in \$000s)

Outcome	A_1 Small Plant	A_2 Medium Plant	A_3 Large Plant
O_1: Little demand	200	100	50
O_2: Medium demand	125	300	100
O_3: Great demand	20	250	500
Minimum or worst possible payoffs:	20	100	50

The maximin chooses the worst (minimum) possible outcome for each alternative. For A_1 it is 20, for A_2 it is 100, and for A_3 it is 50. We now pick the best (maximum) of the worst payoffs. This would be 100 for A_2. Thus, the decision is to build a medium-sized plant and avoid risk. This guarantees at least \$100,000 in profit.

Problem 1: A college fraternity must decide what to sell at Homecoming. It has 2 choices—hot chocolate or cold drinks. What it will earn depends on the weather. Given the following payoff table, find the maximin solution.

Payoff Table (dollars)

Weather	A_1 Hot Chocolate	A_2 Cold Drinks
O_1: Hot	-50	1,000
O_2: Cold	1,500	100

EXPECTED PROFIT UNDER UNCERTAINTY

In the maximin, we do not take into account the probability of the various outcomes (O_i). The expected profit criterion makes some subjective decisions concerning the probabilities of the respective outcomes and uses these probabilities to compute the expected profit of each alternative. The alternative that yields the highest expected value is chosen.

Example 3: Using the payoff table in Example 2 and the following probabilities: $P(O_1) = 0.4$, $P(O_2) = 0.3$, $P(O_3) = 0.3$, find the alternative that maximizes the expected profit.

As shown in the table, the expected profit is obtained by multiplying column (2) by column (3) to obtain column (4). The observations in column (4) are then summed to obtain the expected profit.

Data for Example 3

Computations of Expected Profits

Expected Profit ($000): Alternative A_1—Small Plant

(1)	(2)	(3)	(4)
			Weighted
Outcome	Probability	Profit	Profit
O_1: Little demand	0.4	200	80
O_2: Medium demand	0.3	125	37.5
O_3: Great demand	0.3	20	6
	1.0		123.5

Expected Profit $(A_1) = \$123.5$

Expected Profit ($000): Alternative A_2—Medium Plant

Outcome	Probability	Profit	Weighted Profit
O_1: Little demand	0.4	100	40
O_2: Medium demand	0.3	300	90
O_3: Great demand	0.3	250	75
	1.0		205

Expected profit $(A_2) = \boxed{\$205}$

Expected Profit ($000): Alternative A_3—Large Plant

Outcome	Probability	Profit	Weighted Profit
O_1: Little demand	0.4	50	20
O_2: Medium demand	0.3	100	30
O_3: Great demand	0.3	500	150
	1.0		200

Expected profit $(A_3) = \$200$

From the table in Example 3, we see that A_2 (medium plant) yields the highest expected profit ($205). Using the expected profit criterion, a medium-sized plant should be constructed.

Problem 2: Given the payoff table in Problem 1 and the following probabilities: probability of cold = 0.6 and probability of hot = 0.4, find the alternative that maximizes the expected profit under uncertainty.

EXPECTED OPPORTUNITY LOSS

An opportunity loss is the difference between the best payoff for the outcome and the alternative chosen. For example, using the payoff matrix in Example 2, if O_1 occurs, the best payoff would be obtained by choosing A_1 (200). If you had chosen A_2 (100), your opportunity loss would be $100 (200–100). We can obtain the expected opportunity loss for each alternative. For convenience, the payoff for the best outcome for each alternative is marked with an asterisk. The objective is to choose the alternative that minimizes the expected opportunity loss.

Example 4: Using the payoff table in Example 2, and the probabilities in Example 3, find the alternative that minimizes expected opportunity loss.

Data for Example 4

Payoff Table and Expected Opportunity Loss Table (profit in $000)

| | Payoff Table | | | Opportunity Loss | | |
Outcome	A_1 Small Plant	A_2 Medium Plant	A_3 Large Plant	A_1	A_2	A_3
O_1: Little demand	200*	100	50	0	100	150
O_2: Medium demand	125	300*	100	175	0	200
O_3: Great demand	20	250	500*	480	250	0

* The highest payoff for each outcome

The payoff table is given. To compute the opportunity loss table, first, we mark with an asterisk the highest payoff for each outcome. Next, we compute the opportunity loss for each O_1 by subtracting the payoff matrix value from the asterisk value of each O_1. For example, $O_1A_2 = 100$; the asterisk value is 200. So opportunity loss for O_1A_2 is 100 (200–100). Once we have computed the opportunity loss table, we compute the expected opportunity loss for each alternative (see Table 14-1).

The expected opportunity loss is obtained by multiplying column (2) by column (3) to obtain column (4). The observations in column (4) are then summed to obtain the expected opportunity loss. From Table 14-1 we see that A_2 (medium plant) yields the lowest ($115) expected opportunity loss. Using the expected opportunity loss criterion, a medium-sized plant should be constructed. This is the same conclusion reached under the expected profit criterion.

Problem 3: Given the payoff table in Problem 1 and the probabilities in Problem 2, find the alternative that minimizes the expected opportunity loss.

TABLE 14-1
Computation of expected opportunity loss

Expected Opportunity Loss ($000) for Alternative A_1—Small Plant

(1) Outcome	(2) Probability	(3) Opportunity Loss	(4) Weighted Opp. Loss
O_1: Little demand	0.4	0	0
O_2: Medium demand	0.3	175	52.5
O_3: Great demand	0.3	480	144.0
	1.0		196.5

Expected opportunity loss $(A_1) = \$196.5$

Expected Opportunity Loss ($000), Alternative A_2—Medium Plant

Outcome	Probability	Opportunity Loss	Weighted Opp. Loss
O_1: Little demand	0.4	100	40
O_2: Medium demand	0.3	0	0
O_3: Great demand	0.3	250	75
	1.0		115

Expected opportunity loss $(A_2) = \boxed{\$115}$

Expected Opportunity Loss ($000), Alternative A_3—Large Plant

Outcome	Probability	Opportunity Loss	Weighted Opp. Loss
O_1: Little demand	0.4	150	60
O_2: Medium demand	0.3	200	60
O_3: Great demand	0.3	0	0
	1.0		120

Expected opportunity loss $(A_3) = \$120$

MINIMAX OPPORTUNITY LOSS

Under the minimax opportunity loss, we take the pessimistic or risk-aversion alternative. The minimax chooses the worst (maximum) possible outcome for each alternative. Next we pick the best (minimum) of the worst payoffs. Just as in the maximin, probabilities are not used in the minimax.

Example 5: Using the opportunity loss table in Example 4, find the minimax opportunity loss solution.

As the table on the next page shows, we first pick the worst possible outcome for each alternative: for A_1, it is 480; for A_2, it is 250; for A_3, it is 200. We next pick the best (minimum) of the worst payoffs. This would be 200 for A_3. Using the minimax opportunity loss criterion, we should build a large plant.

As this problem shows, the maximin and the minimax opportunity loss solutions can be different.

Data for Example 5

Opportunity Loss Table

Outcome	A_1 Small Plant	A_2 Medium Plant	A_3 Large Plant
O_1: Little demand	0	100	150
O_2: Medium demand	175	0	200
O_3: Great demand	480	250	0
Worst possible outcome	480	250	200

Problem 4: Using the opportunity loss table in the answer to Problem 3, find the minimax opportunity loss solution.

EXPECTED VALUE OF PERFECT INFORMATION

So far, we have discussed a decision making under uncertainty. The next question is how much would we value perfect information so that we can make a decision with certainty. Alternatively, we could look at the problem in the context of the cost of uncertainty.

The first step in finding the expected value of perfect information is to find the expected profit with perfect information. Once we have computed this value, we subtract the expected profit under uncertainty from it and obtain the expected value of perfect information.

Example 6: Using the payoff table in Example 1 and the probabilities in Example 3, find the expected value of perfect information (EVPI).

If we knew with certainty, which outcome would prevail we would choose the alternative for each possible demand that maximized its payoff. If we knew for certain that O_1 would occur, we would maximize profits (200) by building a small plant. However, if we knew for certain that O_2 would occur we would maximize profits (300) by building a medium sized plant and if we knew for certain that O_3 would occur, we would maximize profits (500) by building a large plant. This gives us column (2) of Table 14-2. Column (3) is the probability of each outcome. Using this information, we can find the expected profit with perfect information. To obtain column (4) we multiply column (2) by column (3). Summing the observation in column (4) we obtain the expected profit with perfect information.

We have just computed the expected profit with perfect information; previously (see Example 3) we computed the expected profit under uncertainty ($205,000). The difference between these two values will give us the expected value of perfect information.

Calculation of expected value of perfect information

Expected profit with perfect information	$320,000
Less: Expected profit under uncertainty	−205,000
Expected value of perfect information	115,000

TABLE 14-2
Calculation of expected profit with perfect information ($000)

(1) Predicted Event	(2) Profit	(3) Probability	(4) Weighted Profit
O_1: Little demand	200	0.4	80
O_2: Medium demand	300	0.3	90
O_3: Great demand	500	0.3	150
		1.0	320

Expected profit with perfect information = $320

If we look at Example 4, the expected opportunity loss (EOL) is $115,000. This is the same as the expected value of perfect information (EVPI). This is no coincidence. The expected value of perfect information is always equal to the expected opportunity loss.

Problem 5: Using the data in Problem 3,

      a. Find the expected value of perfect information.

      b. Show that the EOL is equal to EVPI.

The decision making process can also be shown graphically by the use of a decision diagram (see Figure 14-1). At the end of the outer branches are the payoffs of each outcome. The probability of each outcome is below the outer branch. The expected profit of each decision is at the chance fork represented by a circle. They are computed by multiplying the payoff of each branch by the probability of that outcome and summing the results at each chance fork (circle), for example, for a

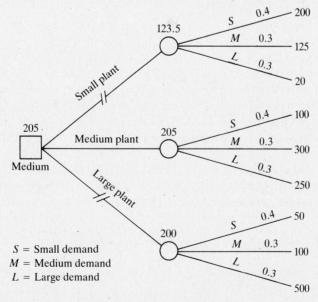

FIGURE 14-1
Decision diagram for manufacturer

small plant we have 0.4(200) + 0.3(125) + 0.3(20) = 123.5. In this case the medium sized plant yields the highest expected profit and should be the plant built. The value of the expected profit ($205) and the decision (medium plant) are placed at the decision fork represented by a square.

DECISION MAKING BASED ON EXPECTED UTILITY

So far, we have assumed that we ought to choose the alternative which maximizes the expected monetary value. However, money itself, for the most part, is useless (it yields no utility). The important issue is how much satisfaction can be obtained with the money. In this section, we develop a method to compute expected utility and choose the alternative which maximizes expected utility. We assume that we can measure how much satisfaction (utility) one can achieve with a given sum of money. It should be noted that different people will achieve different levels of utility with the same amount of money. So, different people may choose different alternatives based on their relative utilities. A person who is a risk taker would have a different utility function from a person who avoids risk. Also, it is assumed that utility can be measured ordinally. We use the measurement of utils to measure utility.

Example 7: You have won a free chance and are given a choice of using that chance on one of two gambling games. The probabilities, payoffs, and utilities are in the following table.

	Game 1			Game 2	
Prob.	**Payoff**	**Utility**	**Prob.**	**Payoff**	**Utility**
0.75	0	0	0.50	100	5
0.25	1,000	30	0.50	400	15

Determine the expected monetary value and expected utility of each game. Which one would you choose on the basis of expected monetary value? Which one would you choose on the basis of expected utility?

Computation of expected monetary value for Example 7

	Game 1			Game 2	
(1)	**(2)**	**(3)** Weighted	**(1)**	**(2)**	**(3)** Weighted
Prob.	**Payoff**	**Payoff**	**Prob.**	**Payoff**	**Payoff**
0.75	0	0	0.50	100	50
0.25	1,000	250	0.50	400	200
		250			250

As shown in the table, the expected monetary value is computed by multiplying column (1) by column (2) to obtain column (3). The observations in column (3) are summed to obtain monetary value. In Games 1 and 2, the expected monetary values are the same ($250), so under the expected monetary value criterion the player is indifferent to which game he plays.

Computation of expected utility for Example 7

Game 1			Game 2		
(1) Prob.	(2) Utility	(3) Weighted Utility	(1) Prob.	(2) Utility	(3) Weighted Utility
0.75	0	0	0.50	5	2.5
0.25	30	7.5	0.50	15	7.5
		7.5			10

As shown in the table, the expected utility is computed by multiplying column (1) by column (2) to obtain column (3). The observations in column (3) are summed to obtain the expected utility. In Game 1 the expected utility is 7.5 utils, and in Game 2 the expected utility is 10 utils. Using the expected utility criterion, Game 2 should be chosen because it maximizes expected utility.

Example 8: Suppose you are given the choice of $5,000 tax free or a chance at $10,000 tax free with a 60% chance of winning. Given the following table, which one would you choose using the expected monetary value and the expected utility methods?

Alternative A			Alternative B		
Prob.	Payoff	Utility	Prob.	Payoff	Utility
1	5,000	20	0.6	10,000	33
0	0	0	0.4	0	0

Computation of expected monetary value for Example 8

Alternative A			Alternative B		
(1) Prob.	(2) Payoff	(3) Weighted Payoff	(1) Prob.	(2) Payoff	(3) Weighted Payoff
1	5,000	5,000	0.6	10,000	6,000
0	0	0	0.4	0	0
		5,000			6,000

As shown in the table, the expected monetary value is computed by multiplying column (1) by column (2) to obtain column (3). The observations in column (3) are summed to obtain the expected monetary value. Alternative B is chosen because it yields the maximum expected monetary value ($6,000). Next, we compute the expected utility.

As shown in the table on the next page, the expected utility is computed by multiplying column (1) by column (2) to obtain column (3). The observations in column (3) are summed to obtain the expected utility. Alternative A is chosen because it yields the maximum expected utility (20).

In comparing the tables in Example 8, you will notice that the expected monetary value and the expected utility methods may yield different results.

Computation of expected utility for Example 8

	Alternative A			Alternative B	
(1)	(2)	(3) Weighted	(1)	(2)	(3) Weighted
Prob.	Utility	Utility	Prob.	Utility	Utility
1	20	20	0.6	33	19.8
0	0	0	0.4	0	0
		20			19.8

Problem 6: Suppose you can choose between two investment decisions. Using the table, decide which investment to make

a. Based on the expected monetary value.

b. Based on the expected utility criterion.

Data for Problem 6

	Investment 1			Investment 2	
Prob.	Payoff	Utility	Prob.	Payoff	Utility
0.2	−20,000	−20	0.2	−40,000	−50
0.4	0	0	0.3	0	0
0.3	10,000	10	0.3	25,000	20
0.1	50,000	40	0.2	50,000	40

CHAPTER 14 REVIEW PROBLEMS

The Following Information is Used for Review Problems 1 Through 5:

A professor has the option of buying 3 stocks, but can buy only one of them, given the following payoff matrix and probabilities.

Payoff Table ($000)

Economic Activity	Prob.	A_1: Stock A	A_2: Stock B	A_3: Stock C
O_1: Growth	0.6	50	75	110
O_2: Recession	0.4	20	−30	−65

1. Find the maximin solution.

2. Find the expected profit under uncertainty solution.

3. Find the expected opportunity loss solution.

4. Find the minimax opportunity loss solution.

5. Find the expected profit with perfect information.

6. You have won $500 on a game show. You are given the choice of giving up that $500 and picking a door at random. Behind one door is $1,000, behind another door is $3,000, and behind another door is $5. Which option should you choose to maximize expected monetary value?

7. You have a choice of three investment decisions. Using the data in the table, decide which investment to make.

   a. Based on the expected monetary value criterion

   b. Based on the expected utility criterion

Data for Review Problem 7

	Investment 1			Investment 2			Investment 3	
Prob.	Payoff	Utility	Prob.	Payoff	Utility	Prob.	Payoff	Utility
0.3	−10,000	−20	0.4	−5,000	−8	0.5	−20,000	−70
0.6	10,000	10	0.4	10,000	10	0.4	25,000	22
0.1	30,000	25	0.2	20,000	18	0.1	100,000	75

The Following Information is Used for Review Problems 8 Through 12:

An inventor has the option of either selling the patent rights or manufacturing the product. Use the data in the payoff table and probabilities.

Data for Review Problems 8–12

Payoff Table ($000)

Outcome	Prob.	A_1 Sell Patent	A_2 Manufacture Product
O_1: Small demand	0.2	150	−100
O_2: Medium demand	0.7	300	500
O_3: Large demand	0.1	750	1250

8. Find the maximin solution.

9. Find the expected profit under uncertainty solution.

10. Find the expected opportunity loss solution.

11. Find the minimax opportunity loss solution.

12. Using the information obtained in Review Problems 9 and 10, find the expected value of perfect information.

15

DECISION MAKING WITH POSTERIOR PROBABILITIES

In the previous chapter, we examined decision making using prior information. In this chapter, we analyze decision making when additional information is obtained. We can revise prior probabilities after additional information has been obtained. These revised probabilities are known as **posterior probabilities**. They are obtained from Bayes' theorem that we examined in Chapter 3. In this chapter, we analyze decisions exclusively in terms of monetary payoffs.

DECISION MAKING AFTER THE OBSERVATION OF SAMPLE EVIDENCE

Suppose in the optimal plant size problem (Examples 2 and 3 in Chapter 14) the owner doesn't want to base his decision solely on the probabilities for demand. (In this chapter, we refer to these probabilities as prior probabilities.) The owner decides to hire a company to conduct a sample. After much analysis, the company concludes that there will be little demand for the product. However, while the company is reliable, it does not have a perfect track record. Sometimes it makes the wrong decision. (Remember, we are still making decisions under uncertainty.) In the past, when little demand actually occurred, it predicted little demand 70% of the time, medium demand 20% of the time, and large demand 10% of the time. If we let X_1, X_2, X_3, denote the sample outcomes,

X_1: Sample indicates little demand will occur.

X_2: Sample indicates medium demand will occur.

X_3: Sample indicates great demand will occur.

and O_1, O_2, O_3 denote the possible outcomes

O_1: little demand

O_2: medium demand

O_3: great demand.

We can now find the conditional probabilities

$P(X_1 \mid O_1) = 0.7 \Rightarrow$ Probability that sample indicates little demand given little demand actually occurs.

$P(X_1 | O_2) = 0.2 \Rightarrow$ Probability that sample indicates little demand given medium demand actually occurs.

$P(X_1 | O_3) = 0.1 \Rightarrow$ Probability that sample indicates little demand given great demand actually occurs.

Note that these probabilities do not have to sum to one.

Example 1: Using the information above and the prior probabilities from Example 1 of Chapter 14 ($P(O_1) = 0.4$, $P(O_2) = 0.3$, $P(O_3) = 0.3$), find the posterior probabilities.

Computation of posterior probabilities for manufacturer in Example 1

Example for the Sample Indication of Little Demand

(1) Event	(2) Prior $P(O_i)$	(3) Conditional $P(X_1 | O_i)$	(4) Joint $P(O_i) \cdot P(X_1 | O_i)$	(5) Posterior $P(O_i | X_1)$
O_1: Little demand	0.4	0.7	0.28	0.76
O_2: Medium demand	0.3	0.2	0.06	0.16
O_3: Great demand	0.3	0.1	0.03	0.08
	1.0		0.37	1.00

As the table shows, column (2) is the prior probabilities and column (3) is the conditional probabilities. If we multiply column (2) by column (3), we can obtain the joint probabilities in column (4). Column (5), the posterior probabilities, is obtained by dividing each observation in column (4) by the sum of column (4). By comparing the prior probabilities in column (2) with the posterior probabilities in column (5), we can observe how the sample information has revised the probabilities. For example, the prior probability of little demand was 0.4; however, because the sample information indicates little demand, the probability of little demand is revised upward to 0.76. Because the sample information indicates little demand, the other possible outcomes of medium demand and great demand are revised downward—from 0.3 to 0.16 and from 0.3 to 0.08, respectively.

We can now use the revised probabilities to compute the posterior expected profits.

Problem 1: The fraternity (in Problems 1 and 2 in Chapter 14) decides to revise the weather probabilities by calling a graduate of the school, a local weatherman. The weatherman predicts that it will be cold, but he is not always correct. In the past when it was actually cold, he predicted it would be cold 80% of the time. However, when it was actually hot, he predicted it would be cold 20% of the time. Find the revised (posterior) probabilities.

Example 2: Using the data in Example 1, and the payoff table in Example 1 of Chapter 14, find the posterior expected profits for the plant size decision and make a decision.

The expected profit for each alternative is obtained by multiplying column (2) by column (3) to obtain column (4). The observations in column (4) are summed to obtain the expected profit.

TABLE 15-1

Calculation of posterior expected profits in the manufacturer's example, using revised probabilities

Expected Profit ($000): Alternative A_1 (small plant)

(1) Outcome	(2) Posterior Probability	(3) Profit	(4) Weighted Profit
O_1: Little demand	0.76	200	152
O_2: Medium demand	0.16	125	20
O_3: Large demand	0.08	20	1.6
			173.6

Expected profit $(A_1) = \boxed{\$173.6}$

Expected Profit ($000): Alternative A_2 (medium plant)

(1) Outcome	(2) Posterior Probability	(3) Profit	(4) Weighted Profit
O_1: Little demand	0.76	100	76
O_2: Medium demand	0.16	300	48
O_3: Large demand	0.08	250	20
			144

Expected profit $(A_2) = \$144$

Expected Profit ($000): Alternative A_3 (large plant)

(1) Outcome	(2) Posterior Probability	(3) Profit	(4) Weighted Profit
O_1: Little demand	0.76	50	38
O_2: Medium demand	0.16	100	16
O_3: Large demand	0.08	500	40
			94

Expected profit $(A_3) = \$94$

As Table 15-1 shows, A_1 (little demand) yields the highest ($173.6) expected profit. Using the posterior expected profits criterion, a small plant should be constructed. Thus, the sample information changes our decision from building a medium plant (Chapter 14) to building a small plant. Figure 15-1 is a graphical presentation of Table 15-1.

Problem 2: Using the data in the answer to Problem 1 and the payoff table in Problem 1 of Chapter 14, find the posterior expected profits for the fraternity's dilemma and use this information to make a decision.

As in Chapter 14, we can determine the posterior expected value of perfect information.

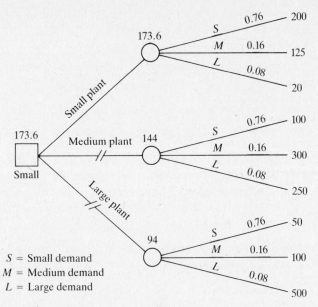

FIGURE 15-1

Decision diagram for posterior analysis of manufacturer

Example 3: Using the payoff table and probabilities in Example 2, find the posterior expected value of perfect information.

If we knew with certainty which outcome would prevail, we would choose the alternative that maximized the payoff of that outcome. For example, if we knew with certainty that little demand would occur, we would build a small plant and have profit of $200. This gives us column (2). Column (3) is the posterior probability of each outcome. Using this information and the payoff table, we can find the posterior expected profit with perfect information table. To obtain column (4) we multiply column (2) by column (3). Summing the observation in column (4), we obtain the posterior expected profit with perfect information.

Calculation of posterior expected profit with
perfect information ($000), for Example 3

(1) Event	(2) Profit	(3) Posterior Probability	(4) Weighted Profit
O_1: Little demand	200	0.76	152
O_2: Medium demand	300	0.16	48
O_3: Large demand	500	0.08	40
			240

Posterior expected profit with perfect information = $240

The posterior expected profit with perfect information is $240. Previously (see Example 2) we computed the posterior expected profit under uncertainty ($173.6). The difference between these two values will give us the posterior expected value of perfect information.

Calculation of posterior expected value
of perfect information

Posterior expected profit with perfect information = $240,000

Less: Posterior expected profit under uncertainty = −173,600

Posterior expected value of perfect information = $ 66,400

Just as before, the posterior expected value of perfect information is equal to the posterior expected opportunity loss. The expected value of perfect information has decreased from $115,000 to $66,400. The sample information has decreased uncertainty, which decreases the value of perfect information.

Problem 3: Using the payoff table in Problem 1 and posterior probabilities in the answer to Problem 2, find the posterior expected value of perfect information.

ACCEPTANCE SAMPLING

Posterior analysis is also used in fields such as acceptance sampling to determine whether a shipment of goods should be accepted or, in terms of quality control, whether a production process should be stopped and adjusted because it doesn't meet the quality specifications. As with the previous example of posterior analysis, a sample is taken to determine which course of action should be taken.

Example 4: Boxes of oranges are to be sampled to determine if the oranges are good and the shipment should be accepted. Historically, the boxes have contained 5% defective 10% of the time, 10% defective 60% of the time, and 15% defective 30% of the time. In the past, the company has accepted boxes with 5% and 10% defective and rejected lots with 15% defective. Using these data, the company has constructed an opportunity losses table. Find the prior expected opportunity losses and make a decision.

Data for Example 4

**Payoff Table Showing Opportunity
Losses for Accepting and Rejecting
Lots with Specific Proportions
of Defectives**

Event (p) Proportion of Defectives	Act	
	A_1 Reject	A_2 Accept
0.05	150	0
0.10	75	0
0.15	0	150

TABLE 15-2

Prior expected opportunity losses for orange example

A_1: Reject the Lot

(1) Event p	(2) Prior Probability $P_0(p)$	(3) Opportunity Loss	(4) Weighted Opportunity Loss
0.05	0.10	150	15
0.10	0.60	75	45
0.15	0.30	0	0
	1.00		60

Prior expected opportunity loss $(A_1) = \$60$

A_2: Accept the Lot

(1) Event p	(2) Prior Probability $P_0(p)$	(3) Opportunity Loss	(4) Weighted Opportunity Loss
0.05	0.10	0	0
0.10	0.60	0	0
0.15	0.30	150	45
	1.00		45

Prior expected opportunity loss $(A_2) = \boxed{\$45}$

Using the payoff table and the prior probabilities we can construct a prior expected opportunity loss table as shown in Table 15-2.

The prior expected opportunity loss is obtained by multiplying column (2) by column (3) to obtain column (4). The observations in column (4) are then summed to obtain the prior expected opportunity loss.

As Table 15-2 shows, A_2 (accept the lot), yields the lowest (\$45) prior expected opportunity loss. Using the prior expected opportunity loss criterion, the lots should be accepted. The prior minimum expected opportunity loss is equal to the prior expected value of perfect information. Both are equal to \$45.

Problem 4: Lightbulbs are to be sampled to determine if the lightbulbs are good and the entire shipment should be accepted. Historically, the shipments have contained 5% defectives 70% of the time and 10% defective 30% of the time. In the past, the company has accepted shipments with 5% defectives and rejected lots with 10% defective. Use the information in the table on the next page to determine the prior expected opportunity loss (EOL) and using this criterion what decision should the firm make.

Data for Problem 4

**Payoff Table Showing Opportunity
Losses for Accepting and Rejecting
Shipments with Specific Proportions
of Defectives**

Event (p) Proportion of Defectives	Act	
	A_1 Reject	A_2 Accept
0.05	50	0
0.10	0	100

An Acceptance Sampling Illustration

Example 5: A sample of 20 oranges is taken and one is found to be defective. Use the posterior expected opportunity loss criterion to determine which action should be taken. (Assume independent trials.)

Data for Example 5

**Computation of Posterior Probabilities for the Orange Problem Incorporating Evidence Based
on a Sample of Size 20**

(1) Event p	(2) Prior Probability $P_0(p)$	(3) Conditional Probability $P(X = 1 \mid n = 20, p)$	(4) Joint Probability $P_0(p) \cdot P(X = 1 \mid n = 20, p)$	(5) Posterior Probability $P_1(p)$
0.05	0.10	0.3774	0.03774	0.15667
0.10	0.60	0.2702	0.16212	0.67297
0.15	0.30	0.1368	0.04104	0.17036
	1.00		0.24090	1.0000

As the table shows, column (2) is the prior probabilities and column (3) is the conditional probabilities. Column (3) is obtained by looking up the values for $n = 20$, $x = 1$, and $p = 0.05$, $p = 0.10$ and $p = 0.15$ in the binomial table (Table A-2). If we multiply column (2) by column (3), we can obtain the joint probabilities in column (4). Column (5), the posterior probabilities, is obtained by dividing each observation in column (4) by the sum of column (4). By comparing the prior probabilities in column (2) with the posterior probabilities in column (5), we can observe how the sample information has revised the probabilities.

We can now use the revised probabilities to compute the posterior expected opportunity losses. As shown in Table 15-3, the posterior expected opportunity loss is obtained by multiplying column (2) by column (3) to obtain column (4). The observations in column (4) are then summed to obtain the posterior expected opportunity loss.

As Table 15-3 shows, A_2 (accept the lot) yields the lowest ($25.55) posterior expected opportunity loss. Under the expected opportunity loss criterion, the lot should be accepted.

TABLE 15-3
Posterior expected opportunity losses for the orange example

A_1: Reject the Lot

(1) Event p	(2) Posterior Probability $P_1(p)$	(3) Opportunity Loss	(4) Weighted Opportunity Loss
0.05	0.15667	150	23.50
0.10	0.67297	75	50.47
0.15	0.17036	0	0
	1.00000		73.97

Posterior expected opportunity loss (A_1) = \$73.97

A_2: Accept the Lot

(1) Event p	(2) Posterior Probability $P_1(p)$	(3) Opportunity Loss	(4) Weighted Probability Loss
0.05	0.15667	0	0
0.10	0.67297	0	0
0.15	0.17036	150	25.55
	1.00000		25.55

Posterior expected opportunity loss (A_2) = $\boxed{\$25.55}$

The decision is still the same to accept the lot. However, the expected opportunity loss after the sample has decreased from \$45 to \$25.55. This means that the value of having perfect information has decreased.

Problem 5: A sample of 20 lightbulbs is taken and 2 are found to be defective. Using the posterior expected opportunity loss criterion and the data in the answer to Problem 4, determine which act should be chosen. Assume independent trials.

PRIOR AND POSTERIOR MEANS

We can compare the mean of the prior and posterior distributions to determine the effect that the sample information has on the mean or expected value of the distribution.

Example 6: Find the prior and posterior mean for the data in Examples 4 and 5.

Data for Example 6

**Calculation of the Prior Mean for
the Proportion of Defectives for the
Orange Example**

(1)	(2)	(3)
Event p	Prior Probability $P_0(p)$	$pP_0(p)$
0.05	0.10	0.005
0.10	0.60	0.060
0.15	0.30	0.045
		0.110

Prior mean $= E_0(p) = 0.11$

As the table shows, columns (1) and (2) are given. Column (3) is obtained by multiplying column (1) by column (2). The mean is computed by summing the observations in column (3).

Data for Example 6

**Calculation of the Posterior Means
for the Proportion of Defectives
for the Orange Example:
Sample Evidence, $X = 1$, $n = 20$**

(1)	(2)	(3)
Event p	Posterior Probability $P_1(p)$	$pP_1(p)$
0.05	0.15667	0.00783
0.10	0.67297	0.06730
0.15	0.04104	0.00616
		0.07129

Posterior mean $= E_1(p) = 0.07$

As the table shows, columns (1) and (2) are given. Column (3) is obtained by multiplying column (1) by column (2). The mean is computed by summing the observations in column (3).

Thus, we can see that the posterior mean is lower than the prior mean when a sample of 20 is taken and 1 defective is found.

Problem 6: Find the prior and posterior mean for the data in the answers to Problems 4 and 5.

CHAPTER 15 REVIEW PROBLEMS

1. The professor (Review Problem 1, Chapter 14) decides to obtain some added information before he invests. He calls a former student who is an economist and asks her what she thinks will happen to the market. The former student predicts that there will be economic growth. However, the economist is not always right. In the past when there was economic growth, she predicted growth 90% of the time. However, when there was a recession she predicted growth 20% of the time. Find the revised (posterior) probabilities.

2. Using the information in the answer to Review Problem 1 and the payoff table in Review Problem 1 in Chapter 14, find the posterior expected profits for the professor's problem and make a decision.

3. Using the payoff table and posterior probabilities in the answer to Review Problem 2, find the posterior expected value of perfect information.

4. A sample of eggs is taken to determine whether the shipment is good and should be accepted. Past records show that the shipments have contained 10% cracked 60% of the time, 15% cracked 30% of the time and 20% cracked 10% of the time. The company has accepted shipments with 10% defectives and rejected shipments with 15% and 20% defectives. Use the information in the table to determine what decision the firm should make using the prior expected opportunity loss (EOL) criterion.

Data for Review Problem 4		
Payoff Table Showing Opportunity Losses for Accepting and Rejecting Shipments with Specific Proportion of Defectives		
Event (p)	*Act*	
Proportion of Defectives	A_1 Reject	A_2 Accept
0.10	50	0
0.15	0	100
0.20	0	200

Data for Review Problem 7		
Payoff Table Showing Opportunity Losses for Accepting and Rejecting Shipments with Specific Proportion of Defectives		
Event (p)	*Act*	
Proportion of Defectives	A_1 Reject	A_2 Accept
0.10	50	0
0.20	0	150

5. A sample of 20 eggs is taken and 3 are found to be cracked. Using the posterior expected opportunity loss criterion and the data in Review Problem 4, determine whether the shipment should be accepted.

6. Using the data in Review Problem 4 and the answer to Review Problem 5, find the prior and posterior means.

7. A sample of sparkplugs is taken to determine if the shipment is good. Historically, the sparkplug company's shipments contain 10% defectives 40% of the time, and 20% defectives 60% of the time. The company buying the sparkplugs has accepted shipments containing 10% defectives and rejected shipments containing 20% defectives. Use the information in the table to determine what decision the firm should make using the prior expected opportunity loss criterion.

8. A sample of 10 is taken, and 1 is found to be defective. Using the posterior expected opportunity loss criterion and the data in Review Problem 7, make a decision concerning the shipment.

9. Using the data in Review Problem 7 and the answer to Review Problem 8, find the prior and posterior means.

10. The inventor (Review Problem 8, Chapter 14), before making a decision, decides to hire a consultant to determine the market demand for his product. The consultant predicts that there

will be medium demand. However, the consultant is not always right. In the past when medium demand actually occurred, he predicted medium demand 80% of the time. However, when small demand actually occurred he predicted medium demand 20% of the time and when large demand actually occurred he predicted medium demand 10% of the time. Find the posterior probabilities.

11. Using the information in the answer to Review Problem 10 and the payoff table in Review Problem 8 in Chapter 14, find the posterior expected profits for the inventor and make a decision.

12. Using the payoff table and posterior probabilities in the answer to Review Problem 11, find the posterior expected value of perfect information.

16

DEVISING OPTIMAL STRATEGIES PRIOR TO SAMPLING

In Chapter 15, we examined decision making under uncertainty with sample information. In this chapter, we examine whether or not a sample should be taken. A sample should be taken only if the potential benefit is greater than the cost of the sample. If it is determined that a sample should be taken, then the best course of action will also be determined. This analysis is referred to as **preposterior analysis** (that is, analysis before a sample is taken). There are two basic forms of preposterior analysis: *extensive-form* and *normal-form*.

EXTENSIVE-FORM ANALYSIS

Extensive-form analysis is a two-stage process. First, determine the correct action and the expected opportunity loss without the sample. The second stage is to determine the expected opportunity loss with the sample. The two stages are compared and the one with the minimum expected opportunity loss (taking into account the cost of the sample) is chosen. Beside determining whether or not a sample should be taken, the optimal action is also determined.

Example 1: The producer of a new play has the following opportunity loss table concerning sale of the rights to a play.

	Opportunity Loss Table ($millions)	
Event	A_1 Sell the Rights	A_2 Keep the Rights
O_1: Success	7	0
O_2: Failure	0	5

The prior probability of success is 0.4. The producer also has the option to take it on tour before it goes on Broadway. Historically, if it is successful on Broadway there are good reviews on tour 90%

TABLE 16-1

Calculation of prior expected opportunity losses ($ millions)

A_1: Sell the Rights

(1)	(2)	(3)	(4)
Event	Probability	Opportunity Loss	Weighted Opportunity Loss
O_1: Success	0.4	7	2.8
O_2: Failure	0.6	0	0
	1.0		2.8

Prior EOL $(A_1) = \boxed{\$2.8}$

A_2: Keep the Rights

Event	Probability	Opportunity Loss	Weighted Opportunity Loss
O_1: Success	0.4	0	0
O_2: Failure	0.6	5	3
			3

EOL $(A_2) = \$3$

of the time, and if it is a failure on Broadway there are good reviews on tour 20% of the time. The cost of the tour is $1 million. What is the optimal action for the producer to take?

The first step is to determine the prior expected opportunity loss of each action.

As Table 16-1 shows, the prior expected opportunity loss is obtained by multiplying column (2) by column (3) to obtain column (4). The observations in column (4) are then summed to obtain the expected prior opportunity loss.

From Table 16-1, we see that A_1 yields the lowest ($2.8) prior expected opportunity loss. Using the prior expected opportunity loss criterion, the producer should sell the rights. Figure 16-1 presents this analysis as a decision diagram.

The next step is to determine the posterior expected opportunity loss with sample information, where $X_1 =$ good reviews and $X_2 =$ bad reviews. The first step is to compute the posterior probabilities.

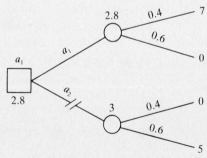

FIGURE 16-1

Decision diagram if no tour is taken

As Table 16-2 shows, columns (2) and (3) are obtained from information in the example. Column (4) is obtained by multiplying column (2) by column (3)—for example, 0.4(0.9) = 0.36, 0.4(0.1) = 0.04. Column (5) is obtained by dividing the observations in column (4) by the sum of column (4). For example, 0.36/0.48 = 0.75, 0.12/0.48 = 0.25, 0.04/0.52 = 0.08, and 0.48/0.52 = 0.92. We now have the posterior probabilities.

We can use these posterior probabilities to compute the posterior expected opportunity loss. First, determine the choice and opportunity loss under good reviews; then determine the choice and opportunity loss under bad reviews.

The posterior expected opportunity loss for good reviews is obtained by multiplying column (2) by column (3) to obtain column (4). The observations in column (4) are then summed to obtain the posterior expected opportunity loss.

From Table 16-3 we see that A_2 yields the lowest ($1.25) expected posterior opportunity loss.

TABLE 16-2
Computation of posterior probabilities

(1)	(2)	(3) Conditional Probabilities $P(X_i \mid O_i)$		(4) Joint Probabilities $P(X_i \text{ and } O_i)$		(5) Posterior Probabilities	
Event	Prior Probabilities $P(O_1)$	X_1	X_2	X_1	X_2	X_1	X_2
O_1: Success	0.4	0.9	0.1	0.36	0.04	0.75	0.077
O_2: Failure	0.6	0.2	0.8	0.12	0.48	0.25	0.923
				0.48	0.52		

TABLE 16-3
Posterior expected opportunity losses for good reviews

A_1: Sell the Rights

(1)	(2)	(3)	(4)
Event	Posterior Probability	Opportunity Loss	Weighted Opportunity Loss
O_1: Success	0.75	7	5.25
O_2: Failure	0.25	0	0
			5.25

Posterior EOL (A_1) = $5.25

A_2: Keep the Rights

(1)	(2)	(3)	(4)
Event	Posterior Probability	Opportunity Loss	Weighted Opportunity Loss
O_1: Success	0.75	0	0
O_2: Failure	0.25	5	1.25
			1.25

Posterior EOL (A_2) = 1.25

TABLE 16-4

Posterior expected opportunity loss for bad reviews ($ millions)

A_1: Sell the Rights

(1)	(2)	(3)	(4)
Event	Posterior Probability	Opportunity Loss	Weighted Opportunity Loss
O_1: Success	0.077	7	0.54
O_2: Failure	0.923	0	0
	1.000		0.54

Posterior EOL $(A_1) = \boxed{\$0.54}$

A_2: Keep the Rights

(1)	(2)	(3)	(4)
Event	Posterior Probability	Opportunity Loss	Weighted Opportunity Loss
O_1: Success	0.077	0	0.0
O_2: Failure	0.923	5	4.6
	1.000		4.6

Posterior EOL $(A_2) = \$4.6$

Using the expected posterior opportunity loss criterion, the producer should keep the rights if there are good reviews.

The posterior expected opportunity loss for a bad review is obtained by multiplying column (2) by column (3) to obtain column (4). The observations in column (4) are then summed to obtain the posterior expected opportunity loss. As Table 16-4 shows, A_1 yields the lowest ($.54) posterior expected opportunity loss. Using the posterior expected opportunity loss criterion, the producer should sell the rights if there are bad reviews.

The probabilities of X_1 and X_2 are obtained from Table 16-2. The values for EOL $| X_i$ are obtained from Tables 16-3 and 16-4.

The prior expected opportunity loss (which is the same as the expected opportunity loss when

TABLE 16-5

Computation of the expected opportunity loss when the tour is taken

X_i	$P(X_i)$	EOL $| X_i$	Weighted Opportunity Loss
X_1: Good reviews	0.48	1.25	0.6
X_2: Bad reviews	0.52	0.54	0.28
	1.00		0.88

Expected opportunity loss when the tour is taken = $0.88

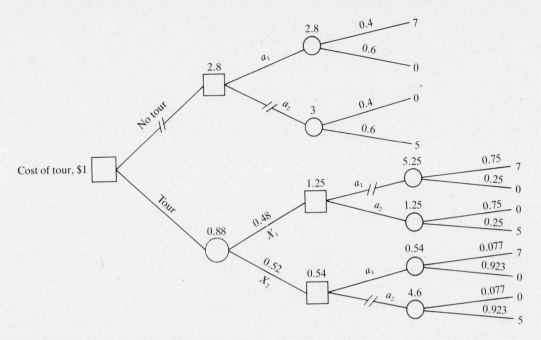

FIGURE 16-2
Decision diagram for preposterior analysis for the producer example

the tour is not taken) is $2.80. The expected value of sample information (EVSI) is equal to

Expected opportunity loss without a sample = $2.80
Less: Expected opportunity loss with a sample = −0.88
$$\overline{}$$
EVSI = $1.92

However, there is a cost in taking the sample, in this case $1 million. To determine if the sample should be taken, this cost must be taken into account. We do this by calculating the expected net gain of sample information (ENGS). If ENGS is positive, the sample should be taken.

ENGS = EVSI − cost of sample information.

In this case, ENGS = 1.92 − 1 = 0.92. The optimal strategy is to take the sample and, if the sample results in good reviews, the producer should keep the rights. If the sample results in bad reviews, the producer should sell the rights.

Figure 16-2 is the decision diagram for Example 1.

Problem 1: Dr. Egan is trying to decide whether to enter a new business venture. The prior probability of success is 0.7, and the prior probability of failure is 0.3. The opportunity loss table ($000) is shown here.

Event	A_1 Enter	A_2 Do not Enter
O_1: Success	0	150
O_2: Failure	100	0

There is also the option of taking a market survey that will cost $25,000. Historically, if the business venture is a success, the survey indicates a success (X_1) 80% of the time, is inconclusive (X_2) 15% of the time, and indicates a failure (X_3) 5% of the time. If the business venture is a failure, the survey indicates a success 10% of the time, inconclusive results 15% of the time, and failure 75% of the time. Using extensive-form analysis, determine Dr. Egan's best strategy.

NORMAL-FORM ANALYSIS

We have just carried out the procedure for extensive-form preposterior analysis. There is another type of preposterior analysis known as normal-form by which we can solve the same problem using a different technique. The first step in **normal-form analysis** is to list all the possible strategies that the decision maker can follow. Next, all strategies that are not feasible are eliminated. The expected opportunity loss for each feasible strategy is obtained and the strategy with the minimum expected opportunity loss is chosen. In some cases there may be only one feasible strategy, which is obviously the one chosen.

The general rule for the number of strategies is n^r, where $n =$ the number of acts and $r =$ the number of sample outcomes.

Example 2: From data in Example 1, devise the optimal strategy using normal-form analysis.
In this example, there are two $(n = 2)$ actions and two $(r = 2)$ possible sample outcomes. Thus the number of strategies is $n^r = 2^2 = 4$. These strategies are listed in Table 16-6.

The next step is to determine which strategies are not feasible. Strategies 1 and 4 entail the same decision regardless of the sample outcome. For example, strategy 1 states that no matter what the outcome of the sample, the producer will sell the rights. If this is true, then there is no sense in taking the sample. The same is true of strategy 4; no matter what the outcome of the sample, the producer will keep the rights. Thus, strategies 1 and 4 are not feasible. Strategy 2 is not feasible because it tells the producer to sell the rights (a_1) if the play has good reviews (X_1) and not to sell the rights (a_2) if the play has bad reviews (X_2). Strategy 2 does not make any sense because the producer should do just the opposite. Thus, strategy 3 is the only feasible strategy—sell if you have bad reviews and keep if you have good reviews.

Next we will compute the expected opportunity loss of strategy 3 and compare it with the expected opportunity loss without a sample. As shown in Table 16-7, column (2) is the opportunity loss table. Column (3) is the conditional probabilities given in the sample information. Column (4) is computed by using the following, where l_{a_i} is the opportunity loss of a_i.

$$R(s_3 \mid O_1) = P(a_2) \cdot l_{a_2} + P(a_1) \cdot l_{a_1} \quad \text{for row } O_1$$
$$R(s_3 \mid O_2) = P(a_2) \cdot l_{a_2} + P(a_1) \cdot l_{a_1} \quad \text{for row } O_2$$

Thus

$$R(s_3 \mid O_1) = 0.9(0) + (0.1)(7) = 0.7$$
$$R(s_3 \mid O_2) = 0.2(5) + 0.8(0) = 1$$

The $\text{EOL}(s_3)$ is then computed by using the following:

$$\text{EOL}(s_3) = P(O_1) \cdot R(s_3 \mid O_1) + P(O_2) \cdot R(s_3 \mid O_2)$$

where $P(O_1)$ and $P(O_2)$ are the prior probabilities. In this example,

$$\text{EOL}(s_3) = 0.4(0.7) + 0.6(1) = 0.28 + 0.6 = \$0.88$$

TABLE 16-6

A listing of all possible strategies in producer example

Sample Outcome	Strategy				
	s_1	s_2	s_3	s_4	
X_1: Good reviews	a_1	a_1	a_2	a_2	a_1 = sell the rights
X_2: Bad reviews	a_1	a_2	a_1	a_2	a_2 = keep the rights

TABLE 16-7

Calculation of risks, or conditional expected opportunity loss of strategy s_3

(1)	(2)		(3)		(4)
State of Nature	Opportunity Loss		Probability of Action $s_3(a_2, a_1)$		Risk (conditional expected loss) $R(s_3 \mid O_1)$
	a_1	a_2	a_2	a_1	
O_1: Success	7	0	0.9	0.1	0.7
O_2: Failure	0	5	0.2	0.8	1.0

The expected opportunity loss of s_3 is $0.88, the same value that was obtained for the expected opportunity loss with a sample using the extensive-form. The extensive-form and the normal-form analysis will always yield the same results.

Once we have computed the expected opportunity loss with a sample using the normal-form analysis, we compare it with the expected opportunity loss without sampling. This was computed in the first part of Example 1 and would have to be computed if we used the normal-form analysis exclusively. However, given that we already computed the value, there is no need to do it again. The expected opportunity loss without a sample is $2.8. Thus, the ENGS is $0.92 and a sample should be taken.

We can see that the normal-form yields the same results as the extensive-form, but with less computation.

Problem 2: Solve Problem 1, using the normal-form analysis.

SENSITIVITY ANALYSIS

In the previous section, we had only one strategy that was feasible. Suppose instead we have two feasible strategies and we want to determine how the values of prior probabilities influence which strategy we choose, that is, for different values of prior probabilities we may choose different strategies. Thus, we want to determine how sensitive is the choice of strategy to the values of the prior probabilities. We can do this by finding the prior probabilities at which the person is indifferent, that is, where the EOL of each strategy is the same. These probabilities will yield the breakeven value for the prior probabilities.

Example 3: Suppose there are two states of nature O_1 and O_2 and two feasible strategies s_2 and s_4. At what value of the prior probabilities would the decision maker be indifferent? Given

$$R(s_2|O_1) = 10.00 \qquad R(s_4|O_1) = 6.00$$
$$R(s_2|O_2) = 15.00 \qquad R(s_4|O_2) = 20.00$$

Rule:
$$EOL(s_2) = P(O_1)R(s_2|O_1) + P(O_2) \cdot R(s_2|O_2)$$
$$EOL(s_4) = P(O_1)R(s_4|O_1) + P(O_2) \cdot R(s_4|O_2)$$

Substituting the values, we obtain

$$EOL(s_2) = P(O_1) \cdot 10 + P(O_2) \cdot 15$$
$$EOL(s_4) = P(O_1) \cdot 6 + P(O_2) \cdot 20$$

If we let $P(O_1) = p$ and $P(O_2) = 1 - p$ and set $EOL(s_2) = EOL(s_4)$, we can now solve for the breakeven p value.

We now have

$$p(10) + (1 - p)(15) = p(6) + (1 - p)(20)$$

Solving for p

$$10p + 15 - 15p = 6p + 20 - 20p$$
$$-5p + 15 = -14p + 20$$
$$9p = 5$$
$$p = 5/9 = 0.55$$

Thus, if $p = 0.55$ the decision maker is indifferent between strategy 2 and strategy 4. However, if $p > 0.55$ the decision maker will choose strategy 4, and if $p < 0.55$ the decision maker will choose strategy 2. For example if $P(O_1) = 0.5$, then $P(O_2) = 0.5$ and

$$EOL(s_2) = 0.5(10) + 0.5(15) = 12.5$$
$$EOL(s_4) = 0.5(6) + 0.5(20) = 13$$

Thus, choose strategy 2 because it minimizes EOL.

Another example: If $P(O_1) = 0.75$, then $P(O_2) = 0.25$ and

$$EOL(s_2) = 0.75(10) + 0.25(15) = 11.25$$
$$EOL(s_4) = 0.75(6) + 0.25(20) = 9.5$$

Thus, choose strategy 4, because it minimizes EOL.

Problem 3: Using the information in Problem 2, at what probability would Dr. Egan be indifferent between feasible strategies?

ACCEPTANCE SAMPLING

We can also use preposterior analysis to decide in cases of acceptance sampling whether or not a sample should be taken. Again the criterion is to take a sample if the expected gain from sampling is positive.

TABLE 16-8

Basic data for acceptance sampling for the orange example

Event p lot proportion of defectives	Prior Probability $P_0(p)$	Opportunity Loss a_1 Reject	Opportunity Loss a_2 Accept
0.05	0.10	150	0
0.10	0.60	75	0
0.15	0.30	0	150

Prior expected opportunity loss $(A_1) = (0.1)(150) + (0.6)(75) + 0.3(0) = \$60$
Prior expected opportunity loss $(A_2) = (0.1)(0) + (0.6)(0) + 0.3(150) = \boxed{\$45}$

TABLE 16-9

A listing of all possible strategies in the orange example

Sample Outcome (number of defectives)	s_1	s_2	s_3	s_4	s_5	s_6	s_7	s_8
$X = 0$	a_1	a_1	a_1	a_1	a_2	a_2	a_2	a_2
$X = 1$	a_1	a_1	a_2	a_2	a_1	a_1	a_2	a_2
$X = 2$	a_1	a_2	a_2	a_1	a_1	a_2	a_1	a_2

a_1: Reject the lot
a_2: Accept the lot

Example 4: Using the data in the orange example (Example 4 in Chapter 15), determine whether a sample of two should be taken. The cost of the sample is $10.

As shown in Table 16-8, the prior probabilities and the payoff table come from the orange example. The prior expected opportunity loss for each action is computed by multiplying the prior probability by the respective opportunity loss for each action. (See Chapter 14, Table 14-4.)

Since A_2 (accept the lot) yields the lowest prior expected opportunity loss, this is the action that should be taken if no sample is taken.

Our next step is to calculate the expected opportunity loss with a sample to determine if a sample should be taken. The first step in preposterior analysis is to determine which of two forms to use, extensive or normal. (Again, remember that if the calculations are done correctly they will yield the same results.)

Let's choose the normal-form because it is the easier to compute. The first step in the normal-form is to determine the number of strategies; in this case there are three possible sample outcomes ($r = 3$) and two actions ($n = 2$). The number of possible strategies is $n^r = 2^3 = 8$. These strategies are listed in Table 16-9.

Strategies s_1 and s_8 are not feasible because the sample information does not change the course of action. That is, regardless of the sample information, we will always reject the lot in s_1 and we will always accept the lot in s_8, so there is no sense in taking a sample that will not change our decision. Strategies s_2, s_3, s_4 and s_6 are not feasible because they reject lots with a smaller number of defectives but accept lots with a greater number of defectives. For example, in s_2 we reject lots with 0 and 1 defective but accept a lot with 2 defectives. This is inconsistent. Thus, s_5 and s_7 are the only feasible strategies.

Our next step is to determine the optimal strategy by calculating the expected opportunity loss of each strategy, as shown in Table 16-10.

Column (1) is the lot proportion of defectives and column (2) is the opportunity loss,

TABLE 16-10

Calculation of risks, or conditional expected opportunity losses, for strategies, s_5 and s_7

s_5

(1) Event p (lot proportion of defectives)	(2) Opportunity Loss		(3) Probability of Action $s_5(a_2, a_1, a_1)$			(4) Risk (conditional expected loss) $R(s_5 \mid p_i, n = 2)$
	a_1	a_2	$X = 0$ a_2	$X = 1$ a_1	$X = 2$ a_1	
0.05	150	0	0.9025	0.0950	0.0025	14.625
0.10	75	0	0.81	0.18	0.01	14.25
0.15	0	150	0.7225	0.2550	0.0225	108.375

$$R(s_5 \mid p = 0.05, n = 2) = 0.9025(0) + 0.0950(150) + 0.0025(150) = 14.625$$
$$R(s_5 \mid p = 0.10, n = 2) = 0.81(0) + 0.18(75) + 0.01(75) = 14.25$$
$$R(s_5 \mid p = 0.15, n = 2) = 0.7225(150) + 0.2550(0) + 0.0225(0) = 108.375$$

s_7

Event p (lot proportion of defectives)	Opportunity Loss		Probability of Action $s_7(a_2, a_2, a_1)$			Risk (conditional expected loss) $R(s_7 \mid p_i, n = 2)$
	a_1	a_2	$X = 0$ a_2	$X = 1$ a_2	$X = 2$ a_1	
0.05	150	0	0.9025	0.0950	0.0025	0.375
0.10	75	0	0.81	0.18	0.01	0.75
0.15	0	150	0.7225	0.2550	0.0225	146.625

$$R(s_7 \mid p = 0.05, n = 2) = 0.9025(0) + 0.0950(0) + 0.0025(150) = 0.375$$
$$R(s_7 \mid p = 0.10, n = 2) = 0.81(0) + 0.18(0) + 0.01(75) = 0.75$$
$$R(s_7 \mid p = 0.15, n = 2) = 0.7225(150) + 0.2550(150) + 0.0225(0) = 146.625$$

Column (3) is the conditional probabilities and can be found in the appendix Table A-2 by looking up the following:

$P(X = 0 \mid p = 0.05, n = 2) = 0.9025$ $\quad P(X = 0 \mid p = 0.10, n = 2) = 0.81$ $\quad P(X = 0 \mid p = 0.15, n = 2) = 0.7225$

$P(X = 1 \mid p = 0.05, n = 2) = 0.0950$ $\quad P(X = 1 \mid p = 0.10, n = 2) = 0.18$ $\quad P(X = 1 \mid p = 0.15, n = 2) = 0.2550$

$P(X = 2 \mid p = 0.05, n = 2) = 0.0025$ $\quad P(X = 2 \mid p = 0.10, n = 2) = 0.01$ $\quad P(X = 2 \mid p = 0.15, n = 2) = 0.0225$

We obtain these values because we want to determine the probability of drawing a sample with X defectives, given a sample of 2 and an assumed value of p [for example $P(X = 0 \mid p = 0.05, n = 2)$]. This can be expressed as "what is the probability of getting no defectives, given a sample of 2 from a population that has 5% defective?"

Column (4) is obtained by multiplying the values in column (3) by the appropriate opportunity loss of that action in column (2) and summing the values.

The expected opportunity loss of each strategy is computed by using the following:

$$\text{EOL}(s_k) = \Sigma P_0(p) \cdot R(s_k \mid p)$$

where $P_0(p)$ is the prior probability and $R(s_k \mid p)$ is the risk or conditional expected loss.

For strategy 5, we have

$$\text{EOL}(s_5) = P_0(p = 0.05) \cdot R(s_5 \mid p = 0.05) + P_0(p = 0.10) \cdot R(s_5 \mid p = 0.10) + P_0(p = 0.15) \cdot p(s_5 \mid p = 0.15)$$

$$= 0.1(14.625) + 0.6(14.25) + 0.3(108.375) = \boxed{42.525}$$

For strategy 7, we have

$$\text{EOL}(s_7) = P_0(p=0.05) \cdot R(s_7 \mid p=0.05) + P_0(p=0.10) \cdot R(s_7 \mid p=0.10) + P_0(p=0.15) \cdot R(s_7 \mid p=0.15)$$
$$= 0.1(0.375) + 0.6(0.75) + 0.3(146.625) = 44.475$$

The $P_0(p)$ are found in Table 16-8, and the $R(s_k \mid p_i)$ are found in Table 16-10.

Strategy 5 is the optimal strategy because it yields the minimum expected opportunity loss ($42.525).

From Table 16-8, the prior expected opportunity loss (which is the same as the expected opportunity loss without a sample) is $45. The expected opportunity loss with a sample is $42.525. We can now compute the expected value of sample information (EVSI) which is equal to

Expected opportunity loss without a sample =   45.

Less: Expected opportunity loss with a sample = -42.525

EVSI = $ 2.475

The expected value of taking the sample is 2.475. However, the cost of taking the sample (in this case, $10) must be taken into account. We do this by calculating the expected net gain of sample information (ENGS). If ENGS is positive, the sample should be taken. The rule for ENGS is

$$\text{ENGS} = \text{EVSI} - \text{cost of sample information}$$
$$= 2.475 - 10 = -\$7.525 \quad (\$ \text{ thousands})$$

Thus, even though there is a gain to taking the sample (2.475), the cost of the sample outweighs the gain and the optimal strategy is not to take a sample.

Problem 4: Find the optimal strategy for the Example 4, using the extensive-form analysis procedure.

CHAPTER 16 REVIEW PROBLEMS

1. One firm wants to buy another firm. However, it is not sure whether the government will allow the merger. Firm X believes the probability that the merger will be allowed is 0.7. It can hire an antitrust consultant Clair Voiant to do a study to predict whether the firms will be allowed to merge. Ms. Voiant's fee is $5,000. Her track record is such that, when the merger is allowed, she predicts that it will be allowed 90% of the time. However, when the merger is not allowed, she predicts the merger will not be allowed 80% of the time. Given the following information, use extensive-form analysis to determine the best strategy.

Opportunity Loss Table ($000)		
	A_1	A_2 Don't
Event	Merge	Merge
O_1: Allowed	0	150
O_2: Disallowed	200	0

2. Solve Review Problem 1, using normal-form analysis.

3. Suppose there are two states of nature, O_1 and O_2, and two feasible strategies, s_1 and s_5. At what value of the prior probability $P(O_1)$ would the decision maker be indifferent? Given:

$$R(s_1 \mid O_1) = 5 \qquad R(s_5 \mid O_1) = 10 \qquad R(s_1 \mid O_2) = 12 \qquad R(s_5 \mid O_2) = 6$$

4. Using the data in Review Problem 4 of Chapter 15, determine whether a sample of two should be taken. The cost of the sample is $5.

5. Using the data in Review Problem 7 of Chapter 15, determine whether a sample of two should be taken. The cost of the sample is $10.

6. A small town is having a parade. If it rains during the parade, many of the costumes will be ruined. However, if the parade is postponed, the town will make less money from the event. The day of the parade comes and it is cloudy. The probability of rain is believed to be 0.6. However, the town can hire an expert meteorologist for $500. When it actually rained, the meteorologist had predicted rain 90% of the time, he was unsure 5% of the time, and he had forecasted no rain 5% of the time. However, when there was no rain, he predicted rain 30% of the time, he was unsure 20% of the time, and he predicted no rain 50% of the time. Given the following information, determine the best strategy for the town.

Opportunity Loss Table ($000)

Event	A_1 Allow	A_2 Postpone
O_1: Rain	5	0
O_2: No rain	0	3

7. In Review Problem 6, at what level of the prior probability $P(O_1)$ would the decision maker be indifferent?

17

COMPARISON OF CLASSICAL AND BAYESIAN STATISTICS

In previous chapters we have examined classical and Bayesian statistics. In this chapter we discuss the differences between these two types of statistics. Finally, the classical hypothesis testing is compared with Bayesian decision theory.

HYPOTHESIS TESTING AND BAYESIAN DECISION THEORY

There are some basic differences between hypothesis testing and Bayesian decision theory. In Bayesian, both prior probabilities and payoffs are used, whereas in hypothesis testing the level of α is used. In the hypothesis, α is used to determine the decision rule; in Bayesian, the optimal decision is based on maximizing expected payoff (minimizing expected opportunity loss). Bayesian decision making is based on subjective prior probabilities, while hypothesis testing does not use prior probabilities. The level of α is central to the hypothesis testing procedure and unless it is chosen with some thoughtfulness, it could lead to undesirable decision choices. Finally, in Bayesian decision theory we have a procedure to determine whether a sample should be taken. Classical statistics does not have a satisfactory procedure to test whether or not a sample should be taken.

Example 1: Use the data in Table 17-1 to compare the results using Bayesian decision theory and classical hypothesis test. We are given the following payoff matrix concerning decision making for a lot of tires. First, we examine the Bayesian approach.

We are dealing with preposterior analysis and the first step is to determine which form to use, extensive or normal. We shall use the normal-form because the amount of computation is less than under the extensive-form. The first step in the normal-form is to determine the number of possible strategies. In this case there are three possible sample outcomes ($r = 3$) and two possible actions ($n = 2$). So the number of possible strategies is $n^r = 2^3 = 8$. We can list these strategies, as shown in Table 17-2.

Let X denote the number of defectives. We can define the type of information we receive from the sample by the number of defectives found in the sample. If $X \leq C_1$, we define it as type E information. If $C_1 < X \leq C_2$, we have type F information and if $X > C_2$, we have type G information.

TABLE 17-1

Payoff table, showing opportunity losses for actions of
acceptance and rejection

State of Nature (p = lot proportion of defectives)	Prior Probability	Act a_1 Reject	Act a_2 Accept
0.04	0.7	100	0
0.08	0.2	0	200
0.12	0.1	0	400

$$\text{EOL}(A_1) = 0.7(100) + 0.2(0) + 0.1(0) = \boxed{\$70}$$

$$\text{EOL}(A_2) = 0.7(0) + 0.2(200) + 0.1(400) = \$80$$

TABLE 17-2

Possible decision rules based on information derived from
single samples of size n

Sample Information	s_1	s_2	s_3	s_4	s_5	s_6	s_7	s_8	
Type E $(X \leq C_1)$	R	A	A	A	A	R	R	R	R: Reject the lot
Type F $(C_1 < X \leq C_2)$	R	A	A	R	R	A	R	A	A: Accept the lot
Type G $(X > C_2)$	R	A	R	R	A	A	A	R	

The next step is to determine which strategies are feasible. Strategies s_1 and s_2 are not feasible because the sample information does not change the course of action. If the sample information has no influence on your course of action, then there is no sense in taking a sample. Strategies s_5, s_6, s_7, and s_8 are not feasible because they reject lots with smaller number of defectives but accept lots with a higher number of defectives. For example, in s_6 we reject all lots with $X \leq C_1$ defectives but accept all lots with $X > C_1$ defectives. This is inconsistent. Thus, s_3 and s_4 are the only feasible strategies.

TABLE 17-3

Joint frequency distribution of sample results and states of nature

(1) State of Nature (p = lot proportion of defectives)	(2) Type E $(X \leq C_1)$	(3) Type F $C_1 < X \leq C_2$	(4) Type G $X > C_2$	(5) Total
0.04	0.50	0.15	0.05	0.70
0.08	0.10	0.08	0.02	0.20
0.12	0.02	0.03	0.05	0.10
	0.62	0.26	0.12	1.00

TABLE 17-4

Calculation of conditional probability for type of sample information given p

State of Nature (p = lot proportion of defectives)	Prior Probability $P_0(p)$	$P(E \mid p)$	Conditional Probability $P(F \mid p)$	$P(G \mid p)$
0.04	0.7	0.71	0.21	0.07*
0.08	0.2	0.50	0.40	0.10
0.12	0.1	0.20	0.30	0.50

* This row does not sum to one due to rounding.

Our next step is to determine the optimal strategy. We can do this by calculating the expected opportunity loss of each strategy and choosing the one with the minimum expected opportunity loss.

In Table 17-3, a joint frequency distribution is given for sample results and states of nature. It is assumed that these frequencies were obtained from a large number of samples and thus can represent probabilities. These are the joint probabilities. Notice that the total values in column (5) are the same as the prior probabilities.

Our next step is to compute the conditional probabilities (see Table 17-4). They can be obtained by dividing the joint probabilities by their marginal probabilities (for example, $0.50 \mid 0.70 = 0.71$), which is the $P(E \mid p = 0.04)$.

Our next step is to determine the optimal strategy by calculating the expected opportunity loss of each strategy (see Table 17-5).

The probability of action is the conditional probabilities that were calculated in Table 17-4. The risk in column (4) is computed by multiplying the values in column (3) by the appropriate opportunity loss of that action in column (2) and summing the values.

The expected opportunity loss of each strategy is computed by using the following rule.

$$\text{EOL}(s_k) = \Sigma P_0(p) \cdot R(s_k \mid p)$$

where $P_0(p)$ is the prior probability and $R(s_k \mid p)$ is the risk.

For strategy 3, we have

$$\text{EOL}(s_3) = P_0(p = 0.04) \cdot R(s_3 \mid p = 0.04) + P_0(p = 0.08) \cdot R(s_3 \mid p = 0.08)$$
$$+ P_0(p = 0.12) \cdot R(s_3 \mid p = 0.12)$$
$$= 0.7(7) + 0.2(180) + 0.1(200) = 60.9$$

For strategy 4, we have

$$\text{EOL}(s_4) = P_0(p = 0.04) \cdot R(s_4 \mid p = 0.04) + P_0(p = 0.08) \cdot R(s_4 \mid p = 0.08)$$
$$+ P_0(p = 0.12) \cdot R(s_4 \mid p = 0.12)$$
$$= 0.7(28) + 0.2(100) + 0.1(80) = 47.6$$

Strategy 4 is the optimal strategy because it yields the minimum expected opportunity loss (47.6). Thus, if $X \leq C_1$, we accept the shipment; however, if $X > C_1$, we reject the shipment.

Next, we examine the classical hypothesis test procedure to make a decision concerning the tire example. There are two hypotheses, the null and alternative. Given the discrete proportions assumed here, we modify somewhat the null and alternative hypotheses.

$$H_0: p = 0.04 \qquad H_1: p = 0.08 \quad \text{or} \quad 0.12$$

If we accept H_0, we accept the lot, if we reject H_0, we reject the lot. From previous analysis, the

TABLE 17-5
Calculations of risk, or conditional expected opportunity losses for strategies s_3 and s_4

Strategy s_3

(1) State of Nature (p = lot proportion of defectives)	(2) Opportunity Loss R A		(3) Probability of Action $s_3(A, A, R)$ A A R			(4) Risk (conditional expected losses) $R(s_3 \mid p_i, n)$
0.04	100	0	0.71	0.21	0.07	7
0.08	0	200	0.50	0.40	0.10	180
0.12	0	400	0.20	0.30	0.50	200

$$R(s_3 \mid p = 0.04, n) = 0.71(0) + 0.21(0) + 0.07(100) = 7$$
$$R(s_3 \mid p = 0.08, n) = 0.50(200) + 0.40(200) + 0.10(0) = 180$$
$$R(s_3 \mid p = 0.12, n) = 0.20(400) + 0.30(400) + 0.50(0) = 200$$

Strategy s_4

State of Nature (p = lot proportion of defectives)	Opportunity Loss R A		Probability of Action $s_4(A, R, R)$ A R R			Risk (conditional expected losses) $R(s_4 \mid p_i, n)$
0.04	100	0	0.71	0.21	0.07	28
0.08	0	200	0.50	0.40	0.10	100
0.12	0	400	0.20	0.30	0.50	80

$$R(s_4 \mid p = 0.04, n) = 0.71(0) + 0.21(100) + 0.07(100) = 28$$
$$R(s_4 \mid p = 0.08, n) = 0.50(200) + 0.40(0) + 0.10(0) = 100$$
$$R(s_4 \mid p = 0.12, n) = 0.20(400) + 0.30(0) + 0.50(0) = 80$$

Type I error, the level of α, is the probability of rejecting H_0 when H_0 is true. In this case let us assume that the level of $\alpha = 0.10$. We can determine the various levels of the Type I error under each strategy. Using Table 17-4, the Type I error of strategy 3 and 4 can be computed.

The Type I error of strategy 3 is the probability of rejecting H_0 when H_0 is true. From Table 17-4 we can find the probability of accepting H_0 when H_0 is true. Under s_3 we will accept H_0 if we observe E or F, given $p = 0.04$. The probability of accepting H_0 when H_0 is true ($p = 0.04$) is $0.71 + 0.21 = 0.92$. The probability of rejecting H_0 when H_0 is true is $1 - 0.92 = 0.08$.

The Type I error of strategy 4 can also be computed from Table 17-4. Again, we can find the probability of accepting H_0 when H_0 is true. Under s_4 we will accept H_0 if we observe E. The probability of accepting H_0 when H_0 is true $P(E \mid p = 0.04)$ is 0.71. The Type I error, the probability of rejecting H_0 when H_0 is true, is $1 - 0.71 = 0.29$.

Thus, under s_3, Type I error is 0.08, and under s_4, Type I error is 0.29. Strategy 3 has a Type I error less than $\alpha = 0.10$ and would be the acceptable strategy under hypothesis testing. However, using Bayesian decision making, s_4 is the optimal strategy. As one can see in this example, the outcome is different under the two analyses. As seen in Chapters 15 and 16, a sample should not be taken under certain cases in Bayesian analysis, whereas a sample must be taken to do a classical hypothesis test.

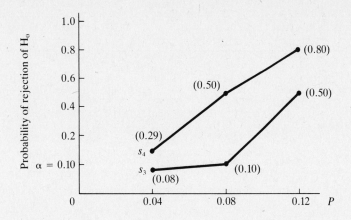

FIGURE 17-1

The power curve for strategies s_3 and s_4 (see Figure 17-1) can be obtained from Table 17-4.

	s_3
$P(\text{Accept } H_0 \mid p = 0.04) = 0.92$	$P(\text{Reject } H_0 \mid p = 0.04) = 0.08$
$P(\text{Accept } H_0 \mid p = 0.08) = 0.90$	$P(\text{Reject } H_0 \mid p = 0.08) = 0.10$
$P(\text{Accept } H_0 \mid p = 0.12) = 0.50$	$P(\text{Reject } H_0 \mid p = 0.12) = 0.50$

	s_4
$P(\text{Accept } H_0 \mid p = 0.04) = 0.71$	$P(\text{Reject } H_0 \mid p = 0.04) = 0.29$
$P(\text{Accept } H_0 \mid p = 0.08) = 0.50$	$P(\text{Reject } H_0 \mid p = 0.08) = 0.50$
$P(\text{Accept } H_0 \mid p = 0.12) = 0.20$	$P(\text{Reject } H_0 \mid p = 0.12) = 0.80$

The $P(\text{Accept } H_0 \mid p = 0.04)$ under s_3 is $P(\text{E} \mid p = 0.04) + P(\text{F} \mid p = 0.04)$ because under s_3, we will accept H_0 if the sample information is E or F. The $P(\text{Reject } H_0 \mid p = 0.04)$ is equal to $1 - P(\text{Accept } H_0 \mid p = 0.04)$, which in this case is $1 - 0.92 = 0.08$. The other Type I errors are computed essentially the same way. Remember, under s_4 we will accept only if E is obtained in the sample information.

Problem 1: Given the payoff matrix, joint frequency of sample results, and states of nature for a shipment of tomatoes (see data on the next page), compare the results using Bayesian decision theory and classical hypothesis testing. Level of $\alpha = 0.10$.

Data for Problem 1

**Payoff Table, Showing Opportunity Losses for Actions
of Acceptance and Rejection**

State of Nature (p = lot proportion of defectives)	Prior Probability	Act	
		a_1 Reject	a_2 Accept
0.02	0.80	200	0
0.04	0.15	0	300
0.06	0.05	0	600

Joint Frequency Distribution of Sample Results and States of Nature

State of Nature (p = lot proportion of defectives)	Sample Results			
	Type E $X \le C_1$	Type F $C_1 < X \le C_2$	Type G $X > C_2$	Total
0.02	0.60	0.15	0.05	0.80
0.04	0.08	0.05	0.02	0.15
0.06	0.01	0.02	0.02	0.05
	0.69	0.22	0.09	1.00

CHAPTER 17 REVIEW PROBLEMS

1. Given the following payoff matrix, joint frequency of sample results, and states of nature for a shipment of lumber, compare the results using Bayesian decision theory and classical hypothesis testing. Test at $\alpha = 0.10$.

Data for Review Problem 1

**Payoff Table, Showing Opportunity Losses for Action
of Acceptance and Rejection**

State of Nature (p = proportion of defectives)	Prior Probability	Act	
		a_1 Reject	a_2 Accept
0.01	0.60	100	0
0.02	0.30	200	0
0.03	0.10	0	400

Joint Frequency Distribution of Sample Results and States of Nature

State of Nature (p = proportion of derivatives)	Sample Results			
	Type E $(X \le C_1)$	Type F $(C_1 < X \le C_2)$	Type G $(X > C_2)$	Total
0.01	0.45	0.10	0.05	0.60
0.02	0.20	0.06	0.04	0.30
0.03	0.02	0.03	0.05	0.10
				1.00

2. Given the following payoff matrix, joint frequency of sample results, and states of nature for a shipment of radios, compare the results using Bayesian decision theory and classical hypothesis testing. Test at $\alpha = 0.05$.

Data for Review Problem 2

Payoff Table, Showing Opportunity Losses for Actions of Acceptance and Rejection

State of Nature (p = lot proportion of defectives)	Prior Probability	Act a_1 Reject	a_2 Accept
0.01	0.90	50	0
0.03	0.06	0	100
0.05	0.04	0	200

Joint Frequency Distribution of Sample Results and States of Nature

State of Nature (p = lot proportion of defectives)	Type E $(X \le C_1)$	Sample Results Type F $(C_1 < X \le C_2)$	Type G $(X > C_2)$	Total
0.01	0.80	0.08	0.02	0.90
0.02	0.03	0.02	0.01	0.06
0.03	0.02	0.01	0.01	0.04

APPENDIX
STATISTICAL TABLES

TABLE A-1

Selected values of the binomial cumulative distribution function

$$F(c) = P(X \leqslant c) = \sum_{x=0}^{c} \binom{n}{x} (1-p)^{n-x} p^x$$

Example If $p = 0.20$, $n = 7$, $c = 2$, then $F(2) = P(X \leqslant 2) = 0.8520$.

						p					
n	c	0.05	0.10	0.15	0.20	0.25	0.30	0.35	0.40	0.45	0.50
2	0	0.9025	0.8100	0.7225	0.6400	0.5625	0.4900	0.4225	0.3600	0.3025	0.2500
	1	0.9975	0.9900	0.9775	0.9600	0.9375	0.9100	0.8775	0.8400	0.7975	0.7500
3	0	0.8574	0.7290	0.6141	0.5120	0.4219	0.3430	0.2746	0.2160	0.1664	0.1250
	1	0.9928	0.9720	0.9392	0.8960	0.8438	0.7840	0.7182	0.6480	0.5748	0.5000
	2	0.9999	0.9990	0.9966	0.9920	0.9844	0.9730	0.9571	0.9360	0.9089	0.8750
4	0	0.8145	0.6561	0.5220	0.4096	0.3164	0.2401	0.1785	0.1296	0.0915	0.0625
	1	0.9860	0.9477	0.8905	0.8192	0.7383	0.6517	0.5630	0.4752	0.3910	0.3125
	2	0.9995	0.9963	0.9880	0.9728	0.9492	0.9163	0.8735	0.8208	0.7585	0.6875
	3	1.0000	0.9999	0.9995	0.9984	0.9961	0.9919	0.9850	0.9744	0.9590	0.9375
5	0	0.7738	0.5905	0.4437	0.3277	0.2373	0.1681	0.1160	0.0778	0.0503	0.0312
	1	0.9774	0.9185	0.8352	0.7373	0.6328	0.5282	0.4284	0.3370	0.2562	0.1875
	2	0.9988	0.9914	0.9734	0.9421	0.8965	0.8369	0.7648	0.6826	0.5931	0.5000
	3	1.0000	0.9995	0.9978	0.9933	0.9844	0.9692	0.9460	0.9130	0.8688	0.8125
	4	1.0000	1.0000	0.9999	0.9997	0.9990	0.9976	0.9947	0.9898	0.9815	0.9688
6	0	0.7351	0.5314	0.3771	0.2621	0.1780	0.1176	0.0754	0.0467	0.0277	0.0156
	1	0.9672	0.8857	0.7765	0.6554	0.5339	0.4202	0.3191	0.2333	0.1636	0.1094
	2	0.9978	0.9842	0.9527	0.9011	0.8306	0.7443	0.6471	0.5443	0.4415	0.3438
	3	0.9999	0.9987	0.9941	0.9830	0.9624	0.9295	0.8826	0.8208	0.7447	0.6562
	4	1.0000	0.9999	0.9996	0.9984	0.9954	0.9891	0.9777	0.9590	0.9308	0.8906
	5	1.0000	1.0000	1.0000	0.9999	0.9998	0.9993	0.9982	0.9959	0.9917	0.9844

Source: From Irwin Miller and John E. Freund, *Probability and Statistics for Engineers*, Second Edition, © 1977, pp. 477–481. Reprinted by permission of Prentice-Hall, Inc., Englewood Cliffs, NJ.

TABLE A-1 (continued)

n	c	0.05	0.10	0.15	0.20	0.25	0.30	0.35	0.40	0.45	0.50
							p				
7	0	0.6983	0.4783	0.3206	0.2097	0.1335	0.0824	0.0490	0.0280	0.0152	0.0078
	1	0.9556	0.8503	0.7166	0.5767	0.4449	0.3294	0.2338	0.1586	0.1024	0.0625
	2	0.9962	0.9743	0.9262	0.8520	0.7564	0.6471	0.5323	0.4199	0.3164	0.2266
	3	0.9998	0.9973	0.9879	0.9667	0.9294	0.8740	0.8002	0.7102	0.6083	0.5000
	4	1.0000	0.9998	0.9988	0.9953	0.9871	0.9712	0.9444	0.9037	0.8471	0.7734
	5	1.0000	1.0000	0.9999	0.9996	0.9987	0.9962	0.9910	0.9812	0.9643	0.9375
	6	1.0000	1.0000	1.0000	1.0000	0.9999	0.9998	0.9994	0.9984	0.9963	0.9922
8	0	0.6634	0.4305	0.2725	0.1678	0.1001	0.0576	0.0319	0.0168	0.0084	0.0039
	1	0.9428	0.8131	0.6572	0.5033	0.3671	0.2553	0.1691	0.1064	0.0632	0.0352
	2	0.9942	0.9619	0.8948	0.7969	0.6785	0.5518	0.4278	0.3154	0.2201	0.1445
	3	0.9996	0.9950	0.9786	0.9437	0.8862	0.8059	0.7064	0.5941	0.4770	0.3633
	4	1.0000	0.9996	0.9971	0.9896	0.9727	0.9420	0.8939	0.8263	0.7396	0.6367
	5	1.0000	1.0000	0.9998	0.9988	0.9958	0.9887	0.9747	0.9502	0.9115	0.8555
	6	1.0000	1.0000	1.0000	0.9999	0.9996	0.9987	0.9964	0.9915	0.9819	0.9648
	7	1.0000	1.0000	1.0000	1.0000	1.0000	0.9999	0.9998	0.9993	0.9983	0.9961
9	0	0.6302	0.3874	0.2316	0.1342	0.0751	0.0404	0.0207	0.0101	0.0046	0.0020
	1	0.9288	0.7748	0.5995	0.4362	0.3003	0.1960	0.1211	0.0705	0.0385	0.0195
	2	0.9916	0.9470	0.8591	0.7382	0.6007	0.4628	0.3373	0.2318	0.1495	0.0898
	3	0.9994	0.9917	0.9661	0.9144	0.8343	0.7297	0.6089	0.4826	0.3614	0.2539
	4	1.0000	0.9991	0.9944	0.9804	0.9511	0.9012	0.8283	0.7334	0.6214	0.5000
	5	1.0000	0.9999	0.9994	0.9969	0.9900	0.9747	0.9464	0.9006	0.8342	0.7461
	6	1.0000	1.0000	1.0000	0.9997	0.9987	0.9957	0.9888	0.9750	0.9502	0.9102
	7	1.0000	1.0000	1.0000	1.0000	0.9999	0.9996	0.9986	0.9962	0.9909	0.9805
	8	1.0000	1.0000	1.0000	1.0000	1.0000	1.0000	0.9999	0.9997	0.9992	0.9980
10	0	0.5987	0.3487	0.1969	0.1074	0.0563	0.0282	0.0135	0.0060	0.0025	0.0010
	1	0.9139	0.7361	0.5443	0.3758	0.2440	0.1493	0.0860	0.0464	0.0232	0.0107
	2	0.9885	0.9298	0.8202	0.6778	0.5256	0.3828	0.2616	0.1673	0.0996	0.0547
	3	0.9990	0.9872	0.9500	0.8791	0.7759	0.6496	0.5138	0.3823	0.2660	0.1719
	4	0.9999	0.9984	0.9901	0.9672	0.9219	0.8497	0.7515	0.6331	0.5044	0.3770
	5	1.0000	0.9999	0.9986	0.9936	0.9803	0.9527	0.9051	0.8338	0.7384	0.6230
	6	1.0000	1.0000	0.9999	0.9991	0.9965	0.9894	0.9740	0.9452	0.8980	0.8281
	7	1.0000	1.0000	1.0000	0.9999	0.9996	0.9984	0.9952	0.9877	0.9726	0.9453
	8	1.0000	1.0000	1.0000	1.0000	1.0000	0.9999	0.9995	0.9983	0.9955	0.9893
	9	1.0000	1.0000	1.0000	1.0000	1.0000	1.0000	1.0000	0.9999	0.9997	0.9990
11	0	0.5688	0.3138	0.1673	0.0859	0.0422	0.0198	0.0088	0.0036	0.0014	0.0005
	1	0.8981	0.6974	0.4922	0.3221	0.1971	0.1130	0.0606	0.0302	0.0139	0.0059
	2	0.9848	0.9104	0.7788	0.6174	0.4552	0.3127	0.2001	0.1189	0.0652	0.0327
	3	0.9984	0.9815	0.9306	0.8389	0.7133	0.5696	0.4256	0.2963	0.1911	0.1133
	4	0.9999	0.9972	0.9841	0.9496	0.8854	0.7897	0.6683	0.5328	0.3971	0.2744

TABLE A-1   (continued)

n	c	0.05	0.10	0.15	0.20	0.25	0.30	0.35	0.40	0.45	0.50
							p				
	5	1.0000	0.9997	0.9973	0.9883	0.9657	0.9218	0.8513	0.7535	0.6331	0.5000
	6	1.0000	1.0000	0.9997	0.9980	0.9924	0.9784	0.9499	0.9006	0.8262	0.7256
	7	1.0000	1.0000	1.0000	0.9998	0.9988	0.9957	0.9878	0.9707	0.9390	0.8867
	8	1.0000	1.0000	1.0000	1.0000	0.9999	0.9994	0.9980	0.9941	0.9852	0.9673
	9	1.0000	1.0000	1.0000	1.0000	1.0000	1.0000	0.9998	0.9993	0.9978	0.9941
	10	1.0000	1.0000	1.0000	1.0000	1.0000	1.0000	1.0000	1.0000	0.9998	0.9995
12	0	0.5404	0.2824	0.1422	0.0687	0.0317	0.0138	0.0057	0.0022	0.0008	0.0002
	1	0.8816	0.6590	0.4435	0.2749	0.1584	0.0850	0.0424	0.0196	0.0083	0.0032
	2	0.9804	0.8891	0.7358	0.5583	0.3907	0.2528	0.1513	0.0834	0.0421	0.0193
	3	0.9978	0.9744	0.9078	0.7946	0.6488	0.4925	0.3467	0.2253	0.1345	0.0730
	4	0.9998	0.9957	0.9761	0.9274	0.8424	0.7237	0.5833	0.4382	0.3044	0.1938
	5	1.0000	0.9995	0.9954	0.9806	0.9456	0.8822	0.7873	0.6652	0.5269	0.3872
	6	1.0000	0.9999	0.9993	0.9961	0.9857	0.9614	0.9154	0.8418	0.7393	0.6128
	7	1.0000	1.0000	0.9999	0.9994	0.9972	0.9905	0.9745	0.9427	0.8883	0.8062
	8	1.0000	1.0000	1.0000	0.9999	0.9996	0.9983	0.9944	0.9847	0.9644	0.9270
	9	1.0000	1.0000	1.0000	1.0000	1.0000	0.9998	0.9992	0.9972	0.9921	0.9807
	10	1.0000	1.0000	1.0000	1.0000	1.0000	1.0000	0.9999	0.9997	0.9989	0.9968
	11	1.0000	1.0000	1.0000	1.0000	1.0000	1.0000	1.0000	1.0000	0.9999	0.9998
13	0	0.5133	0.2542	0.1209	0.0550	0.0238	0.0097	0.0037	0.0013	0.0004	0.0001
	1	0.8646	0.6213	0.3983	0.2336	0.1267	0.0637	0.0296	0.0126	0.0049	0.0017
	2	0.9755	0.8661	0.6920	0.5017	0.3326	0.2025	0.1132	0.0579	0.0269	0.0112
	3	0.9969	0.9658	0.8820	0.7473	0.5843	0.4206	0.2783	0.1686	0.0929	0.0461
	4	0.9997	0.9935	0.9658	0.9009	0.7940	0.6543	0.5005	0.3530	0.2279	0.1334
	5	1.0000	0.9991	0.9925	0.9700	0.9198	0.8346	0.7159	0.5744	0.4268	0.2905
	6	1.0000	0.9999	0.9987	0.9930	0.9757	0.9376	0.8705	0.7712	0.6437	0.5000
	7	1.0000	1.0000	0.9998	0.9988	0.9944	0.9818	0.9538	0.9023	0.8212	0.7095
	8	1.0000	1.0000	1.0000	0.9998	0.9990	0.9960	0.9874	0.9679	0.9302	0.8666
	9	1.0000	1.0000	1.0000	1.0000	0.9999	0.9993	0.9975	0.9922	0.9797	0.9539
	10	1.0000	1.0000	1.0000	1.0000	1.0000	0.9999	0.9997	0.9987	0.9959	0.9888
	11	1.0000	1.0000	1.0000	1.0000	1.0000	1.0000	1.0000	0.9999	0.9995	0.9983
	12	1.0000	1.0000	1.0000	1.0000	1.0000	1.0000	1.0000	1.0000	1.0000	0.9999
14	0	0.4877	0.2288	0.1028	0.0440	0.0178	0.0068	0.0024	0.0008	0.0002	0.0001
	1	0.8470	0.5846	0.3567	0.1979	0.1010	0.0475	0.0205	0.0081	0.0029	0.0009
	2	0.9699	0.8416	0.6479	0.4481	0.2811	0.1608	0.0839	0.0398	0.0170	0.0065
	3	0.9958	0.9559	0.8535	0.6982	0.5213	0.3552	0.2205	0.1243	0.0632	0.0287
	4	0.9996	0.9908	0.9533	0.8702	0.7415	0.5842	0.4227	0.2793	0.1672	0.0898

TABLE A-1   (continued)

n	c	0.05	0.10	0.15	0.20	0.25	0.30	0.35	0.40	0.45	0.50
							p				
	5	1.0000	0.9985	0.9885	0.9561	0.8883	0.7805	0.6405	0.4859	0.3373	0.2120
	6	1.0000	0.9998	0.9978	0.9884	0.9617	0.9067	0.8164	0.6925	0.5461	0.3953
	7	1.0000	1.0000	0.9997	0.9976	0.9897	0.9685	0.9247	0.8499	0.7414	0.6047
	8	1.0000	1.0000	1.0000	0.9996	0.9978	0.9917	0.9757	0.9417	0.8811	0.7880
	9	1.0000	1.0000	1.0000	1.0000	0.9997	0.9983	0.9940	0.9825	0.9574	0.9102
	10	1.0000	1.0000	1.0000	1.0000	1.0000	0.9998	0.9989	0.9961	0.9886	0.9713
	11	1.0000	1.0000	1.0000	1.0000	1.0000	1.0000	0.9999	0.9994	0.9978	0.9935
	12	1.0000	1.0000	1.0000	1.0000	1.0000	1.0000	1.0000	0.9999	0.9997	0.9991
	13	1.0000	1.0000	1.0000	1.0000	1.0000	1.0000	1.0000	1.0000	1.0000	0.9999
15	0	0.4633	0.2059	0.0874	0.0352	0.0134	0.0047	0.0016	0.0005	0.0001	0.0000
	1	0.8290	0.5490	0.3186	0.1671	0.0802	0.0353	0.0142	0.0052	0.0017	0.0005
	2	0.9638	0.8159	0.6042	0.3980	0.2361	0.1268	0.0617	0.0271	0.0107	0.0037
	3	0.9945	0.9444	0.8227	0.6482	0.4613	0.2969	0.1727	0.0905	0.0424	0.0176
	4	0.9994	0.9873	0.9383	0.8358	0.6865	0.5155	0.3519	0.2173	0.1204	0.0592
	5	0.9999	0.9978	0.9832	0.9389	0.8516	0.7216	0.5643	0.4032	0.2608	0.1509
	6	1.0000	0.9997	0.9964	0.9819	0.9434	0.8689	0.7548	0.6098	0.4522	0.3036
	7	1.0000	1.0000	0.9996	0.9958	0.9827	0.9500	0.8868	0.7869	0.6535	0.5000
	8	1.0000	1.0000	0.9999	0.9992	0.9958	0.9848	0.9578	0.9050	0.8182	0.6964
	9	1.0000	1.0000	1.0000	0.9999	0.9992	0.9963	0.9876	0.9662	0.9231	0.8491
	10	1.0000	1.0000	1.0000	1.0000	0.9999	0.9993	0.9972	0.9907	0.9745	0.9408
	11	1.0000	1.0000	1.0000	1.0000	1.0000	0.9999	0.9995	0.9981	0.9937	0.9824
	12	1.0000	1.0000	1.0000	1.0000	1.0000	1.0000	0.9999	0.9997	0.9989	0.9963
	13	1.0000	1.0000	1.0000	1.0000	1.0000	1.0000	1.0000	1.0000	0.9999	0.9995
	14	1.0000	1.0000	1.0000	1.0000	1.0000	1.0000	1.0000	1.0000	1.0000	1.0000
16	0	0.4401	0.1853	0.0743	0.0281	0.0100	0.0033	0.0010	0.0003	0.0001	0.0000
	1	0.8108	0.5147	0.2839	0.1407	0.0635	0.0261	0.0098	0.0033	0.0010	0.0003
	2	0.9571	0.7892	0.5614	0.3518	0.1971	0.0994	0.0451	0.0183	0.0066	0.0021
	3	0.9930	0.9316	0.7899	0.5981	0.4050	0.2459	0.1339	0.0651	0.0281	0.0106
	4	0.9991	0.9830	0.9209	0.7982	0.6302	0.4499	0.2892	0.1666	0.0853	0.0384
	5	0.9999	0.9967	0.9765	0.9183	0.8103	0.6598	0.4900	0.3288	0.1976	0.1051
	6	1.0000	0.9995	0.9944	0.9733	0.9204	0.8247	0.6881	0.5272	0.3660	0.2272
	7	1.0000	0.9999	0.9989	0.9930	0.9729	0.9256	0.8406	0.7161	0.5629	0.4018
	8	1.0000	1.0000	0.9998	0.9985	0.9925	0.9743	0.9329	0.8577	0.7441	0.5982
	9	1.0000	1.0000	1.0000	0.9998	0.9984	0.9929	0.9771	0.9417	0.8759	0.7728
	10	1.0000	1.0000	1.0000	1.0000	0.9997	0.9984	0.9938	0.9809	0.9514	0.8949
	11	1.0000	1.0000	1.0000	1.0000	1.0000	0.9997	0.9987	0.9951	0.9851	0.9616
	12	1.0000	1.0000	1.0000	1.0000	1.0000	1.0000	0.9998	0.9991	0.9965	0.9894
	13	1.0000	1.0000	1.0000	1.0000	1.0000	1.0000	1.0000	0.9999	0.9994	0.9979
	14	1.0000	1.0000	1.0000	1.0000	1.0000	1.0000	1.0000	1.0000	1.0000	0.9997
	15	1.0000	1.0000	1.0000	1.0000	1.0000	1.0000	1.0000	1.0000	1.0000	1.0000

TABLE A-1 (continued)

n	c	0.05	0.10	0.15	0.20	0.25	0.30	0.35	0.40	0.45	0.50
17	0	0.4181	0.1668	0.0631	0.0225	0.0075	0.0023	0.0007	0.0002	0.0000	0.0000
	1	0.7922	0.4818	0.2525	0.1182	0.0501	0.0193	0.0067	0.0021	0.0006	0.0001
	2	0.9497	0.7618	0.5198	0.3096	0.1637	0.0774	0.0327	0.0123	0.0041	0.0012
	3	0.9912	0.9174	0.7556	0.5489	0.3530	0.2019	0.1028	0.0464	0.0184	0.0064
	4	0.9988	0.9779	0.9013	0.7582	0.5739	0.3887	0.2348	0.1260	0.0596	0.0245
	5	0.9999	0.9953	0.9681	0.8943	0.7653	0.5968	0.4197	0.2639	0.1471	0.0717
	6	1.0000	0.9992	0.9917	0.9623	0.8929	0.7752	0.6188	0.4478	0.2902	0.1662
	7	1.0000	0.9999	0.9983	0.9891	0.9598	0.8954	0.7872	0.6405	0.4743	0.3145
	8	1.0000	1.0000	0.9997	0.9974	0.9876	0.9597	0.9006	0.8011	0.6626	0.5000
	9	1.0000	1.0000	1.0000	0.9995	0.9969	0.9873	0.9617	0.9081	0.8166	0.6855
	10	1.0000	1.0000	1.0000	0.9999	0.9994	0.9968	0.9880	0.9652	0.9174	0.8338
	11	1.0000	1.0000	1.0000	1.0000	0.9999	0.9993	0.9970	0.9894	0.9699	0.9283
	12	1.0000	1.0000	1.0000	1.0000	1.0000	0.9999	0.9994	0.9975	0.9914	0.9755
	13	1.0000	1.0000	1.0000	1.0000	1.0000	1.0000	0.9999	0.9995	0.9981	0.9936
	14	1.0000	1.0000	1.0000	1.0000	1.0000	1.0000	1.0000	0.9999	0.9997	0.9988
	15	1.0000	1.0000	1.0000	1.0000	1.0000	1.0000	1.0000	1.0000	1.0000	0.9999
	16	1.0000	1.0000	1.0000	1.0000	1.0000	1.0000	1.0000	1.0000	1.0000	1.0000
18	0	0.3972	0.1501	0.0536	0.0180	0.0056	0.0016	0.0004	0.0001	0.0000	0.0000
	1	0.7735	0.4503	0.2241	0.0991	0.0395	0.0142	0.0046	0.0013	0.0003	0.0001
	2	0.9419	0.7338	0.4797	0.2713	0.1353	0.0600	0.0236	0.0082	0.0025	0.0007
	3	0.9891	0.9018	0.7202	0.5010	0.3057	0.1646	0.0783	0.0328	0.0120	0.0038
	4	0.9985	0.9718	0.8794	0.7164	0.5187	0.3327	0.1886	0.0942	0.0411	0.0154
	5	0.9998	0.9936	0.9581	0.8671	0.7175	0.5344	0.3550	0.2088	0.1077	0.0481
	6	1.0000	0.9988	0.9882	0.9487	0.8610	0.7217	0.5491	0.3743	0.2258	0.1189
	7	1.0000	0.9998	0.9973	0.9837	0.9431	0.8593	0.7283	0.5634	0.3915	0.2403
	8	1.0000	1.0000	0.9995	0.9957	0.9807	0.9404	0.8609	0.7368	0.5778	0.4073
	9	1.0000	1.0000	0.9999	0.9991	0.9946	0.9790	0.9403	0.8653	0.7473	0.5927
	10	1.0000	1.0000	1.0000	0.9998	0.9988	0.9939	0.9788	0.9424	0.8720	0.7597
	11	1.0000	1.0000	1.0000	1.0000	0.9998	0.9986	0.9938	0.9797	0.9463	0.8811
	12	1.0000	1.0000	1.0000	1.0000	1.0000	0.9997	0.9986	0.9942	0.9817	0.9519
	13	1.0000	1.0000	1.0000	1.0000	1.0000	1.0000	0.9997	0.9987	0.9951	0.9846
	14	1.0000	1.0000	1.0000	1.0000	1.0000	1.0000	1.0000	0.9998	0.9990	0.9962
	15	1.0000	1.0000	1.0000	1.0000	1.0000	1.0000	1.0000	1.0000	0.9999	0.9993
	16	1.0000	1.0000	1.0000	1.0000	1.0000	1.0000	1.0000	1.0000	1.0000	0.9999
19	0	0.3774	0.1351	0.0456	0.0144	0.0042	0.0011	0.0003	0.0001	0.0000	0.0000
	1	0.7547	0.4203	0.1985	0.0829	0.0310	0.0104	0.0031	0.0008	0.0002	0.0000
	2	0.9335	0.7054	0.4413	0.2369	0.1113	0.0462	0.0170	0.0055	0.0015	0.0004
	3	0.9868	0.8850	0.6841	0.4551	0.2630	0.1332	0.0591	0.0230	0.0077	0.0022
	4	0.9980	0.9648	0.8556	0.6733	0.4654	0.2822	0.1500	0.0696	0.0280	0.0096

TABLE A-1 (continued)

n	c	0.05	0.10	0.15	0.20	0.25	p 0.30	0.35	0.40	0.45	0.50
	5	0.9998	0.9914	0.9463	0.8369	0.6678	0.4739	0.2968	0.1629	0.0777	0.0318
	6	1.0000	0.9983	0.9837	0.9324	0.8251	0.6655	0.4812	0.3081	0.1727	0.0835
	7	1.0000	0.9997	0.9959	0.9767	0.9225	0.8180	0.6656	0.4878	0.3169	0.1796
	8	1.0000	1.0000	0.9992	0.9933	0.9713	0.9161	0.8145	0.6675	0.4940	0.3238
	9	1.0000	1.0000	0.9999	0.9984	0.9911	0.9674	0.9125	0.8139	0.6710	0.5000
	10	1.0000	1.0000	1.0000	0.9997	0.9977	0.9895	0.9653	0.9115	0.8159	0.6762
	11	1.0000	1.0000	1.0000	1.0000	0.9995	0.9972	0.9886	0.9648	0.9129	0.8204
	12	1.0000	1.0000	1.0000	1.0000	0.9999	0.9994	0.9969	0.9884	0.9658	0.9165
	13	1.0000	1.0000	1.0000	1.0000	1.0000	0.9999	0.9993	0.9969	0.9891	0.9682
	14	1.0000	1.0000	1.0000	1.0000	1.0000	1.0000	0.9999	0.9994	0.9972	0.9904
	15	1.0000	1.0000	1.0000	1.0000	1.0000	1.0000	1.0000	0.9999	0.9995	0.9978
	16	1.0000	1.0000	1.0000	1.0000	1.0000	1.0000	1.0000	1.0000	0.9999	0.9996
	17	1.0000	1.0000	1.0000	1.0000	1.0000	1.0000	1.0000	1.0000	1.0000	1.0000
20	0	0.3585	0.1216	0.0388	0.0115	0.0032	0.0008	0.0002	0.0000	0.0000	0.0000
	1	0.7358	0.3917	0.1756	0.0692	0.0243	0.0076	0.0021	0.0005	0.0001	0.0000
	2	0.9245	0.6769	0.4049	0.2061	0.0913	0.0355	0.0121	0.0036	0.0009	0.0002
	3	0.9841	0.8670	0.6477	0.4114	0.2252	0.1071	0.0444	0.0160	0.0049	0.0013
	4	0.9974	0.9568	0.8298	0.6296	0.4148	0.2375	0.1182	0.0510	0.0189	0.0059
	5	0.9997	0.9887	0.9327	0.8042	0.6172	0.4164	0.2454	0.1256	0.0553	0.0207
	6	1.0000	0.9976	0.9781	0.9133	0.7858	0.6080	0.4166	0.2500	0.1299	0.0577
	7	1.0000	0.9996	0.9941	0.9679	0.8982	0.7723	0.6010	0.4159	0.2520	0.1316
	8	1.0000	0.9999	0.9987	0.9900	0.9591	0.8867	0.7624	0.5956	0.4143	0.2517
	9	1.0000	1.0000	0.9998	0.9974	0.9861	0.9520	0.8782	0.7553	0.5914	0.4119
	10	1.0000	1.0000	1.0000	0.9994	0.9961	0.9829	0.9468	0.8725	0.7507	0.5881
	11	1.0000	1.0000	1.0000	0.9999	0.9991	0.9949	0.9804	0.9435	0.8692	0.7483
	12	1.0000	1.0000	1.0000	1.0000	0.9998	0.9987	0.9940	0.9790	0.9420	0.8684
	13	1.0000	1.0000	1.0000	1.0000	1.0000	0.9997	0.9985	0.9935	0.9786	0.9423
	14	1.0000	1.0000	1.0000	1.0000	1.0000	1.0000	0.9997	0.9984	0.9936	0.9793
	15	1.0000	1.0000	1.0000	1.0000	1.0000	1.0000	1.0000	0.9997	0.9985	0.9941
	16	1.0000	1.0000	1.0000	1.0000	1.0000	1.0000	1.0000	1.0000	0.9997	0.9987
	17	1.0000	1.0000	1.0000	1.0000	1.0000	1.0000	1.0000	1.0000	1.0000	0.9998
	18	1.0000	1.0000	1.0000	1.0000	1.0000	1.0000	1.0000	1.0000	1.0000	1.0000

TABLE A-2

Selected values of the binomial probability distribution

$$P(x) = \binom{n}{x}(1-p)^{n-x}p^x$$

Example   If $p = 0.15$, $n = 4$, and $x = 3$, then $P(3) = 0.0115$. When $p > 0.5$, the value of $P(x)$ for a given n, x, and p is obtained by finding the tabular entry for the given n, with $n - x$ in place of the given x and $1 - p$ in place of the given p.

n	x	0.05	0.10	0.15	0.20	0.25	p 0.30	0.35	0.40	0.45	0.50
1	0	0.9500	0.9000	0.8500	0.8000	0.7500	0.7000	0.6500	0.6000	0.5500	0.5000
	1	0.0500	0.1000	0.1500	0.2000	0.2500	0.3000	0.3500	0.4000	0.4500	0.5000
2	0	0.9025	0.8100	0.7225	0.6400	0.5625	0.4900	0.4225	0.3600	0.3025	0.2500
	1	0.0950	0.1800	0.2550	0.3200	0.3750	0.4200	0.4550	0.4800	0.4950	0.5000
	2	0.0025	0.0100	0.0225	0.0400	0.0625	0.0900	0.1225	0.1600	0.2025	0.2500
3	0	0.8574	0.7290	0.6141	0.5120	0.4219	0.3430	0.2746	0.2160	0.1664	0.1250
	1	0.1354	0.2430	0.3251	0.3840	0.4219	0.4410	0.4436	0.4320	0.4084	0.3750
	2	0.0071	0.0270	0.0574	0.0960	0.1406	0.1890	0.2389	0.2880	0.3341	0.3750
	3	0.0001	0.0010	0.0034	0.0080	0.0156	0.0270	0.0429	0.0640	0.0911	0.1250
4	0	0.8145	0.6561	0.5220	0.4096	0.3164	0.2401	0.1785	0.1296	0.0915	0.0625
	1	0.1715	0.2916	0.3685	0.4096	0.4219	0.4116	0.3845	0.3456	0.2995	0.2500
	2	0.0135	0.0486	0.0975	0.1536	0.2109	0.2646	0.3105	0.3456	0.3675	0.3750
	3	0.0005	0.0036	0.0115	0.0256	0.0469	0.0756	0.1115	0.1536	0.2005	0.2500
	4	0.0000	0.0001	0.0005	0.0016	0.0039	0.0081	0.0150	0.0256	0.0410	0.0625
5	0	0.7738	0.5905	0.4437	0.3277	0.2373	0.1681	0.1160	0.0778	0.0503	0.0312
	1	0.2036	0.3280	0.3915	0.4096	0.3955	0.3602	0.3124	0.2592	0.2059	0.1562
	2	0.0214	0.0729	0.1382	0.2048	0.2637	0.3087	0.3364	0.3456	0.3369	0.3125
	3	0.0011	0.0081	0.0244	0.0512	0.0879	0.1323	0.1811	0.2304	0.2757	0.3125
	4	0.0000	0.0004	0.0022	0.0064	0.0146	0.0284	0.0488	0.0768	0.1128	0.1562
	5	0.0000	0.0000	0.0001	0.0003	0.0010	0.0024	0.0053	0.0102	0.0185	0.0312
6	0	0.7351	0.5314	0.3771	0.2621	0.1780	0.1176	0.0754	0.0467	0.0277	0.0156
	1	0.2321	0.3543	0.3993	0.3932	0.3560	0.3025	0.2437	0.1866	0.1359	0.0938
	2	0.0305	0.0984	0.1762	0.2458	0.2966	0.3241	0.3280	0.3110	0.2780	0.2344
	3	0.0021	0.0146	0.0415	0.0819	0.1318	0.1852	0.2355	0.2765	0.3032	0.3125
	4	0.0001	0.0012	0.0055	0.0154	0.0330	0.0595	0.0951	0.1382	0.1861	0.2344
	5	0.0000	0.0001	0.0004	0.0015	0.0044	0.0102	0.0205	0.0369	0.0609	0.0938
	6	0.0000	0.0000	0.0000	0.0001	0.0002	0.0007	0.0018	0.0041	0.0083	0.0156
7	0	0.6983	0.4783	0.3206	0.2097	0.1335	0.0824	0.0490	0.0280	0.0152	0.0078
	1	0.2573	0.3720	0.3960	0.3670	0.3115	0.2471	0.1848	0.1306	0.0872	0.0547
	2	0.0406	0.1240	0.2097	0.2753	0.3115	0.3177	0.2985	0.2613	0.2140	0.1641
	3	0.0036	0.0230	0.0617	0.1147	0.1730	0.2269	0.2679	0.2903	0.2918	0.2734
	4	0.0002	0.0026	0.0109	0.0287	0.0577	0.0972	0.1442	0.1935	0.2388	0.2734

TABLE A-2   (continued)

n	x	0.05	0.10	0.15	0.20	0.25	p 0.30	0.35	0.40	0.45	0.50
	5	0.0000	0.0002	0.0012	0.0043	0.0115	0.0250	0.0466	0.0774	0.1172	0.1641
	6	0.0000	0.0000	0.0001	0.0004	0.0013	0.0036	0.0084	0.0172	0.0320	0.0547
	7	0.0000	0.0000	0.0000	0.0000	0.0001	0.0002	0.0006	0.0016	0.0037	0.0078
8	0	0.6634	0.4305	0.2725	0.1678	0.1001	0.0576	0.0319	0.0168	0.0084	0.0039
	1	0.2793	0.3826	0.3847	0.3355	0.2670	0.1977	0.1373	0.0896	0.0548	0.0312
	2	0.0515	0.1488	0.2376	0.2936	0.3115	0.2965	0.2587	0.2090	0.1569	0.1094
	3	0.0054	0.0331	0.0839	0.1468	0.2076	0.2541	0.2786	0.2787	0.2568	0.2188
	4	0.0004	0.0046	0.0185	0.0459	0.0865	0.1361	0.1875	0.2322	0.2627	0.2734
	5	0.0000	0.0004	0.0026	0.0092	0.0231	0.0467	0.0808	0.1239	0.1719	0.2188
	6	0.0000	0.0000	0.0002	0.0011	0.0038	0.0100	0.0217	0.0413	0.0703	0.1094
	7	0.0000	0.0000	0.0000	0.0001	0.0004	0.0012	0.0033	0.0079	0.0164	0.0312
	8	0.0000	0.0000	0.0000	0.0000	0.0000	0.0001	0.0002	0.0007	0.0017	0.0039
9	0	0.6302	0.3874	0.2316	0.1342	0.0751	0.0404	0.0207	0.0101	0.0046	0.0020
	1	0.2985	0.3874	0.3679	0.3020	0.2253	0.1556	0.1004	0.0605	0.0339	0.0176
	2	0.0629	0.1722	0.2597	0.3020	0.3003	0.2668	0.2162	0.1612	0.1110	0.0703
	3	0.0077	0.0446	0.1069	0.1762	0.2336	0.2668	0.2716	0.2508	0.2119	0.1641
	4	0.0006	0.0074	0.0283	0.0661	0.1168	0.1715	0.2194	0.2508	0.2600	0.2461
	5	0.0000	0.0008	0.0050	0.0165	0.0389	0.0735	0.1181	0.1672	0.2128	0.2461
	6	0.0000	0.0001	0.0006	0.0028	0.0087	0.0210	0.0424	0.0743	0.1160	0.1641
	7	0.0000	0.0000	0.0000	0.0003	0.0012	0.0039	0.0098	0.0212	0.0407	0.0703
	8	0.0000	0.0000	0.0000	0.0000	0.0001	0.0004	0.0013	0.0035	0.0083	0.0176
	9	0.0000	0.0000	0.0000	0.0000	0.0000	0.0000	0.0001	0.0003	0.0008	0.0020
10	0	0.5987	0.3487	0.1969	0.1074	0.0563	0.0282	0.0135	0.0060	0.0025	0.0010
	1	0.3151	0.3874	0.3474	0.2684	0.1877	0.1211	0.0725	0.0403	0.0207	0.0098
	2	0.0746	0.1937	0.2759	0.3020	0.2816	0.2335	0.1757	0.1209	0.0763	0.0439
	3	0.0105	0.0574	0.1298	0.2013	0.2503	0.2668	0.2522	0.2150	0.1665	0.1172
	4	0.0010	0.0112	0.0401	0.0881	0.1460	0.2001	0.2377	0.2508	0.2384	0.2051
	5	0.0001	0.0015	0.0085	0.0264	0.0584	0.1029	0.1536	0.2007	0.2340	0.2461
	6	0.0000	0.0001	0.0012	0.0055	0.0162	0.0368	0.0689	0.1115	0.1596	0.2051
	7	0.0000	0.0000	0.0001	0.0008	0.0031	0.0090	0.0212	0.0425	0.0746	0.1172
	8	0.0000	0.0000	0.0000	0.0001	0.0004	0.0014	0.0043	0.0106	0.0229	0.0439
	9	0.0000	0.0000	0.0000	0.0000	0.0000	0.0001	0.0005	0.0016	0.0042	0.0098
	10	0.0000	0.0000	0.0000	0.0000	0.0000	0.0000	0.0000	0.0001	0.0003	0.0010
11	0	0.5688	0.3138	0.1673	0.0859	0.0422	0.0198	0.0088	0.0036	0.0014	0.0005
	1	0.3293	0.3835	0.3248	0.2362	0.1549	0.0932	0.0518	0.0266	0.0125	0.0054
	2	0.0867	0.2131	0.2866	0.2953	0.2581	0.1998	0.1395	0.0887	0.0513	0.0269
	3	0.0137	0.0710	0.1517	0.2215	0.2581	0.2568	0.2254	0.1774	0.1259	0.0806
	4	0.0014	0.0158	0.0536	0.1107	0.1721	0.2201	0.2428	0.2365	0.2060	0.1611

TABLE A-2 (continued)

n	x	0.05	0.10	0.15	0.20	0.25	p 0.30	0.35	0.40	0.45	0.50
	5	0.0001	0.0025	0.0132	0.0388	0.0803	0.1321	0.1830	0.2207	0.2360	0.2256
	6	0.0000	0.0003	0.0023	0.0097	0.0268	0.0566	0.0985	0.1471	0.1931	0.2256
	7	0.0000	0.0000	0.0003	0.0017	0.0064	0.0173	0.0379	0.0701	0.1128	0.1611
	8	0.0000	0.0000	0.0000	0.0002	0.0011	0.0037	0.0102	0.0234	0.0462	0.0806
	9	0.0000	0.0000	0.0000	0.0000	0.0001	0.0005	0.0018	0.0052	0.0126	0.0269
	10	0.0000	0.0000	0.0000	0.0000	0.0000	0.0000	0.0002	0.0007	0.0021	0.0054
	11	0.0000	0.0000	0.0000	0.0000	0.0000	0.0000	0.0000	0.0000	0.0002	0.0005
12	0	0.5404	0.2824	0.1422	0.0687	0.0317	0.0138	0.0057	0.0022	0.0008	0.0002
	1	0.3413	0.3766	0.3012	0.2062	0.1267	0.0712	0.0368	0.0174	0.0075	0.0029
	2	0.0988	0.2301	0.2924	0.2835	0.2323	0.1678	0.1088	0.0639	0.0339	0.0161
	3	0.0173	0.0852	0.1720	0.2362	0.2581	0.2397	0.1954	0.1419	0.0923	0.0537
	4	0.0021	0.0213	0.0683	0.1329	0.1936	0.2311	0.2367	0.2128	0.1700	0.1208
	5	0.0002	0.0038	0.0193	0.0532	0.1032	0.1585	0.2039	0.2270	0.2225	0.1934
	6	0.0000	0.0005	0.0040	0.0155	0.0401	0.0792	0.1281	0.1766	0.2124	0.2256
	7	0.0000	0.0000	0.0006	0.0033	0.0115	0.0291	0.0591	0.1009	0.1489	0.1934
	8	0.0000	0.0000	0.0001	0.0005	0.0024	0.0078	0.0199	0.0420	0.0762	0.1208
	9	0.0000	0.0000	0.0000	0.0001	0.0004	0.0015	0.0048	0.0125	0.0277	0.0537
	10	0.0000	0.0000	0.0000	0.0000	0.0000	0.0002	0.0008	0.0025	0.0068	0.0161
	11	0.0000	0.0000	0.0000	0.0000	0.0000	0.0000	0.0001	0.0003	0.0010	0.0029
	12	0.0000	0.0000	0.0000	0.0000	0.0000	0.0000	0.0000	0.0000	0.0001	0.0002
13	0	0.5133	0.2542	0.1209	0.0550	0.0238	0.0097	0.0037	0.0013	0.0004	0.0001
	1	0.3512	0.3672	0.2774	0.1787	0.1029	0.0540	0.0259	0.0113	0.0045	0.0016
	2	0.1109	0.2448	0.2937	0.2680	0.2059	0.1388	0.0836	0.0453	0.0220	0.0095
	3	0.0214	0.0997	0.1900	0.2457	0.2517	0.2181	0.1651	0.1107	0.0660	0.0349
	4	0.0028	0.0277	0.0838	0.1535	0.2097	0.2337	0.2222	0.1845	0.1350	0.0873
	5	0.0003	0.0055	0.0266	0.0691	0.1258	0.1803	0.2154	0.2214	0.1989	0.1571
	6	0.0000	0.0008	0.0063	0.0230	0.0559	0.1030	0.1546	0.1968	0.2169	0.2095
	7	0.0000	0.0001	0.0011	0.0058	0.0186	0.0442	0.0833	0.1312	0.1775	0.2095
	8	0.0000	0.0000	0.0001	0.0011	0.0047	0.0142	0.0336	0.0656	0.1089	0.1571
	9	0.0000	0.0000	0.0000	0.0001	0.0009	0.0034	0.0101	0.0243	0.0495	0.0873
	10	0.0000	0.0000	0.0000	0.0000	0.0001	0.0006	0.0022	0.0065	0.0162	0.0349
	11	0.0000	0.0000	0.0000	0.0000	0.0000	0.0001	0.0003	0.0012	0.0036	0.0095
	12	0.0000	0.0000	0.0000	0.0000	0.0000	0.0000	0.0000	0.0001	0.0005	0.0016
	13	0.0000	0.0000	0.0000	0.0000	0.0000	0.0000	0.0000	0.0000	0.0000	0.0001
14	0	0.4877	0.2288	0.1028	0.0440	0.0178	0.0068	0.0024	0.0008	0.0002	0.0001
	1	0.3593	0.3559	0.2539	0.1539	0.0832	0.0407	0.0181	0.0073	0.0027	0.0009
	2	0.1229	0.2570	0.2912	0.2501	0.1802	0.1134	0.0634	0.0317	0.0141	0.0056
	3	0.0259	0.1142	0.2056	0.2501	0.2402	0.1943	0.1366	0.0845	0.0462	0.0222
	4	0.0037	0.0349	0.0998	0.1720	0.2202	0.2290	0.2022	0.1549	0.1040	0.0611

TABLE A-2   (continued)

n	x	0.05	0.10	0.15	0.20	0.25	0.30	0.35	0.40	0.45	0.50
	5	0.0004	0.0078	0.0352	0.0860	0.1468	0.1963	0.2178	0.2066	0.1701	0.1222
	6	0.0000	0.0013	0.0093	0.0322	0.0734	0.1262	0.1759	0.2066	0.2088	0.1833
	7	0.0000	0.0002	0.0019	0.0092	0.0280	0.0618	0.1082	0.1574	0.1952	0.2095
	8	0.0000	0.0000	0.0003	0.0020	0.0082	0.0232	0.0510	0.0918	0.1398	0.1833
	9	0.0000	0.0000	0.0000	0.0003	0.0018	0.0066	0.0183	0.0408	0.0762	0.1222
	10	0.0000	0.0000	0.0000	0.0000	0.0003	0.0014	0.0049	0.0136	0.0312	0.0611
	11	0.0000	0.0000	0.0000	0.0000	0.0000	0.0002	0.0010	0.0033	0.0093	0.0222
	12	0.0000	0.0000	0.0000	0.0000	0.0000	0.0000	0.0001	0.0005	0.0019	0.0056
	13	0.0000	0.0000	0.0000	0.0000	0.0000	0.0000	0.0000	0.0001	0.0002	0.0009
	14	0.0000	0.0000	0.0000	0.0000	0.0000	0.0000	0.0000	0.0000	0.0000	0.0001
15	0	0.4633	0.2059	0.0874	0.0352	0.0134	0.0047	0.0016	0.0005	0.0001	0.0000
	1	0.3658	0.3432	0.2312	0.1319	0.0668	0.0305	0.0126	0.0047	0.0016	0.0005
	2	0.1348	0.2669	0.2856	0.2309	0.1559	0.0916	0.0476	0.0219	0.0090	0.0032
	3	0.0307	0.1285	0.2184	0.2501	0.2252	0.1700	0.1110	0.0634	0.0318	0.0139
	4	0.0049	0.0428	0.1156	0.1876	0.2252	0.2186	0.1792	0.1268	0.0780	0.0417
	5	0.0006	0.0105	0.0449	0.1032	0.1651	0.2061	0.2123	0.1859	0.1404	0.0916
	6	0.0000	0.0019	0.0132	0.0430	0.0917	0.1472	0.1906	0.2066	0.1914	0.1527
	7	0.0000	0.0003	0.0030	0.0138	0.0393	0.0811	0.1319	0.1771	0.2013	0.1964
	8	0.0000	0.0000	0.0005	0.0035	0.0131	0.0348	0.0710	0.1181	0.1647	0.1964
	9	0.0000	0.0000	0.0001	0.0007	0.0034	0.0116	0.0298	0.0612	0.1048	0.1527
	10	0.0000	0.0000	0.0000	0.0001	0.0007	0.0030	0.0096	0.0245	0.0515	0.0916
	11	0.0000	0.0000	0.0000	0.0000	0.0001	0.0006	0.0024	0.0074	0.0191	0.0417
	12	0.0000	0.0000	0.0000	0.0000	0.0000	0.0001	0.0004	0.0016	0.0052	0.0139
	13	0.0000	0.0000	0.0000	0.0000	0.0000	0.0000	0.0001	0.0003	0.0010	0.0032
	14	0.0000	0.0000	0.0000	0.0000	0.0000	0.0000	0.0000	0.0000	0.0001	0.0005
	15	0.0000	0.0000	0.0000	0.0000	0.0000	0.0000	0.0000	0.0000	0.0000	0.0000
16	0	0.4401	0.1853	0.0743	0.0281	0.0100	0.0033	0.0010	0.0003	0.0001	0.0000
	1	0.3706	0.3294	0.2097	0.1126	0.0535	0.0228	0.0087	0.0030	0.0009	0.0002
	2	0.1463	0.2745	0.2775	0.2111	0.1336	0.0732	0.0353	0.0150	0.0056	0.0018
	3	0.0359	0.1423	0.2285	0.2463	0.2079	0.1465	0.0888	0.0468	0.0215	0.0085
	4	0.0061	0.0514	0.1311	0.2001	0.2252	0.2040	0.1553	0.1014	0.0572	0.0278
	5	0.0008	0.0137	0.0555	0.1201	0.1802	0.2099	0.2008	0.1623	0.1123	0.0667
	6	0.0001	0.0028	0.0180	0.0550	0.1101	0.1649	0.1982	0.1983	0.1684	0.1222
	7	0.0000	0.0004	0.0045	0.0197	0.0524	0.1010	0.1524	0.1889	0.1969	0.1746
	8	0.0000	0.0001	0.0009	0.0055	0.0197	0.0487	0.0923	0.1417	0.1812	0.1964
	9	0.0000	0.0000	0.0001	0.0012	0.0058	0.0185	0.0442	0.0840	0.1318	0.1746
	10	0.0000	0.0000	0.0000	0.0002	0.0014	0.0056	0.0167	0.0392	0.0755	0.1222
	11	0.0000	0.0000	0.0000	0.0000	0.0002	0.0013	0.0049	0.0142	0.0337	0.0667
	12	0.0000	0.0000	0.0000	0.0000	0.0000	0.0002	0.0011	0.0040	0.0115	0.0278
	13	0.0000	0.0000	0.0000	0.0000	0.0000	0.0000	0.0002	0.0008	0.0029	0.0085
	14	0.0000	0.0000	0.0000	0.0000	0.0000	0.0000	0.0000	0.0001	0.0005	0.0018

TABLE A-2 (continued)

n	x	0.05	0.10	0.15	0.20	0.25	0.30	0.35	0.40	0.45	0.50
							p				
	15	0.0000	0.0000	0.0000	0.0000	0.0000	0.0000	0.0000	0.0000	0.0001	0.0002
	16	0.0000	0.0000	0.0000	0.0000	0.0000	0.0000	0.0000	0.0000	0.0000	0.0000
17	0	0.4181	0.1668	0.0631	0.0225	0.0075	0.0023	0.0007	0.0002	0.0000	0.0000
	1	0.3741	0.3150	0.1893	0.0957	0.0426	0.0169	0.0060	0.0019	0.0005	0.0001
	2	0.1575	0.2800	0.2673	0.1914	0.1136	0.0581	0.0260	0.0102	0.0035	0.0010
	3	0.0415	0.1556	0.2359	0.2393	0.1893	0.1245	0.0701	0.0341	0.0144	0.0052
	4	0.0076	0.0605	0.1457	0.2093	0.2209	0.1868	0.1320	0.0796	0.0411	0.0182
	5	0.0010	0.0175	0.0668	0.1361	0.1914	0.2081	0.1849	0.1379	0.0875	0.0472
	6	0.0001	0.0039	0.0236	0.0680	0.1276	0.1784	0.1991	0.1839	0.1432	0.0944
	7	0.0000	0.0007	0.0065	0.0267	0.0668	0.1201	0.1685	0.1927	0.1841	0.1484
	8	0.0000	0.0001	0.0014	0.0084	0.0279	0.0644	0.1134	0.1606	0.1883	0.1855
	9	0.0000	0.0000	0.0003	0.0021	0.0093	0.0276	0.0611	0.1070	0.1540	0.1855
	10	0.0000	0.0000	0.0000	0.0004	0.0025	0.0095	0.0263	0.0571	0.1008	0.1484
	11	0.0000	0.0000	0.0000	0.0001	0.0005	0.0026	0.0090	0.0242	0.0525	0.0944
	12	0.0000	0.0000	0.0000	0.0000	0.0001	0.0006	0.0024	0.0081	0.0215	0.0472
	13	0.0000	0.0000	0.0000	0.0000	0.0000	0.0001	0.0005	0.0021	0.0068	0.0182
	14	0.0000	0.0000	0.0000	0.0000	0.0000	0.0000	0.0001	0.0004	0.0016	0.0052
	15	0.0000	0.0000	0.0000	0.0000	0.0000	0.0000	0.0000	0.0001	0.0003	0.0010
	16	0.0000	0.0000	0.0000	0.0000	0.0000	0.0000	0.0000	0.0000	0.0000	0.0001
	17	0.0000	0.0000	0.0000	0.0000	0.0000	0.0000	0.0000	0.0000	0.0000	0.0000
18	0	0.3972	0.1501	0.0536	0.0180	0.0056	0.0016	0.0004	0.0001	0.0000	0.0000
	1	0.3763	0.3002	0.1704	0.0811	0.0338	0.0126	0.0042	0.0012	0.0003	0.0001
	2	0.1683	0.2835	0.2556	0.1723	0.0958	0.0458	0.0190	0.0069	0.0022	0.0006
	3	0.0473	0.1680	0.2406	0.2297	0.1704	0.1046	0.0547	0.0246	0.0095	0.0031
	4	0.0093	0.0700	0.1592	0.2153	0.2130	0.1681	0.1104	0.0614	0.0291	0.0117
	5	0.0014	0.0218	0.0787	0.1507	0.1988	0.2017	0.1664	0.1146	0.0666	0.0327
	6	0.0002	0.0052	0.0301	0.0816	0.1436	0.1873	0.1941	0.1655	0.1181	0.0708
	7	0.0000	0.0010	0.0091	0.0350	0.0820	0.1376	0.1792	0.1892	0.1657	0.1214
	8	0.0000	0.0002	0.0022	0.0120	0.0376	0.0811	0.1327	0.1734	0.1864	0.1669
	9	0.0000	0.0000	0.0004	0.0033	0.0139	0.0386	0.0794	0.1284	0.1694	0.1855
	10	0.0000	0.0000	0.0001	0.0008	0.0042	0.0149	0.0385	0.0771	0.1248	0.1669
	11	0.0000	0.0000	0.0000	0.0001	0.0010	0.0046	0.0151	0.0374	0.0742	0.1214
	12	0.0000	0.0000	0.0000	0.0000	0.0002	0.0012	0.0047	0.0145	0.0354	0.0708
	13	0.0000	0.0000	0.0000	0.0000	0.0000	0.0002	0.0012	0.0045	0.0134	0.0327
	14	0.0000	0.0000	0.0000	0.0000	0.0000	0.0000	0.0002	0.0011	0.0039	0.0117
	15	0.0000	0.0000	0.0000	0.0000	0.0000	0.0000	0.0000	0.0002	0.0009	0.0031
	16	0.0000	0.0000	0.0000	0.0000	0.0000	0.0000	0.0000	0.0000	0.0001	0.0006
	17	0.0000	0.0000	0.0000	0.0000	0.0000	0.0000	0.0000	0.0000	0.0000	0.0001
	18	0.0000	0.0000	0.0000	0.0000	0.0000	0.0000	0.0000	0.0000	0.0000	0.0000

TABLE A-2 (continued)

n	x	0.05	0.10	0.15	0.20	0.25	0.30	0.35	0.40	0.45	0.50
19	0	0.3774	0.1351	0.0456	0.0144	0.0042	0.0011	0.0003	0.0001	0.0000	0.0000
	1	0.3774	0.2852	0.1529	0.0685	0.0268	0.0093	0.0029	0.0008	0.0002	0.0000
	2	0.1787	0.2852	0.2428	0.1540	0.0803	0.0358	0.0138	0.0046	0.0013	0.0003
	3	0.0533	0.1796	0.2428	0.2182	0.1517	0.0869	0.0422	0.0175	0.0062	0.0018
	4	0.0112	0.0798	0.1714	0.2182	0.2023	0.1491	0.0909	0.0467	0.0203	0.0074
	5	0.0018	0.0266	0.0907	0.1636	0.2023	0.1916	0.1468	0.0933	0.0497	0.0222
	6	0.0002	0.0069	0.0374	0.0955	0.1574	0.1916	0.1844	0.1451	0.0949	0.0518
	7	0.0000	0.0014	0.0122	0.0443	0.0974	0.1525	0.1844	0.1797	0.1443	0.0961
	8	0.0000	0.0002	0.0032	0.0166	0.0487	0.0981	0.1489	0.1797	0.1771	0.1442
	9	0.0000	0.0000	0.0007	0.0051	0.0198	0.0514	0.0980	0.1464	0.1771	0.1762
	10	0.0000	0.0000	0.0001	0.0013	0.0066	0.0220	0.0528	0.0976	0.1449	0.1762
	11	0.0000	0.0000	0.0000	0.0003	0.0018	0.0077	0.0233	0.0532	0.0970	0.1442
	12	0.0000	0.0000	0.0000	0.0000	0.0004	0.0022	0.0083	0.0237	0.0529	0.0961
	13	0.0000	0.0000	0.0000	0.0000	0.0001	0.0005	0.0024	0.0085	0.0233	0.0518
	14	0.0000	0.0000	0.0000	0.0000	0.0000	0.0001	0.0006	0.0024	0.0082	0.0222
	15	0.0000	0.0000	0.0000	0.0000	0.0000	0.0000	0.0001	0.0005	0.0022	0.0074
	16	0.0000	0.0000	0.0000	0.0000	0.0000	0.0000	0.0000	0.0001	0.0005	0.0018
	17	0.0000	0.0000	0.0000	0.0000	0.0000	0.0000	0.0000	0.0000	0.0001	0.0003
	18	0.0000	0.0000	0.0000	0.0000	0.0000	0.0000	0.0000	0.0000	0.0000	0.0000
	19	0.0000	0.0000	0.0000	0.0000	0.0000	0.0000	0.0000	0.0000	0.0000	0.0000
20	0	0.3585	0.1216	0.0388	0.0115	0.0032	0.0008	0.0002	0.0000	0.0000	0.0000
	1	0.3774	0.2702	0.1368	0.0576	0.0211	0.0068	0.0020	0.0005	0.0001	0.0000
	2	0.1887	0.2852	0.2293	0.1369	0.0669	0.0278	0.0100	0.0031	0.0008	0.0002
	3	0.0596	0.1901	0.2428	0.2054	0.1339	0.0716	0.0323	0.0123	0.0040	0.0011
	4	0.0133	0.0898	0.1821	0.2182	0.1897	0.1304	0.0738	0.0350	0.0139	0.0046
	5	0.0022	0.0319	0.1028	0.1746	0.2023	0.1789	0.1272	0.0746	0.0365	0.0148
	6	0.0003	0.0089	0.0454	0.1091	0.1686	0.1916	0.1712	0.1244	0.0746	0.0370
	7	0.0000	0.0020	0.0160	0.0545	0.1124	0.1643	0.1844	0.1659	0.1221	0.0739
	8	0.0000	0.0004	0.0046	0.0222	0.0609	0.1144	0.1614	0.1797	0.1623	0.1201
	9	0.0000	0.0001	0.0011	0.0074	0.0271	0.0654	0.1158	0.1597	0.1771	0.1602
	10	0.0000	0.0000	0.0002	0.0020	0.0099	0.0308	0.0686	0.1171	0.1593	0.1762
	11	0.0000	0.0000	0.0000	0.0005	0.0030	0.0120	0.0336	0.0710	0.1185	0.1602
	12	0.0000	0.0000	0.0000	0.0001	0.0008	0.0039	0.0136	0.0355	0.0727	0.1201
	13	0.0000	0.0000	0.0000	0.0000	0.0002	0.0010	0.0045	0.0146	0.0366	0.0739
	14	0.0000	0.0000	0.0000	0.0000	0.0000	0.0002	0.0012	0.0049	0.0150	0.0370
	15	0.0000	0.0000	0.0000	0.0000	0.0000	0.0000	0.0003	0.0013	0.0049	0.0148
	16	0.0000	0.0000	0.0000	0.0000	0.0000	0.0000	0.0000	0.0003	0.0013	0.0046
	17	0.0000	0.0000	0.0000	0.0000	0.0000	0.0000	0.0000	0.0000	0.0002	0.0011
	18	0.0000	0.0000	0.0000	0.0000	0.0000	0.0000	0.0000	0.0000	0.0000	0.0002
	19	0.0000	0.0000	0.0000	0.0000	0.0000	0.0000	0.0000	0.0000	0.0000	0.0000
	20	0.0000	0.0000	0.0000	0.0000	0.0000	0.0000	0.0000	0.0000	0.0000	0.0000

TABLE A-3

Selected values of the Poisson Cumulative Distribution

$$F(c) = P(X \leq c) = \sum_{x=0}^{c} \frac{\mu^x e^{-\mu}}{x!}$$

Example   If $\mu = 1.00$, then $F(2) = P(X \leq 2) = 0.920$.

μ \ c	0	1	2	3	4	5	6	7	8	9
0.02	0.980	1.000								
0.04	0.961	0.999	1.000							
0.06	0.942	0.998	1.000							
0.08	0.923	0.997	1.000							
0.10	0.905	0.995	1.000							
0.15	0.861	0.990	0.999	1.000						
0.20	0.819	0.982	0.999	1.000						
0.25	0.779	0.974	0.998	1.000						
0.30	0.741	0.963	0.996	1.000						
0.35	0.705	0.951	0.994	1.000						
0.40	0.670	0.938	0.992	0.999	1.000					
0.45	0.638	0.925	0.989	0.999	1.000					
0.50	0.607	0.910	0.986	0.998	1.000					
0.55	0.577	0.894	0.982	0.998	1.000					
0.60	0.549	0.878	0.977	0.997	1.000					
0.65	0.522	0.861	0.972	0.996	0.999	1.000				
0.70	0.497	0.844	0.966	0.994	0.999	1.000				
0.75	0.472	0.827	0.959	0.993	0.999	1.000				
0.80	0.449	0.809	0.953	0.991	0.999	1.000				
0.85	0.427	0.791	0.945	0.989	0.998	1.000				
0.90	0.407	0.772	0.937	0.987	0.998	1.000				
0.95	0.387	0.754	0.929	0.984	0.997	1.000				
1.00	0.368	0.736	0.920	0.981	0.996	0.999	1.000			
1.10	0.333	0.699	0.900	0.974	0.995	0.999	1.000			
1.20	0.301	0.663	0.879	0.966	0.992	0.998	1.000			
1.30	0.273	0.627	0.857	0.957	0.989	0.998	1.000			
1.40	0.247	0.592	0.833	0.946	0.986	0.997	0.999	1.000		
1.50	0.223	0.558	0.809	0.934	0.981	0.996	0.999	1.000		
1.60	0.202	0.525	0.783	0.921	0.976	0.994	0.999	1.000		
1.70	0.183	0.493	0.757	0.907	0.970	0.992	0.998	1.000		
1.80	0.165	0.463	0.731	0.891	0.964	0.990	0.997	0.999	1.000	
1.90	0.150	0.434	0.704	0.875	0.956	0.987	0.997	0.999	1.000	
2.00	0.135	0.406	0.677	0.857	0.947	0.983	0.995	0.999	1.000	
2.20	0.111	0.355	0.623	0.819	0.928	0.975	0.993	0.998	1.000	
2.40	0.091	0.308	0.570	0.779	0.904	0.964	0.988	0.997	0.999	1.000
2.60	0.074	0.267	0.518	0.736	0.877	0.951	0.983	0.995	0.999	1.000
2.80	0.061	0.231	0.469	0.692	0.848	0.935	0.976	0.992	0.998	0.999
3.00	0.050	0.199	0.423	0.647	0.815	0.916	0.966	0.988	0.996	0.999

Source: From Eugene L. Grant, *Statistical Quality Control*, Copyright 1964 by McGraw-Hill Book Company. Used with permission of McGraw-Hill Book Company.

TABLE A-3   (continued)

μ＼c	0	1	2	3	4	5	6	7	8	9
3.20	0.041	0.171	0.380	0.603	0.781	0.895	0.955	0.983	0.994	0.998
3.40	0.033	0.147	0.340	0.558	0.744	0.871	0.942	0.977	0.992	0.997
3.60	0.027	0.126	0.303	0.515	0.706	0.844	0.927	0.969	0.988	0.996
3.80	0.022	0.107	0.269	0.473	0.668	0.816	0.909	0.960	0.984	0.994
4.00	0.018	0.092	0.238	0.433	0.629	0.785	0.889	0.949	0.979	0.992
4.20	0.015	0.078	0.210	0.395	0.590	0.753	0.867	0.936	0.972	0.989
4.40	0.012	0.066	0.185	0.359	0.551	0.720	0.844	0.921	0.964	0.985
4.60	0.010	0.056	0.163	0.326	0.513	0.686	0.818	0.905	0.955	0.980
4.80	0.008	0.048	0.143	0.294	0.476	0.651	0.791	0.887	0.944	0.975
5.00	0.007	0.040	0.125	0.265	0.440	0.616	0.762	0.867	0.932	0.968
5.20	0.006	0.034	0.109	0.238	0.406	0.581	0.732	0.845	0.918	0.960
5.40	0.005	0.029	0.095	0.213	0.373	0.546	0.702	0.822	0.903	0.951
5.60	0.004	0.024	0.082	0.191	0.342	0.512	0.670	0.797	0.886	0.941
5.80	0.003	0.021	0.072	0.170	0.313	0.478	0.638	0.771	0.867	0.929
6.00	0.002	0.017	0.062	0.151	0.285	0.446	0.606	0.744	0.847	0.916

μ	10	11	12	13	14	15	16
2.80	1.000						
3.00	1.000						
3.20	1.000						
3.40	0.999	1.000					
3.60	0.999	1.000					
3.80	0.998	0.999	1.000				
4.00	0.997	0.999	1.000				
4.20	0.996	0.999	1.000				
4.40	0.994	0.998	0.999	1.000			
4.60	0.992	0.997	0.999	1.000			
4.80	0.990	0.996	0.999	1.000			
5.00	0.986	0.995	0.998	0.999	1.000		
5.20	0.982	0.993	0.997	0.999	1.000		
5.40	0.977	0.990	0.996	0.999	1.000		
5.60	0.972	0.988	0.995	0.998	0.999	1.000	
5.80	0.965	0.984	0.993	0.997	0.999	1.000	
6.00	0.957	0.980	0.991	0.996	0.999	0.999	1.000

μ＼c	0	1	2	3	4	5	6	7	8	9
6.20	0.002	0.015	0.054	0.134	0.259	0.414	0.574	0.716	0.826	0.902
6.40	0.002	0.012	0.046	0.119	0.235	0.384	0.542	0.687	0.803	0.886
6.60	0.001	0.010	0.040	0.105	0.213	0.355	0.511	0.658	0.780	0.869
6.80	0.001	0.009	0.034	0.093	0.192	0.327	0.480	0.628	0.755	0.850
7.00	0.001	0.007	0.030	0.082	0.173	0.301	0.450	0.599	0.729	0.830

TABLE A-3   (continued)

μ \ c	0	1	2	3	4	5	6	7	8	9
7.20	0.001	0.006	0.025	0.072	0.156	0.276	0.420	0.569	0.703	0.810
7.40	0.001	0.005	0.022	0.063	0.140	0.253	0.392	0.539	0.676	0.788
7.60	0.001	0.004	0.019	0.055	0.125	0.231	0.365	0.510	0.648	0.765
7.80	0.000	0.004	0.016	0.048	0.112	0.210	0.338	0.481	0.620	0.741
8.00	0.000	0.003	0.014	0.042	0.100	0.191	0.313	0.453	0.593	0.717
8.50	0.000	0.002	0.009	0.030	0.074	0.150	0.256	0.386	0.523	0.653
9.00	0.000	0.001	0.006	0.021	0.055	0.116	0.207	0.324	0.456	0.587
9.50	0.000	0.001	0.004	0.015	0.040	0.089	0.165	0.269	0.392	0.522
10.00	0.000	0.000	0.003	0.010	0.029	0.067	0.130	0.220	0.333	0.458

μ \ c	10	11	12	13	14	15	16	17	18	19
6.20	0.949	0.975	0.989	0.995	0.998	0.999	1.000			
6.40	0.939	0.969	0.986	0.994	0.997	0.999	1.000			
6.60	0.927	0.963	0.982	0.992	0.997	0.999	0.999	1.000		
6.80	0.915	0.955	0.978	0.990	0.996	0.998	0.999	1.000		
7.00	0.901	0.947	0.973	0.987	0.994	0.998	0.999	1.000		
7.20	0.887	0.937	0.967	0.984	0.993	0.997	0.999	0.999	1.000	
7.40	0.871	0.926	0.961	0.980	0.991	0.996	0.998	0.999	1.000	
7.60	0.854	0.915	0.954	0.976	0.989	0.995	0.998	0.999	1.000	
7.80	0.835	0.902	0.945	0.971	0.986	0.993	0.997	0.999	1.000	
8.00	0.816	0.888	0.936	0.966	0.983	0.992	0.996	0.998	0.999	1.000
8.50	0.763	0.849	0.909	0.949	0.973	0.986	0.993	0.997	0.999	0.999
9.00	0.706	0.803	0.876	0.926	0.959	0.978	0.989	0.995	0.998	0.999
9.50	0.645	0.752	0.836	0.898	0.940	0.967	0.982	0.991	0.996	0.998
10.00	0.583	0.697	0.792	0.864	0.917	0.951	0.973	0.986	0.993	0.997

μ \ c	20	21	22
8.50	1.000		
9.00	1.000		
9.50	0.999	1.000	
10.00	0.998	0.999	1.000

μ \ c	0	1	2	3	4	5	6	7	8	9
10.50	0.000	0.000	0.002	0.007	0.021	0.050	0.102	0.179	0.279	0.397
11.00	0.000	0.000	0.001	0.005	0.015	0.038	0.079	0.143	0.232	0.341
11.50	0.000	0.000	0.001	0.003	0.011	0.028	0.060	0.114	0.191	0.289
12.00	0.000	0.000	0.001	0.002	0.008	0.020	0.046	0.090	0.155	0.242
12.50	0.000	0.000	0.000	0.002	0.005	0.015	0.035	0.070	0.125	0.201
13.00	0.000	0.000	0.000	0.001	0.004	0.011	0.026	0.054	0.100	0.166
13.50	0.000	0.000	0.000	0.001	0.003	0.008	0.019	0.041	0.079	0.135
14.00	0.000	0.000	0.000	0.000	0.002	0.006	0.014	0.032	0.062	0.109
14.50	0.000	0.000	0.000	0.000	0.001	0.004	0.010	0.024	0.048	0.088
15.00	0.000	0.000	0.000	0.000	0.001	0.003	0.008	0.018	0.037	0.070

TABLE A-3   (continued)

	10	11	12	13	14	15	16	17	18	19
10.50	0.521	0.639	0.742	0.825	0.888	0.932	0.960	0.978	0.988	0.994
11.00	0.460	0.579	0.689	0.781	0.854	0.907	0.944	0.968	0.982	0.991
11.50	0.402	0.520	0.633	0.733	0.815	0.878	0.924	0.954	0.974	0.986
12.00	0.347	0.462	0.576	0.682	0.772	0.844	0.899	0.937	0.963	0.979
12.50	0.297	0.406	0.519	0.628	0.725	0.806	0.869	0.916	0.948	0.969
13.00	0.252	0.353	0.463	0.573	0.675	0.764	0.835	0.890	0.930	0.957
13.50	0.211	0.304	0.409	0.518	0.623	0.718	0.798	0.861	0.908	0.942
14.00	0.176	0.260	0.358	0.464	0.570	0.669	0.756	0.827	0.883	0.923
14.50	0.145	0.220	0.311	0.413	0.518	0.619	0.711	0.790	0.853	0.901
15.00	0.118	0.185	0.268	0.363	0.466	0.568	0.664	0.749	0.819	0.875

	20	21	22	23	24	25	26	27	28	29
10.50	0.997	0.999	0.999	1.000						
11.00	0.995	0.998	0.999	1.000						
11.50	0.992	0.996	0.998	0.999	1.000					
12.00	0.988	0.994	0.997	0.999	0.999	1.000				
12.50	0.983	0.991	0.995	0.998	0.999	0.999	1.000			
13.00	0.975	0.986	0.992	0.996	0.998	0.999	1.000			
13.50	0.965	0.980	0.989	0.994	0.997	0.998	0.999	1.000		
14.00	0.952	0.971	0.983	0.991	0.995	0.997	0.999	0.999	1.000	
14.50	0.936	0.960	0.976	0.986	0.992	0.996	0.998	0.999	0.999	1.000
15.00	0.917	0.947	0.967	0.981	0.989	0.994	0.997	0.998	0.999	1.000

μ \ c	4	5	6	7	8	9	10	11	12	13
16.00	0.000	0.001	0.004	0.010	0.022	0.043	0.077	0.127	0.193	0.275
17.00	0.000	0.001	0.002	0.005	0.013	0.026	0.049	0.085	0.135	0.201
18.00	0.000	0.000	0.001	0.003	0.007	0.015	0.030	0.055	0.092	0.143
19.00	0.000	0.000	0.001	0.002	0.004	0.009	0.018	0.035	0.061	0.098
20.00	0.000	0.000	0.000	0.001	0.002	0.005	0.011	0.021	0.039	0.066
21.00	0.000	0.000	0.000	0.000	0.001	0.003	0.006	0.013	0.025	0.043
22.00	0.000	0.000	0.000	0.000	0.001	0.002	0.004	0.008	0.015	0.028
23.00	0.000	0.000	0.000	0.000	0.000	0.001	0.002	0.004	0.009	0.017
24.00	0.000	0.000	0.000	0.000	0.000	0.000	0.001	0.003	0.005	0.011
25.00	0.000	0.000	0.000	0.000	0.000	0.000	0.001	0.001	0.003	0.006

	14	15	16	17	18	19	20	21	22	23
16.00	0.368	0.467	0.566	0.659	0.742	0.812	0.868	0.911	0.942	0.963
17.00	0.281	0.371	0.468	0.564	0.655	0.736	0.805	0.861	0.905	0.937
18.00	0.208	0.287	0.375	0.469	0.562	0.651	0.731	0.799	0.855	0.899
19.00	0.150	0.215	0.292	0.378	0.469	0.561	0.647	0.725	0.793	0.849
20.00	0.105	0.157	0.221	0.297	0.381	0.470	0.559	0.644	0.721	0.787
21.00	0.072	0.111	0.163	0.227	0.302	0.384	0.471	0.558	0.640	0.716

TABLE A-3 (continued)

	14	15	16	17	18	19	20	21	22	23
22.00	0.048	0.077	0.117	0.169	0.232	0.306	0.387	0.472	0.556	0.637
23.00	0.031	0.052	0.082	0.123	0.175	0.238	0.310	0.389	0.472	0.555
24.00	0.020	0.034	0.056	0.087	0.128	0.180	0.243	0.314	0.392	0.473
25.00	0.012	0.022	0.038	0.060	0.092	0.134	0.185	0.247	0.318	0.394

	24	25	26	27	28	29	30	31	32	33
16.00	0.978	0.987	0.993	0.996	0.998	0.999	0.999	1.000		
17.00	0.959	0.975	0.985	0.991	0.995	0.997	0.999	0.999	1.000	
18.00	0.932	0.955	0.972	0.983	0.990	0.994	0.997	0.998	0.999	1.000
19.00	0.893	0.927	0.951	0.969	0.980	0.988	0.993	0.996	0.998	0.999
20.00	0.843	0.888	0.922	0.948	0.966	0.978	0.987	0.992	0.995	0.997
21.00	0.782	0.838	0.883	0.917	0.944	0.963	0.976	0.985	0.991	0.994
22.00	0.712	0.777	0.832	0.877	0.913	0.940	0.959	0.973	0.983	0.989
23.00	0.635	0.708	0.772	0.827	0.873	0.908	0.936	0.956	0.971	0.981
24.00	0.554	0.632	0.704	0.768	0.823	0.868	0.904	0.932	0.953	0.969
25.00	0.473	0.553	0.629	0.700	0.763	0.818	0.863	0.900	0.929	0.950

	34	35	36	37	38	39	40	41	42	43
19.00	0.999	1.000								
20.00	0.999	0.999	1.000	1.000						
21.00	0.997	0.998	0.999	0.999	1.000					
22.00	0.994	0.996	0.998	0.999	0.999	1.000				
23.00	0.988	0.993	0.996	0.997	0.999	0.999	1.000	1.000		
24.00	0.979	0.987	0.992	0.995	0.997	0.998	0.999	0.999	1.000	
25.00	0.966	0.978	0.985	0.991	0.994	0.997	0.998	0.999	0.999	1.000

TABLE A-4
Four-place common logarithms

N	0	1	2	3	4	5	6	7	8	9	Proportional Parts 1	2	3	4	5	6	7	8	9
10	0000	0043	0086	0128	0170	0212	0253	0294	0334	0374	4	8	12	17	21	25	29	33	37
11	0414	0453	0492	0531	0569	0607	0645	0682	0719	0755	4	8	11	15	19	23	26	30	34
12	0792	0828	0864	0899	0934	0969	1004	1038	1072	1106	3	7	10	14	17	21	24	28	31
13	1139	1173	1206	1239	1271	1303	1335	1367	1399	1430	3	6	10	13	16	19	23	26	29
14	1461	1492	1523	1553	1584	1614	1644	1673	1703	1732	3	6	9	12	15	18	21	24	27
15	1761	1790	1818	1847	1875	1903	1931	1959	1987	2014	3	6	8	11	14	17	20	22	25
16	2041	2068	2095	2122	2148	2175	2201	2227	2253	2279	3	5	8	11	13	16	18	21	24
17	2304	2330	2355	2380	2405	2430	2455	2480	2504	2529	2	5	7	10	12	15	17	20	22
18	2553	2577	2601	2625	2648	2672	2695	2718	2742	2765	2	5	7	9	12	14	16	19	21
19	2788	2810	2833	2856	2878	2900	2923	2945	2967	2989	2	4	7	9	11	13	16	18	20
20	3010	3032	3054	3075	3096	3118	3139	3160	3181	3201	2	4	6	8	11	13	15	17	19
21	3222	3243	3263	3284	3304	3324	3345	3365	3385	3404	2	4	6	8	10	12	14	16	18
22	3424	3444	3464	3483	3502	3522	3541	3560	3579	3598	2	4	6	8	10	12	14	15	17
23	3617	3636	3655	3674	3692	3711	3729	3747	3766	3784	2	4	6	7	9	11	13	15	17
24	3802	3820	3838	3856	3874	3892	3909	3927	3945	3962	2	4	5	7	9	11	12	14	16
25	3979	3997	4014	4031	4048	4065	4082	4099	4116	4133	2	3	5	7	9	10	12	14	15
26	4150	4166	4183	4200	4216	4232	4249	4265	4281	4298	2	3	5	7	8	10	11	13	15
27	4314	4330	4346	4362	4378	4393	4409	4425	4440	4456	2	3	5	6	8	9	11	13	14
28	4472	4487	4502	4518	4533	4548	4564	4579	4594	4609	2	3	5	6	8	9	11	12	14
29	4624	4639	4654	4669	4683	4698	4713	4728	4742	4757	1	3	4	6	7	9	10	12	13
30	4771	4786	4800	4814	4829	4843	4857	4871	4886	4900	1	3	4	6	7	9	10	11	13
31	4914	4928	4942	4955	4969	4983	4997	5011	5024	5038	1	3	4	6	7	8	10	11	12
32	5051	5065	5079	5092	5105	5119	5132	5145	5159	5172	1	3	4	5	7	8	9	11	12
33	5185	5198	5211	5224	5237	5250	5263	5276	5289	5302	1	3	4	5	6	8	9	10	12
34	5315	5328	5340	5353	5366	5378	5391	5403	5416	5428	1	3	4	5	6	8	9	10	11
35	5441	5453	5465	5478	5490	5502	5514	5527	5539	5551	1	2	4	5	6	7	9	10	11
36	5563	5575	5587	5599	5611	5623	5635	5647	5658	5670	1	2	4	5	6	7	8	10	11
37	5682	5694	5705	5717	5729	5740	5752	5763	5775	5786	1	2	3	5	6	7	8	9	10
38	5798	5809	5821	5832	5843	5855	5866	5877	5888	5899	1	2	3	5	6	7	8	9	10
39	5911	5922	5933	5944	5955	5966	5977	5988	5999	6010	1	2	3	4	5	7	8	9	10
40	6021	6031	6042	6053	6064	6075	6085	6096	6107	6117	1	2	3	4	5	6	8	9	10
41	6128	6138	6149	6160	6170	6180	6191	6201	6212	6222	1	2	3	4	5	6	7	8	9
42	6232	6243	6253	6263	6274	6284	6294	6304	6314	6325	1	2	3	4	5	6	7	8	9
43	6335	6345	6355	6365	6375	6385	6395	6405	6415	6425	1	2	3	4	5	6	7	8	9
44	6435	6444	6454	6464	6474	6484	6493	6503	6513	6522	1	2	3	4	5	6	7	8	9
45	6532	6542	6551	6561	6571	6580	6590	6599	6609	6618	1	2	3	4	5	6	7	8	9
46	6628	6637	6646	6656	6665	6675	6684	6693	6702	6712	1	2	3	4	5	6	7	7	8
47	6721	6730	6739	6749	6758	6767	6776	6785	6794	6803	1	2	3	4	5	5	6	7	8
48	6812	6821	6830	6839	6848	6857	6866	6875	6884	6893	1	2	3	4	4	5	6	7	8
49	6902	6911	6920	6928	6937	6946	6955	6964	6972	6981	1	2	3	4	4	5	6	7	8
50	6990	6998	7007	7016	7024	7033	7042	7050	7059	7067	1	2	3	3	4	5	6	7	8
51	7076	7084	7093	7101	7110	7118	7126	7135	7143	7152	1	2	3	3	4	5	6	7	8
52	7160	7168	7177	7185	7193	7202	7210	7218	7226	7235	1	2	2	3	4	5	6	7	7
53	7243	7251	7259	7267	7275	7284	7292	7300	7308	7316	1	2	2	3	4	5	6	6	7
54	7324	7332	7340	7348	7356	7364	7372	7380	7388	7396	1	2	2	3	4	5	6	6	7
N	0	1	2	3	4	5	6	7	8	9	1	2	3	4	5	6	7	8	9

TABLE A-4   (continued)

N	0	1	2	3	4	5	6	7	8	9	1	2	3	4	5	6	7	8	9
														Proportional Parts					
55	7404	7412	7419	7427	7435	7443	7451	7459	7466	7474	1	2	2	3	4	5	5	6	7
56	7482	7490	7497	7505	7513	7520	7528	7536	7543	7551	1	2	2	3	4	5	5	6	7
57	7559	7566	7574	7582	7589	7597	7604	7612	7619	7627	1	2	2	3	4	5	5	6	7
58	7634	7642	7649	7657	7664	7672	7679	7686	7694	7701	1	1	2	3	4	4	5	6	7
59	7709	7716	7723	7731	7738	7745	7752	7760	7767	7774	1	1	2	3	4	4	5	6	7
60	7782	7789	7796	7803	7810	7818	7825	7823	7839	7846	1	1	2	3	4	4	5	6	6
61	7853	7860	7868	7875	7882	7889	7896	7903	7910	7917	1	1	2	3	4	4	5	6	6
62	7924	7931	7938	7945	7952	7959	7966	7973	7980	7987	1	1	2	3	3	4	5	6	6
63	7993	8000	8007	8014	8021	8028	8035	8041	8048	8055	1	1	2	3	3	4	5	5	6
64	8062	8069	8075	8082	8089	8096	8102	8109	8116	8122	1	1	2	3	3	4	5	5	6
65	8129	8136	8142	8149	8156	8162	8169	8176	8182	8189	1	1	2	3	3	4	5	5	6
66	8195	8202	8209	8215	8222	8228	8235	8241	8248	8254	1	1	2	3	3	4	5	5	6
67	8261	8267	8274	8280	8287	8293	8299	8306	8312	8319	1	1	2	3	3	4	5	5	6
68	8325	8331	8338	8344	8351	8357	8363	8370	8376	8382	1	1	2	3	3	4	4	5	6
69	8388	8395	8401	8407	8414	8420	8426	8432	8439	8445	1	1	2	2	3	4	4	5	6
70	8451	8457	8463	8470	8476	8482	8488	8494	8500	8506	1	1	2	2	3	4	4	5	6
71	8513	8519	8525	8531	8537	8543	8549	8555	8561	8567	1	1	2	2	3	4	4	5	5
72	8573	8579	8585	8591	8597	8603	8609	8615	8621	8627	1	1	2	2	3	4	4	5	5
73	8633	8639	8645	8651	8657	8663	8669	8675	8681	8686	1	1	2	2	3	4	4	5	5
74	8692	8698	8704	8710	8716	8722	8727	8733	8739	8745	1	1	2	2	3	4	4	5	5
75	8751	8756	8762	8768	8774	8779	8785	8791	8797	8802	1	1	2	2	3	3	4	5	5
76	8808	8814	8820	8825	8831	8837	8842	8848	8854	8859	1	1	2	2	3	3	4	5	5
77	8865	8871	8876	8882	8887	8893	8899	8904	8910	8915	1	1	2	2	3	3	4	4	5
78	8921	8927	8932	8938	8943	8949	8954	8960	8965	8971	1	1	2	2	3	3	4	4	5
79	8976	8982	8987	8993	8998	9004	9009	9015	9020	9025	1	1	2	2	3	3	4	4	5
80	9031	9036	9042	9047	9053	9058	9063	9069	9074	9079	1	1	2	2	3	3	4	4	5
81	9085	9090	9096	9101	9106	9112	9117	9122	9128	9133	1	1	2	2	3	3	4	4	5
82	9138	9143	9149	9154	9159	9165	9170	9175	9180	9186	1	1	2	2	3	3	4	4	5
83	9191	9196	9201	9206	9212	9217	9222	9227	9232	9238	1	1	2	2	3	3	4	4	5
84	9243	9248	9253	9258	9263	9269	9274	9279	9284	9289	1	1	2	2	3	3	4	4	5
85	9294	9299	9304	9309	9315	9320	9325	9330	9335	9340	1	1	2	2	3	3	4	4	5
86	9345	9350	9355	9360	9365	9370	9375	9380	9385	9390	1	1	2	2	3	3	4	4	5
87	9395	9400	9405	9410	9415	9420	9425	9430	9435	9440	0	1	1	2	2	3	3	4	4
88	9445	9450	9455	9460	9465	9469	9474	9479	9484	9489	0	1	1	2	2	3	3	4	4
89	9494	9499	9504	9509	9513	9518	9523	9528	9533	9538	0	1	1	2	2	3	3	4	4
90	9542	9547	9552	9557	9562	9566	9571	9576	9581	9586	0	1	1	2	2	3	3	4	4
91	9590	9595	9600	9605	9609	9614	9619	9624	9628	9633	0	1	1	2	2	3	3	4	4
92	9638	9643	9647	9652	9657	9661	9666	9671	9675	9680	0	1	1	2	2	3	3	4	4
93	9685	9689	9694	9699	9703	9708	9713	9717	9722	9727	0	1	1	2	2	3	3	4	4
94	9731	9736	9741	9745	9750	9754	9759	9763	9768	9773	0	1	1	2	2	3	3	4	4
95	9777	9782	9786	9791	9795	9800	9805	9809	9814	9818	0	1	1	2	2	3	3	4	4
96	9823	9827	9832	9836	9841	9845	9850	9854	9859	9863	0	1	1	2	2	3	3	4	4
97	9868	9872	9877	9881	9886	9890	9894	9899	9903	9908	0	1	1	2	2	3	3	4	4
98	9912	9917	9921	9926	9930	9934	9939	9943	9948	9952	0	1	1	2	2	3	3	4	4
99	9956	9961	9965	9969	9974	9978	9983	9987	9991	9996	0	1	1	2	2	3	3	3	4
N	0	1	2	3	4	5	6	7	8	9	1	2	3	4	5	6	7	8	9

TABLE A-5

Areas under the standard normal probability distribution between the mean and successive values of z

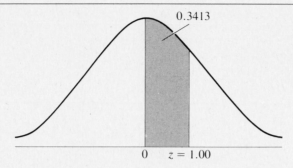

0.3413

0   z = 1.00

Example   If $z = 1.00$, then the area between the mean and this value of z is 0.3413.

z	0.00	0.01	0.02	0.03	0.04	0.05	0.06	0.07	0.08	0.09
0.0	0.0000	0.0040	0.0080	0.0120	0.0160	0.0199	0.0239	0.0279	0.0319	0.0359
0.1	0.0398	0.0438	0.0478	0.0517	0.0557	0.0596	0.0636	0.0675	0.0714	0.0753
0.2	0.0793	0.0832	0.0871	0.0910	0.0948	0.0987	0.1026	0.1064	0.1103	0.1141
0.3	0.1179	0.1217	0.1255	0.1293	0.1331	0.1368	0.1406	0.1443	0.1480	0.1517
0.4	0.1554	0.1591	0.1628	0.1664	0.1700	0.1736	0.1772	0.1808	0.1844	0.1879
0.5	0.1915	0.1950	0.1985	0.2019	0.2054	0.2088	0.2123	0.2157	0.2190	0.2224
0.6	0.2257	0.2291	0.2324	0.2357	0.2389	0.2422	0.2454	0.2486	0.2518	0.2549
0.7	0.2580	0.2612	0.2642	0.2673	0.2704	0.2734	0.2764	0.2794	0.2823	0.2852
0.8	0.2881	0.2910	0.2939	0.2967	0.2995	0.3023	0.3051	0.3078	0.3106	0.3133
0.9	0.3159	0.3186	0.3212	0.3238	0.3264	0.3289	0.3315	0.3340	0.3365	0.3389
1.0	0.3413	0.3438	0.3461	0.3485	0.3508	0.3531	0.3554	0.3577	0.3599	0.3621
1.1	0.3643	0.3665	0.3686	0.3708	0.3729	0.3749	0.3770	0.3790	0.3810	0.3830
1.2	0.3849	0.3869	0.3888	0.3907	0.3925	0.3944	0.3962	0.3980	0.3997	0.4015
1.3	0.4032	0.4049	0.4066	0.4082	0.4099	0.4115	0.4131	0.4147	0.4162	0.4177
1.4	0.4192	0.4207	0.4222	0.4236	0.4251	0.4265	0.4279	0.4292	0.4306	0.4319
1.5	0.4332	0.4345	0.4357	0.4370	0.4382	0.4394	0.4406	0.4418	0.4429	0.4441
1.6	0.4452	0.4463	0.4474	0.4484	0.4495	0.4505	0.4515	0.4525	0.4535	0.4545
1.7	0.4554	0.4564	0.4573	0.4582	0.4591	0.4599	0.4608	0.4616	0.4625	0.4633
1.8	0.4641	0.4649	0.4656	0.4664	0.4671	0.4678	0.4686	0.4693	0.4699	0.4706
1.9	0.4713	0.4719	0.4726	0.4732	0.4738	0.4744	0.4750	0.4756	0.4761	0.4767
2.0	0.4772	0.4778	0.4783	0.4788	0.4793	0.4798	0.4803	0.4808	0.4812	0.4817
2.1	0.4821	0.4826	0.4830	0.4834	0.4838	0.4842	0.4846	0.4850	0.4854	0.4857
2.2	0.4861	0.4864	0.4868	0.4871	0.4875	0.4878	0.4881	0.4884	0.4887	0.4890
2.3	0.4893	0.4896	0.4898	0.4901	0.4904	0.4906	0.4909	0.4911	0.4913	0.4916
2.4	0.4918	0.4920	0.4922	0.4925	0.4927	0.4929	0.4931	0.4932	0.4934	0.4936
2.5	0.4938	0.4940	0.4941	0.4943	0.4945	0.4946	0.4948	0.4949	0.4951	0.4952
2.6	0.4953	0.4955	0.4956	0.4957	0.4959	0.4960	0.4961	0.4962	0.4963	0.4964
2.7	0.4965	0.4966	0.4967	0.4968	0.4969	0.4970	0.4971	0.4972	0.4973	0.4974
2.8	0.4974	0.4975	0.4976	0.4977	0.4977	0.4978	0.4979	0.4979	0.4980	0.4981
2.9	0.4981	0.4982	0.4982	0.4983	0.4984	0.4984	0.4985	0.4985	0.4986	0.4986
3.0	0.49865	0.4987	0.4987	0.4988	0.4988	0.4989	0.4989	0.4989	0.4990	0.4990
4.0	0.49997									

TABLE A-6
Student's *t* distribution

Example For 15 degrees of freedom, the *t* value that corresponds to an area of 0.05 in both tails combined is 2.131.

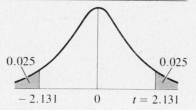

0.025   0.025
− 2.131   0   *t* = 2.131

Degrees of Freedom	Area in Both Tails Combined			
	0.10	0.05	0.02	0.01
1	6.314	12.706	31.821	63.657
2	2.920	4.303	6.965	9.925
3	2.353	3.182	4.541	5.841
4	2.132	2.776	3.747	4.604
5	2.015	2.571	3.365	4.032
6	1.943	2.447	3.143	3.707
7	1.895	2.365	2.998	3.499
8	1.860	2.306	2.896	3.355
9	1.833	2.262	2.821	3.250
10	1.812	2.228	2.764	3.169
11	1.796	2.201	2.718	3.106
12	1.782	2.179	2.681	3.055
13	1.771	2.160	2.650	3.012
14	1.761	2.145	2.624	2.977
15	1.753	2.131	2.602	2.947
16	1.746	2.120	2.583	2.921
17	1.740	2.110	2.567	2.898
18	1.734	2.101	2.552	2.878
19	1.729	2.093	2.539	2.861
20	1.725	2.086	2.528	2.845
21	1.721	2.080	2.518	2.831
22	1.717	2.074	2.508	2.819
23	1.714	2.069	2.500	2.807
24	1.711	2.064	2.492	2.797
25	1.708	2.060	2.485	2.787
26	1.706	2.056	2.479	2.779
27	1.703	2.052	2.473	2.771
28	1.701	2.048	2.467	2.763
29	1.699	2.045	2.462	2.756
30	1.697	2.042	2.457	2.750
40	1.684	2.021	2.423	2.704
60	1.671	2.000	2.390	2.660
120	1.658	1.980	2.358	2.617
Normal Distribution	1.645	1.960	2.326	2.576

Source: From Table III of Fisher and Yates: *Statistical Tables for Biological, Agricultural and Medical Research*, published by Longman Group, Ltd., London (1974) 6th edition (previously published by Oliver and Boyd, Ltd., Edinburgh), and by permission of the authors and publishers.

TABLE A-7

Chi-square (χ^2) distribution

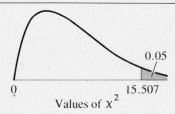

Values of χ^2

Example   In a chi-square distribution with $v = 8$ degrees of freedom, the area to the right of a chi-square value of 15.507 is 0.05.

Degrees of Freedom v	Area in Right Tail				
	0.20	0.10	0.05	0.02	0.01
1	1.642	2.706	3.841	5.412	6.635
2	3.219	4.605	5.991	7.824	9.210
3	4.642	6.251	7.815	9.837	11.345
4	5.989	7.779	9.488	11.668	13.277
5	7.289	9.236	11.070	13.388	15.086
6	8.558	10.645	12.592	15.033	16.812
7	9.803	12.017	14.067	16.622	18.475
8	11.030	13.362	15.507	18.168	20.090
9	12.242	14.684	16.919	19.679	21.666
10	13.442	15.987	18.307	21.161	23.209
11	14.631	17.275	19.675	22.618	24.725
12	15.812	18.549	21.026	24.054	26.217
13	16.985	19.812	22.362	25.472	27.688
14	18.151	21.064	23.685	26.873	29.141
15	19.311	22.307	24.996	28.259	30.578
16	20.465	23.542	26.296	29.633	32.000
17	21.615	24.769	27.587	30.995	33.409
18	22.760	25.989	28.869	32.346	34.805
19	23.900	27.204	30.144	33.687	36.191
20	25.038	28.412	31.410	35.020	37.566
21	26.171	29.615	32.671	36.343	38.932
22	27.301	30.813	33.924	37.659	40.289
23	28.429	32.007	35.172	38.968	41.638
24	29.553	33.196	36.415	40.270	42.980
25	30.675	34.382	37.652	41.566	44.314
26	31.795	35.563	38.885	42.856	45.642
27	32.912	36.741	40.113	44.140	46.963
28	34.027	37.916	41.337	45.419	48.278
29	35.139	39.087	42.557	46.693	49.588
30	36.250	40.256	43.773	47.962	50.892

Source: From Table IV of Fisher and Yates: *Statistical Tables for Biological, Agricultural and Medical Research*, published by Longman Group, Ltd., London (1974) 6th edition (previously published by Oliver and Boyd, Ltd., Edinburgh), and by permission of the authors and publishers.

TABLE A-8

F distribution

Example In an F distribution with $v_1 = 5$ and $v_2 = 6$ degrees of freedom, the area to the right of an F value of 4.39 is 0.05. The value on the F scale to the right of which lies 0.05 of the area is in lightface type. The value on the F scale to the right of which lies 0.01 of the area is in boldface type. For the numerator, v_1 = number of degrees of freedom; v_2 = number of degrees of freedom for the denominator.

Values of F

Each cell shows the 0.05 value (lightface) / 0.01 value (boldface).

v_2 \ v_1	1	2	3	4	5	6	7	8	9	10	11	12	14	16	20	24	30	40	50	75	100	200	500	∞
1	161 / **4,052**	200 / **4,999**	216 / **5,403**	225 / **5,625**	230 / **5,764**	234 / **5,859**	237 / **5,928**	239 / **5,981**	241 / **6,022**	242 / **6,056**	243 / **6,082**	244 / **6,106**	245 / **6,142**	246 / **6,169**	248 / **6,208**	249 / **6,234**	250 / **6,261**	251 / **6,286**	252 / **6,302**	253 / **6,323**	253 / **6,334**	254 / **6,352**	254 / **6,361**	254 / **6,366**
2	18.51 / **98.49**	19.00 / **99.00**	19.16 / **99.17**	19.25 / **99.25**	19.30 / **99.30**	19.33 / **99.33**	19.36 / **99.36**	19.37 / **99.37**	19.38 / **99.39**	19.39 / **99.40**	19.40 / **99.41**	19.41 / **99.42**	19.42 / **99.43**	19.43 / **99.44**	19.44 / **99.45**	19.45 / **99.46**	19.46 / **99.47**	19.47 / **99.48**	19.47 / **98.48**	19.48 / **99.49**	19.49 / **99.49**	19.49 / **99.49**	19.50 / **99.50**	19.50 / **99.50**
3	10.13 / **34.12**	9.55 / **30.82**	9.28 / **29.46**	9.12 / **28.71**	9.01 / **28.24**	8.94 / **27.91**	8.88 / **27.67**	8.84 / **27.49**	8.81 / **27.34**	8.78 / **27.23**	8.76 / **27.13**	8.74 / **27.05**	8.71 / **26.92**	8.69 / **26.83**	8.66 / **26.69**	8.64 / **26.60**	8.62 / **26.50**	8.60 / **26.41**	8.58 / **26.35**	8.57 / **26.27**	8.56 / **26.23**	8.54 / **26.18**	8.54 / **26.14**	8.53 / **26.12**
4	7.71 / **21.20**	6.94 / **18.00**	6.59 / **16.69**	6.39 / **15.98**	6.26 / **15.52**	6.16 / **15.21**	6.09 / **14.98**	6.04 / **14.80**	6.00 / **14.66**	5.96 / **14.54**	5.93 / **14.45**	5.91 / **14.37**	5.87 / **14.24**	5.84 / **14.15**	5.80 / **14.02**	5.77 / **13.93**	5.74 / **13.83**	5.71 / **13.74**	5.70 / **13.69**	5.68 / **13.61**	5.66 / **13.57**	5.65 / **13.52**	5.64 / **13.48**	5.63 / **13.46**
5	6.61 / **16.26**	5.79 / **13.27**	5.41 / **12.06**	5.19 / **11.39**	5.05 / **10.97**	4.95 / **10.67**	4.88 / **10.45**	4.82 / **10.29**	4.78 / **10.15**	4.74 / **10.05**	4.70 / **9.96**	4.68 / **9.89**	4.64 / **9.77**	4.60 / **9.68**	4.56 / **9.55**	4.53 / **9.47**	4.50 / **9.38**	4.46 / **9.29**	4.44 / **9.24**	4.42 / **9.17**	4.40 / **9.13**	4.38 / **9.07**	4.37 / **9.04**	4.36 / **9.02**
6	5.99 / **13.74**	5.14 / **10.92**	4.76 / **9.78**	4.53 / **9.15**	4.39 / **8.75**	4.28 / **8.47**	4.21 / **8.26**	4.15 / **8.10**	4.10 / **7.98**	4.06 / **7.87**	4.03 / **7.79**	4.00 / **7.72**	3.96 / **7.60**	3.92 / **7.52**	3.87 / **7.39**	3.84 / **7.31**	3.81 / **7.23**	3.77 / **7.14**	3.75 / **7.09**	3.72 / **7.02**	3.71 / **6.99**	3.69 / **6.94**	3.68 / **6.90**	3.67 / **6.88**
7	5.59 / **12.25**	4.74 / **9.55**	4.35 / **8.45**	4.12 / **7.85**	3.97 / **7.46**	3.87 / **7.19**	3.79 / **7.00**	3.73 / **6.84**	3.68 / **6.71**	3.63 / **6.62**	3.60 / **6.54**	3.57 / **6.47**	3.52 / **6.35**	3.49 / **6.27**	3.44 / **6.15**	3.41 / **6.07**	3.38 / **5.98**	3.34 / **5.90**	3.32 / **5.85**	3.29 / **5.78**	3.28 / **5.75**	3.25 / **5.70**	3.24 / **5.67**	3.23 / **5.65**
8	5.32 / **11.26**	4.46 / **8.65**	4.07 / **7.59**	3.84 / **7.01**	3.69 / **6.63**	3.58 / **6.37**	3.50 / **6.19**	3.44 / **6.03**	3.39 / **5.91**	3.34 / **5.82**	3.31 / **5.74**	3.28 / **5.67**	3.23 / **5.56**	3.20 / **5.48**	3.15 / **5.36**	3.12 / **5.28**	3.08 / **5.20**	3.05 / **5.11**	3.03 / **5.06**	3.00 / **5.00**	2.98 / **4.96**	2.96 / **4.91**	2.94 / **4.88**	2.93 / **4.86**
9	5.12 / **10.56**	4.26 / **8.02**	3.86 / **6.99**	3.63 / **6.42**	3.48 / **6.06**	3.37 / **5.80**	3.29 / **5.62**	3.23 / **5.47**	3.18 / **5.35**	3.13 / **5.26**	3.10 / **5.18**	3.07 / **5.11**	3.02 / **5.00**	2.98 / **4.92**	2.93 / **4.80**	2.90 / **4.73**	2.86 / **4.64**	2.82 / **4.56**	2.80 / **4.51**	2.77 / **4.45**	2.76 / **4.41**	2.73 / **4.36**	2.72 / **4.33**	2.71 / **4.31**
10	4.96 / **10.04**	4.10 / **7.56**	3.71 / **6.55**	3.48 / **5.99**	3.33 / **5.64**	3.22 / **5.39**	3.14 / **5.21**	3.07 / **5.06**	3.02 / **4.95**	2.97 / **4.85**	2.94 / **4.78**	2.91 / **4.71**	2.86 / **4.60**	2.82 / **4.52**	2.77 / **4.41**	2.74 / **4.33**	2.70 / **4.25**	2.67 / **4.17**	2.64 / **4.12**	2.61 / **4.05**	2.59 / **4.01**	2.56 / **3.96**	2.55 / **3.93**	2.54 / **3.91**
11	4.84 / **9.65**	3.98 / **7.20**	3.59 / **6.22**	3.36 / **5.67**	3.20 / **5.32**	3.09 / **5.07**	3.01 / **4.88**	2.95 / **4.74**	2.90 / **4.63**	2.86 / **4.54**	2.82 / **4.46**	2.79 / **4.40**	2.74 / **4.29**	2.70 / **4.21**	2.65 / **4.10**	2.61 / **4.02**	2.57 / **3.94**	2.53 / **3.86**	2.50 / **3.80**	2.47 / **3.74**	2.45 / **3.70**	2.42 / **3.66**	2.41 / **3.62**	2.40 / **3.60**
12	4.75 / **9.33**	3.88 / **6.93**	3.49 / **5.95**	3.26 / **5.41**	3.11 / **5.06**	3.00 / **4.82**	2.92 / **4.65**	2.85 / **4.50**	2.80 / **4.39**	2.76 / **4.30**	2.72 / **4.22**	2.69 / **4.16**	2.64 / **4.05**	2.60 / **3.98**	2.54 / **3.86**	2.50 / **3.78**	2.46 / **3.70**	2.42 / **3.61**	2.40 / **3.56**	2.36 / **3.49**	2.35 / **3.46**	2.32 / **3.41**	2.31 / **3.38**	2.30 / **3.36**

Source: From George W. Snedecor and William G. Cochran, *Statistical Methods*, Seventh Edition, © 1980 by the Iowa State University Press, Ames, 1A, 50010. Reprinted by permission.

TABLE A-8 (continued)

v_2＼v_1	1	2	3	4	5	6	7	8	9	10	11	12	14	16	20	24	30	40	50	75	100	200	500	∞
13	4.67 9.07	3.80 6.70	3.41 5.74	3.18 5.20	3.02 4.86	2.92 4.62	2.84 4.44	2.77 4.30	2.72 4.19	2.67 4.10	2.63 4.02	2.60 3.96	2.55 3.85	2.51 3.78	2.46 3.67	2.42 3.59	2.38 3.51	2.34 3.42	2.32 3.37	2.28 3.30	2.26 3.27	2.24 3.21	2.22 3.18	2.21 3.16
14	4.60 8.86	3.74 6.51	3.34 5.56	3.11 5.03	2.96 4.69	2.85 4.46	2.77 4.28	2.70 4.14	2.65 4.03	2.60 3.94	2.56 3.86	2.53 3.80	2.48 3.70	2.44 3.62	2.39 3.51	2.35 3.43	2.31 3.34	2.27 3.26	2.24 3.21	2.21 3.14	2.19 3.11	2.16 3.06	2.14 3.02	2.13 3.00
15	4.54 8.68	3.68 6.36	3.29 5.42	3.06 4.89	2.90 4.56	2.79 4.32	2.70 4.14	2.64 4.00	2.59 3.89	2.55 3.80	2.51 3.73	2.48 3.67	2.43 3.56	2.39 3.48	2.33 3.36	2.29 3.29	2.25 3.20	2.21 3.12	2.18 3.07	2.15 3.00	2.12 2.97	2.10 2.92	2.08 2.89	2.07 2.87
16	4.49 8.53	3.63 6.23	3.24 5.29	3.01 4.77	2.85 4.44	2.74 4.20	2.66 4.03	2.59 3.89	2.54 3.78	2.49 3.69	2.45 3.61	2.42 3.55	2.37 3.45	2.33 3.37	2.28 3.25	2.24 3.18	2.20 3.10	2.16 3.01	2.13 2.96	2.09 2.88	2.07 2.86	2.04 2.80	2.02 2.77	2.01 2.75
17	4.45 8.40	3.59 6.11	3.20 5.18	2.96 4.67	2.81 4.34	2.70 4.10	2.62 3.93	2.55 3.79	2.50 3.68	2.45 3.59	2.41 3.52	2.38 3.45	2.33 3.35	2.29 3.27	2.23 3.16	2.19 3.08	2.15 3.00	2.11 2.92	2.08 2.86	2.04 2.79	2.02 2.76	1.99 2.70	1.97 2.67	1.96 2.65
18	4.41 8.28	3.55 6.01	3.16 5.09	2.93 4.58	2.77 4.25	2.66 4.01	2.58 3.85	2.51 3.71	2.46 3.60	2.41 3.51	2.37 3.44	2.34 3.37	2.29 3.27	2.25 3.19	2.19 3.07	2.15 3.00	2.11 2.91	2.07 2.83	2.04 2.78	2.00 2.71	1.98 2.68	1.95 2.62	1.93 2.59	1.92 2.57
19	4.38 8.18	3.52 5.93	3.13 5.01	2.90 4.50	2.74 4.17	2.63 3.94	2.55 3.77	2.48 3.63	2.43 3.52	2.38 3.43	2.34 3.36	2.31 3.30	2.26 3.19	2.21 3.12	2.15 3.00	2.11 2.92	2.07 2.84	2.02 2.76	2.00 2.70	1.96 2.63	1.94 2.60	1.91 2.54	1.90 2.51	1.88 2.49
20	4.35 8.10	3.49 5.85	3.10 4.94	2.87 4.43	2.71 4.10	2.60 3.87	2.52 3.71	2.45 3.56	2.40 3.45	2.35 3.37	2.31 3.30	2.28 3.23	2.23 3.13	2.18 3.05	2.12 2.94	2.08 2.86	2.04 2.77	1.99 2.69	1.96 2.63	1.92 2.56	1.90 2.53	1.87 2.47	1.85 2.44	1.84 2.42
21	4.32 8.02	3.47 5.78	3.07 4.87	2.84 4.37	2.68 4.04	2.57 3.81	2.49 3.65	2.42 3.51	2.37 3.40	2.32 3.31	2.28 3.24	2.25 3.17	2.20 3.07	2.15 2.99	2.09 2.88	2.05 2.80	2.00 2.72	1.96 2.63	1.93 2.58	1.89 2.51	1.87 2.47	1.84 2.42	1.82 2.38	1.81 2.36
22	4.30 7.94	3.44 5.72	3.05 4.82	2.82 4.31	2.66 3.99	2.55 3.76	2.47 3.59	2.40 3.45	2.35 3.35	2.30 3.26	2.26 3.18	2.23 3.12	2.18 3.02	2.13 2.94	2.07 2.83	2.03 2.75	1.98 2.67	1.93 2.58	1.91 2.53	1.87 2.46	1.84 2.42	1.81 2.37	1.80 2.33	1.78 2.31
23	4.28 7.88	3.42 5.66	3.03 4.76	2.80 4.26	2.64 3.94	2.53 3.71	2.45 3.54	2.38 3.41	2.32 3.30	2.28 3.21	2.24 3.14	2.20 3.07	2.14 2.97	2.10 2.89	2.04 2.78	2.00 2.70	1.96 2.62	1.91 2.53	1.88 2.48	1.84 2.41	1.82 2.37	1.79 2.32	1.77 2.28	1.76 2.26
24	4.26 7.82	3.40 5.61	3.01 4.72	2.78 4.22	2.62 3.90	2.51 3.67	2.43 3.50	2.36 3.36	2.30 3.25	2.26 3.17	2.22 3.09	2.18 3.03	2.13 2.93	2.09 2.85	2.02 2.74	1.98 2.66	1.94 2.58	1.89 2.49	1.86 2.44	1.82 2.36	1.80 2.33	1.76 2.27	1.74 2.23	1.73 2.21
25	4.24 7.77	3.38 5.57	2.99 4.68	2.76 4.18	2.60 3.86	2.49 3.63	2.41 3.46	2.34 3.32	2.28 3.21	2.24 3.13	2.20 3.05	2.16 2.99	2.11 2.89	2.06 2.81	2.00 2.70	1.96 2.62	1.92 2.54	1.87 2.45	1.84 2.40	1.80 2.32	1.77 2.29	1.74 2.23	1.72 2.19	1.71 2.17
26	4.22 7.72	3.37 5.53	2.98 4.64	2.74 4.14	2.59 3.82	2.47 3.59	2.39 3.42	2.32 3.29	2.27 3.17	2.22 3.09	2.18 3.02	2.15 2.96	2.10 2.86	2.05 2.77	1.99 2.66	1.95 2.58	1.90 2.50	1.85 2.41	1.82 2.36	1.78 2.28	1.76 2.25	1.72 2.19	1.70 2.15	1.69 2.13

v_2 \ v_1	1	2	3	4	5	6	7	8	9	10	11	12	14	16	20	24	30	40	50	75	100	200	500	∞
27	4.21 **7.68**	3.35 **5.49**	2.96 **4.60**	2.73 **4.11**	2.57 **3.79**	2.46 **3.56**	2.37 **3.39**	2.30 **3.26**	2.25 **3.14**	2.20 **3.06**	2.16 **2.98**	2.13 **2.93**	2.08 **2.83**	2.03 **2.74**	1.97 **2.63**	1.93 **2.55**	1.88 **2.47**	1.84 **2.38**	1.80 **2.33**	1.76 **2.25**	1.74 **2.21**	1.71 **2.16**	1.68 **2.12**	1.67 **2.10**
28	4.20 **7.64**	3.34 **5.45**	2.95 **4.57**	2.71 **4.07**	2.56 **3.76**	2.44 **3.53**	2.36 **3.36**	2.29 **3.23**	2.24 **3.11**	2.19 **3.03**	2.15 **2.95**	2.12 **2.90**	2.06 **2.80**	2.02 **2.71**	1.96 **2.60**	1.91 **2.52**	1.87 **2.44**	1.81 **2.35**	1.78 **2.30**	1.75 **2.22**	1.72 **2.18**	1.69 **2.13**	1.67 **2.09**	1.65 **2.06**
29	4.18 **7.60**	3.33 **5.42**	2.93 **4.54**	2.70 **4.04**	2.54 **3.73**	2.43 **3.50**	2.35 **3.33**	2.28 **3.20**	2.22 **3.08**	2.18 **3.00**	2.14 **2.92**	2.10 **2.87**	2.05 **2.77**	2.00 **2.68**	1.94 **2.57**	1.90 **2.49**	1.85 **2.41**	1.80 **2.32**	1.77 **2.27**	1.73 **2.19**	1.71 **2.15**	1.68 **2.10**	1.65 **2.06**	1.64 **2.03**
30	4.17 **7.56**	3.32 **5.39**	2.92 **4.51**	2.69 **4.02**	2.53 **3.70**	2.42 **3.47**	2.34 **3.30**	2.27 **3.17**	2.21 **3.06**	2.16 **2.98**	2.12 **2.90**	2.09 **2.84**	2.04 **2.74**	1.99 **2.66**	1.93 **2.55**	1.89 **2.47**	1.84 **2.38**	1.79 **2.29**	1.76 **2.24**	1.72 **2.16**	1.69 **2.13**	1.66 **2.07**	1.64 **2.03**	1.62 **2.01**
32	4.15 **7.50**	3.30 **5.34**	2.90 **4.46**	2.67 **3.97**	2.51 **3.66**	2.40 **3.42**	2.32 **3.25**	2.25 **3.12**	2.19 **3.01**	2.14 **2.94**	2.10 **2.86**	2.07 **2.80**	2.02 **2.70**	1.97 **2.62**	1.91 **2.51**	1.86 **2.42**	1.82 **2.34**	1.76 **2.25**	1.74 **2.20**	1.69 **2.12**	1.67 **2.08**	1.64 **2.02**	1.61 **1.98**	1.59 **1.96**
34	4.13 **7.44**	3.28 **5.29**	2.88 **4.42**	2.65 **3.93**	2.49 **3.61**	2.38 **3.38**	2.30 **3.21**	2.23 **3.08**	2.17 **2.97**	2.12 **2.89**	2.08 **2.82**	2.05 **2.76**	2.00 **2.66**	1.95 **2.58**	1.89 **2.47**	1.84 **2.38**	1.80 **2.30**	1.74 **2.21**	1.71 **2.15**	1.67 **2.08**	1.64 **2.04**	1.61 **1.98**	1.59 **1.94**	1.57 **1.91**
36	4.11 **7.39**	3.26 **5.25**	2.86 **4.38**	2.63 **3.89**	2.48 **3.58**	2.36 **3.35**	2.28 **3.18**	2.21 **3.04**	2.15 **2.94**	2.10 **2.86**	2.06 **2.78**	2.03 **2.72**	1.98 **2.62**	1.93 **2.54**	1.87 **2.43**	1.82 **2.35**	1.78 **2.26**	1.72 **2.17**	1.69 **2.12**	1.65 **2.04**	1.62 **2.00**	1.59 **1.94**	1.56 **1.90**	1.55 **1.87**
38	4.10 **7.35**	3.25 **5.21**	2.85 **4.34**	2.62 **3.86**	2.46 **3.54**	2.35 **3.32**	2.26 **3.15**	2.19 **3.02**	2.14 **2.91**	2.09 **2.82**	2.05 **2.75**	2.02 **2.69**	1.96 **2.59**	1.92 **2.51**	1.85 **2.40**	1.80 **2.32**	1.76 **2.22**	1.71 **2.14**	1.67 **2.08**	1.63 **2.00**	1.60 **1.97**	1.57 **1.90**	1.54 **1.86**	1.53 **1.84**
40	4.08 **7.31**	3.23 **5.18**	2.84 **4.31**	2.61 **3.83**	2.45 **3.51**	2.34 **3.29**	2.25 **3.12**	2.18 **2.99**	2.12 **2.88**	2.07 **2.80**	2.04 **2.73**	2.00 **2.66**	1.95 **2.56**	1.90 **2.49**	1.84 **2.37**	1.79 **2.29**	1.74 **2.20**	1.69 **2.11**	1.66 **2.05**	1.61 **1.97**	1.59 **1.94**	1.55 **1.88**	1.53 **1.84**	1.51 **1.81**
42	4.07 **7.27**	3.22 **5.15**	2.83 **4.29**	2.59 **3.80**	2.44 **3.49**	2.32 **3.26**	2.24 **3.10**	2.17 **2.96**	2.11 **2.86**	2.06 **2.77**	2.02 **2.70**	1.99 **2.64**	1.94 **2.54**	1.89 **2.46**	1.82 **2.35**	1.78 **2.26**	1.73 **2.17**	1.68 **2.08**	1.64 **2.02**	1.60 **1.94**	1.57 **1.91**	1.54 **1.85**	1.51 **1.80**	1.49 **1.78**
44	4.06 **7.24**	3.21 **5.12**	2.82 **4.26**	2.58 **3.78**	2.43 **3.46**	2.31 **3.24**	2.23 **3.07**	2.16 **2.94**	2.10 **2.84**	2.05 **2.75**	2.01 **2.68**	1.98 **2.62**	1.92 **2.52**	1.88 **2.44**	1.81 **2.32**	1.76 **2.24**	1.72 **2.15**	1.66 **2.06**	1.63 **2.00**	1.58 **1.92**	1.56 **1.88**	1.52 **1.82**	1.50 **1.78**	1.48 **1.75**
46	4.05 **7.21**	3.20 **5.10**	2.81 **4.24**	2.57 **3.76**	2.42 **3.44**	2.30 **3.22**	2.22 **3.05**	2.14 **2.92**	2.09 **2.82**	2.04 **2.73**	2.00 **2.66**	1.97 **2.60**	1.91 **2.50**	1.87 **2.42**	1.80 **2.30**	1.75 **2.22**	1.71 **2.13**	1.65 **2.04**	1.62 **1.98**	1.57 **1.90**	1.54 **1.86**	1.51 **1.80**	1.48 **1.76**	1.46 **1.72**
48	4.04 **7.19**	3.19 **5.08**	2.80 **4.22**	2.56 **3.74**	2.41 **3.42**	2.30 **3.20**	2.21 **3.04**	2.14 **2.90**	2.08 **2.80**	2.03 **2.71**	1.99 **2.64**	1.96 **2.58**	1.90 **2.48**	1.86 **2.40**	1.79 **2.28**	1.74 **2.20**	1.70 **2.11**	1.64 **2.02**	1.61 **1.96**	1.56 **1.88**	1.53 **1.84**	1.50 **1.78**	1.47 **1.73**	1.45 **1.70**

TABLE A-8 (continued)

v_2 \ v_1	1	2	3	4	5	6	7	8	9	10	11	12	14	16	20	24	30	40	50	75	100	200	500	∞
50	4.03 **7.17**	3.18 **5.06**	2.79 **4.20**	2.56 **3.72**	2.40 **3.41**	2.29 **3.18**	2.20 **3.02**	2.13 **2.88**	2.07 **2.78**	2.02 **2.70**	1.98 **2.62**	1.95 **2.56**	1.90 **2.46**	1.85 **2.39**	1.78 **2.26**	1.74 **2.18**	1.69 **2.10**	1.63 **2.00**	1.60 **1.94**	1.55 **1.86**	1.52 **1.82**	1.48 **1.76**	1.46 **1.71**	1.44 **1.68**
55	4.02 **7.12**	3.17 **5.01**	2.78 **4.16**	2.54 **3.68**	2.38 **3.37**	2.27 **3.15**	2.18 **2.98**	2.11 **2.85**	2.05 **2.75**	2.00 **2.66**	1.97 **2.59**	1.93 **2.53**	1.88 **2.43**	1.83 **2.35**	1.76 **2.23**	1.72 **2.15**	1.67 **2.06**	1.61 **1.96**	1.58 **1.90**	1.52 **1.82**	1.50 **1.78**	1.46 **1.71**	1.43 **1.66**	1.41 **1.64**
60	4.00 **7.08**	3.15 **4.98**	2.76 **4.13**	2.52 **3.65**	2.37 **3.34**	2.25 **3.12**	2.17 **2.95**	2.10 **2.82**	2.04 **2.72**	1.99 **2.63**	1.95 **2.56**	1.92 **2.50**	1.86 **2.40**	1.81 **2.32**	1.75 **2.20**	1.70 **2.12**	1.65 **2.03**	1.59 **1.93**	1.56 **1.87**	1.50 **1.79**	1.48 **1.74**	1.44 **1.68**	1.41 **1.63**	1.39 **1.60**
65	3.99 **7.04**	3.14 **4.95**	2.75 **4.10**	2.51 **3.62**	2.36 **3.31**	2.24 **3.09**	2.15 **2.93**	2.08 **2.79**	2.02 **2.70**	1.98 **2.61**	1.94 **2.54**	1.90 **2.47**	1.85 **2.37**	1.80 **2.30**	1.73 **2.18**	1.68 **2.09**	1.63 **2.00**	1.57 **1.90**	1.54 **1.84**	1.49 **1.76**	1.46 **1.71**	1.42 **1.64**	1.39 **1.60**	1.37 **1.56**
70	3.98 **7.01**	3.13 **4.92**	2.74 **4.08**	2.50 **3.60**	2.35 **3.29**	2.23 **3.07**	2.14 **2.91**	2.07 **2.77**	2.01 **2.67**	1.97 **2.59**	1.93 **2.51**	1.89 **2.45**	1.84 **2.35**	1.79 **2.28**	1.72 **2.15**	1.67 **2.07**	1.62 **1.98**	1.56 **1.88**	1.53 **1.82**	1.47 **1.74**	1.45 **1.69**	1.40 **1.62**	1.37 **1.56**	1.35 **1.53**
80	3.96 **6.96**	3.11 **4.88**	2.72 **4.04**	2.48 **3.56**	2.33 **3.25**	2.21 **3.04**	2.12 **2.87**	2.05 **2.74**	1.99 **2.64**	1.95 **2.55**	1.91 **2.48**	1.88 **2.41**	1.82 **2.32**	1.77 **2.24**	1.70 **2.11**	1.65 **2.03**	1.60 **1.94**	1.54 **1.84**	1.51 **1.78**	1.45 **1.70**	1.42 **1.65**	1.38 **1.57**	1.35 **1.52**	1.32 **1.49**
100	3.94 **6.90**	3.09 **4.82**	2.70 **3.98**	2.46 **3.51**	2.30 **3.20**	2.19 **2.99**	2.10 **2.82**	2.03 **2.69**	1.97 **2.59**	1.92 **2.51**	1.88 **2.43**	1.85 **2.36**	1.79 **2.26**	1.75 **2.19**	1.68 **2.06**	1.63 **1.98**	1.57 **1.89**	1.51 **1.79**	1.48 **1.73**	1.42 **1.64**	1.39 **1.59**	1.34 **1.51**	1.30 **1.46**	1.28 **1.43**
125	3.92 **6.84**	3.07 **4.78**	2.68 **3.94**	2.44 **3.47**	2.29 **3.17**	2.17 **2.95**	2.08 **2.79**	2.01 **2.65**	1.95 **2.56**	1.90 **2.47**	1.86 **2.40**	1.83 **2.33**	1.77 **2.23**	1.72 **2.15**	1.65 **2.03**	1.60 **1.94**	1.55 **1.85**	1.49 **1.75**	1.45 **1.68**	1.39 **1.59**	1.36 **1.54**	1.31 **1.46**	1.27 **1.40**	1.25 **1.37**
150	3.91 **6.81**	3.06 **4.75**	2.67 **3.91**	2.43 **3.44**	2.27 **3.14**	2.16 **2.92**	2.07 **2.76**	2.00 **2.62**	1.94 **2.53**	1.89 **2.44**	1.85 **2.37**	1.82 **2.30**	1.76 **2.20**	1.71 **2.12**	1.64 **2.00**	1.59 **1.91**	1.54 **1.83**	1.47 **1.72**	1.44 **1.66**	1.37 **1.56**	1.34 **1.51**	1.29 **1.43**	1.25 **1.37**	1.22 **1.33**
200	3.89 **6.76**	3.04 **4.71**	2.65 **3.88**	2.41 **3.41**	2.26 **3.11**	2.14 **2.90**	2.05 **2.73**	1.98 **2.60**	1.92 **2.50**	1.87 **2.41**	1.83 **2.34**	1.80 **2.28**	1.74 **2.17**	1.69 **2.09**	1.62 **1.97**	1.57 **1.88**	1.52 **1.79**	1.45 **1.69**	1.42 **1.62**	1.35 **1.53**	1.32 **1.48**	1.26 **1.39**	1.22 **1.33**	1.19 **1.28**
400	3.86 **6.70**	3.02 **4.66**	2.62 **3.83**	2.39 **3.36**	2.23 **3.06**	2.12 **2.85**	2.03 **2.69**	1.96 **2.55**	1.90 **2.46**	1.85 **2.37**	1.81 **2.29**	1.78 **2.23**	1.72 **2.12**	1.67 **2.04**	1.60 **1.92**	1.54 **1.84**	1.49 **1.74**	1.42 **1.64**	1.38 **1.57**	1.32 **1.47**	1.28 **1.42**	1.22 **1.32**	1.16 **1.24**	1.13 **1.19**
1,000	3.85 **6.66**	3.00 **4.62**	2.61 **3.80**	2.38 **3.34**	2.22 **3.04**	2.10 **2.82**	2.02 **2.66**	1.95 **2.53**	1.89 **2.43**	1.84 **2.34**	1.80 **2.26**	1.76 **2.20**	1.70 **2.09**	1.65 **2.01**	1.58 **1.89**	1.53 **1.81**	1.47 **1.71**	1.41 **1.61**	1.36 **1.54**	1.30 **1.44**	1.26 **1.38**	1.19 **1.28**	1.13 **1.19**	1.08 **1.11**
∞	3.84 **6.63**	2.99 **4.60**	2.60 **3.78**	2.37 **3.32**	2.21 **3.02**	2.09 **2.80**	2.01 **2.64**	1.94 **2.51**	1.88 **2.41**	1.83 **2.32**	1.79 **2.24**	1.75 **2.18**	1.69 **2.07**	1.64 **1.99**	1.57 **1.87**	1.52 **1.79**	1.46 **1.69**	1.40 **1.59**	1.35 **1.52**	1.28 **1.41**	1.24 **1.36**	1.17 **1.25**	1.11 **1.15**	1.00 **1.00**

TABLE A-9
Critical values of T in the Wilcoxon matched-pairs signed-ranks test
Critical values of T at various levels of probability

The symbol T denotes the smaller sum of ranks associated with differences that are all of the same sign. For any given N (number of ranked differences), the obtained T is significant at a given level if it is equal to or *less than* the value shown in the table.

	Level of Significance for One-tailed Test					Level of Significance for One-tailed Test			
	0.05	0.025	0.01	0.005		0.05	0.025	0.01	0.005
	Level of Significance for Two-tailed Test					Level of Significance for Two-tailed Test			
N	0.10	0.05	0.02	0.01	N	0.10	0.05	0.02	0.01
5	0	—	—	—	28	130	116	101	91
6	2	0	—	—	29	140	126	110	100
7	3	2	0	—	30	151	137	120	109
8	5	3	1	0	31	163	147	130	118
9	8	5	3	1	32	175	159	140	128
10	10	8	5	3	33	187	170	151	138
11	13	10	7	5	34	200	182	162	148
12	17	13	9	7	35	213	195	173	159
13	21	17	12	9	36	227	208	185	171
14	25	21	15	12	37	241	221	198	182
15	30	25	19	15	38	256	235	211	194
16	35	29	23	19	39	271	249	224	207
17	41	34	27	23	40	286	264	238	220
18	47	40	32	27	41	302	279	252	233
19	53	46	37	32	42	319	294	266	247
20	60	52	43	37	43	336	310	281	261
21	67	58	49	42	44	353	327	296	276
22	75	65	55	48	45	371	343	312	291
23	83	73	62	54	46	389	361	328	307
24	91	81	69	61	47	407	378	345	322
25	100	89	76	68	48	426	396	362	339
26	110	98	84	75	49	446	415	379	355
27	119	107	92	83	50	466	434	397	373

(Slight discrepancies will be found between the critical values appearing in the table above and in Table 2 of the 1964 revision of F. Wilcoxon and R.A. Wilcox, *Some Rapid Approximate Statistical Procedures*, New York, Lederle Laboratories, 1964. The disparity reflects the latter's policy of selecting the critical value nearest a given significance level, occasionally overstepping that level. For example, for $N = 8$, the probability of a T of three equals 0.0390 (two-tail), and the probability of a T of four equals 0.0546 (two-tail). Wilcoxon and Wilcox select a T of four as the critical value at the 0.05 level of significance (two-tail), whereas Table A-9 reflects a more conservative policy by setting a T of three as the critical value at this level.)

Source: From Frank Wilcoxon and Roberta A. Wilcox, *Some Rapid Approximate Statistical Procedures*. Revised 1964 by Lederle Laboratories, Pearl River, NY. Reproduced with the permission of the American Cyanamid Company.

TABLE A-10

Table of exponential functions

x	e^x	e^{-x}	x	e^x	e^{-x}
0.00	1.000	1.000	3.00	20.086	0.050
0.10	1.105	0.905	3.10	22.198	0.045
0.20	1.221	0.819	3.20	24.533	0.041
0.30	1.350	0.741	3.30	27.113	0.037
0.40	1.492	0.670	3.40	29.964	0.033
0.50	1.649	0.607	3.50	33.115	0.030
0.60	1.822	0.549	3.60	36.598	0.027
0.70	2.014	0.497	3.70	40.447	0.025
0.80	2.226	0.449	3.80	44.701	0.022
0.90	2.460	0.407	3.90	49.402	0.020
1.00	2.718	0.368	4.00	54.598	0.018
1.10	3.004	0.333	4.10	60.340	0.017
1.20	3.320	0.301	4.20	66.686	0.015
1.30	3.669	0.273	4.30	73.700	0.014
1.40	4.055	0.247	4.40	81.451	0.012
1.50	4.482	0.223	4.50	90.017	0.011
1.60	4.953	0.202	4.60	99.484	0.010
1.70	5.474	0.183	4.70	109.95	0.009
1.80	6.050	0.165	4.80	121.51	0.008
1.90	6.686	0.150	4.90	134.29	0.007
2.00	7.389	0.135	5.00	148.41	0.007
2.10	8.166	0.122	5.10	164.02	0.006
2.20	9.025	0.111	5.20	181.27	0.006
2.30	9.974	0.100	5.30	200.34	0.005
2.40	11.023	0.091	5.40	221.41	0.005
2.50	12.182	0.082	5.50	244.69	0.004
2.60	13.464	0.074	5.60	270.43	0.004
2.70	14.880	0.067	5.70	298.87	0.003
2.80	16.445	0.061	5.80	330.30	0.003
2.90	18.174	0.055	5.90	365.04	0.003
3.00	20.086	0.050	6.00	403.43	0.002

ANSWERS TO PROBLEMS AND REVIEW PROBLEMS

CHAPTER 1

Answers to Problems

1.

	Lower Class Limits	Higher Class Limits	Midpoints
1st Class	10	20	15
2nd Class	20	30	25
3rd Class	30	40	35
4th Class	40	50	45
5th Class	50	60	55

The class size (i) of each class is 10.

2. a. The first and second classes are not mutually exclusive. The second and third classes are not all inclusive.

   b. The classes are mutually exclusive and all-inclusive.

   c. The first and second classes are not mutually exclusive.

3.

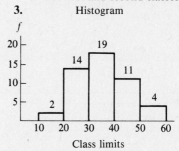

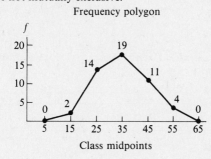

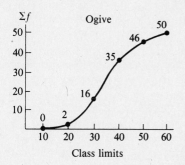

4. $\bar{X} = \dfrac{\Sigma X}{n} = \dfrac{136}{8} = 17$

5.

X	w	wX
0.02	100,000	2,000
0.04	50,000	2,000
0.06	1,000,000	60,000
	1,150,000	64,000

$$\bar{X}_w = \frac{\Sigma wX}{\Sigma w} = \frac{64,000}{1,150,000} = 0.056 = 5.6\%$$

The observations carry different weights. This makes the weighted average the appropriate measure.

6. Position of median: $\dfrac{n+1}{2} = \dfrac{8+1}{2} = 4.5^{\text{th}}$ position

Ranking data from lowest to highest: 10, 13, 14, 17, 18, 21, 21, 22

Value of $P_{4.5} = \dfrac{P_4 + P_5}{2} = \dfrac{17 + 18}{2} = 17.5$

Value of the median: 17.5

7. Position of the median: $(n + 1)/2 = 9 + 1 = 5^{\text{th}}$ position

Ranking data from lowest to highest: 4, 5, 7, 8, 10, 12, 12, 19, 21.

Value of median = 10

8. Mode is 12. It occurs twice. All the others occur only once.

9. Range = Highest value − Lowest value

$= 22 - 10 = 12$

10. $\Sigma(X - \bar{X})^2 = (10 - 17)^2 + (13 - 17)^2 + (21 - 17)^2 + (17 - 17)^2 + (14 - 17)^2 + (22 - 17)^2$

$+ (18 - 17)^2 + (21 - 17)^2$

$= (-7)^2 + (-4)^2 + 4^2 + 0^2 + (-3)^2 + 5^2 + 1^2 + 4^2$

$= 49 + 16 + 16 + 0 + 9 + 25 + 1 + 16$

$= 132$

$s^2 = \Sigma(X - \bar{X})^2/(n - 1) = 132/(8 - 1) = 132/7 = 18.857$

$s = 4.34$

11.

x	f	m	fm	fm²	Σf
10 and under 20	2	15	30	450	2
20 and under 30	14	25	350	8,750	16
30 and under 40	19	35	665	23,275	35
40 and under 50	11	45	495	22,275	46
50 and under 60	4	55	220	12,100	50
	50		1,760	66,850	

$\bar{X} = (\Sigma fm/n) = 1,760/50 = 35.2$

Median: $\text{Md} = L_{Md} + \dfrac{(n/2) - \Sigma f_p}{f_{Md}}(i) = 30 + \dfrac{(50/2) - 16}{19}(10) = 30 + 4.74 = 34.74$

Mode = 35

$$\text{Variance} = \frac{n\Sigma fm^2 - (\Sigma fm)^2}{n(n-1)} = \frac{50(66,850) - (1760)^2}{50(49)} = 99.96$$

Standard deviation: $s = 9.998$

12. $CV = s/\bar{X} = .284$

13. $\mu = \Sigma X/N = 162/6 = 27$

$\sigma^2 = \Sigma(X - \mu)^2/N = 166/6 = 27.67$

Answers to Review Problems

1. $\bar{X} = \Sigma X/n = 220/10 = 22$

Median: position: $\dfrac{n+1}{2} = \dfrac{10+1}{2} = 5.5^{\text{th}}$ position

Lowest to highest: 15, 18, 19, 19, 21, 22, 22, 22, 27, 35
Value of 5.5^{th} position: $P_5 = 21$, $P_6 = 22$

$$\frac{(P_5 + P_6)}{2} = \frac{21 + 22}{2} = 21.5$$

Value of median: 21.5
Mode: 22, it occurs three times
Range: Highest − Lowest = 35 − 15 = 20
Variance: $s^2 = \Sigma(X - \bar{X})^2/(n-1) = 278/(10-1) = 30.89$
Standard deviation: $s = 5.56$

2. $\bar{X} = \dfrac{\Sigma X}{n} = \dfrac{100}{5} = 20$

Median = 20
Mode = 20

$$\text{Variance: } s^2 = \frac{\Sigma(X - \bar{X})^2}{n-1} = \frac{0}{4} = 0$$

All the observation are the same value, so there is no dispersion.

3. Sample 1: $\bar{X} = \Sigma X/n = 265/5 = 53$

$s^2 = \Sigma(X - \bar{X})^2/(n-1) = 10/(5-1) = 2.5$

Sample 2: $\bar{X} = \Sigma X/n = 265/5 = 53$

$s^2 = \Sigma(X - \bar{X})^2/(n-1) = 416/(5-1) = 104$

The means of each sample are equal. However, the variance of the second is much greater than the variance of the first.

4.

Product	Profit per Item X	Quantity w	wX
A	50	1,000	50,000
B	100	5,000	500,000
C	400	500	200,000
D	1,000	200	200,000
		6,700	950,000

$\bar{X}_w = \Sigma wX/\Sigma w = 950,000/6,700 = \$141.79$

The weighted average should be used because there are different quantities sold of each item and therefore each mark-up has a different weight.

5.

x	f	m	fm	fm²	Σf
0 and under 20	2	10	20	200	2
20 and under 40	5	30	150	4500	7
40 and under 60	12	50	600	30000	19
60 and under 80	25	70	1750	122500	44
80 and under 100	6	90	540	48600	50
	50		3060	205800	

$$\bar{X} = \frac{\Sigma fm}{n} = \frac{3060}{50} = 61.2$$

$$s^2 = \frac{n\Sigma fm^2 - (\Sigma fm)^2}{n(n-1)} = \frac{50(205,800) - (3,060)^2}{50(49)} = 378.1$$

$$s = 19.4$$

$$\text{Median} = L_{md} + \frac{n/2 - \Sigma f_p}{f_{md}}(i) = 60 + \frac{25 - 19}{25}(20) = 64.8$$

$$\text{Mode} = 70$$

6.

x	f	m	fm	fm²	Σf
0 and under 100	10	50	500	25000	10
100 and under 200	40	150	6000	900000	50
200 and under 300	120	250	30000	7500000	170
300 and under 400	25	350	8750	3062500	195
400 and under 500	5	450	2250	1012500	200
	200		47500	12500000	

$$\bar{X} = \frac{\Sigma fm}{n} = \frac{47500}{200} = 237.5$$

$$s^2 = \frac{n\Sigma fm^2 - (\Sigma fm)^2}{n(n-1)} = \frac{200(12500000) - (47500)^2}{200(199)} = 6124.4$$

$$s = 78.26$$

$$\text{Median} = L_{md} + \frac{n/2 - \Sigma f_p}{f_{md}}(i) = 200 + \frac{100 - 50}{120}(100) = 241.67$$

$$\text{Mode} = 250$$

7. The mean and standard deviation cannot be computed because the last class is open ended, and a midpoint cannot be found for an open-ended class.

$$\text{Median} = L_{Md} + \frac{n/2 - \Sigma f_p}{f_{Md}}(i)$$

$$= 30 + \frac{122.5 - 60}{85}(10) = 37.35$$

$$\text{Mode} = 35$$

8.

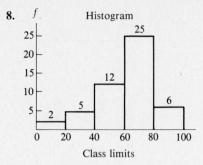

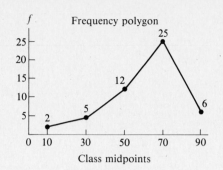

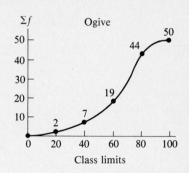

9. $CV = s/\bar{X} = 19.4/61.2 = 0.317$
10. $CV = s/\bar{X} = 78.26/237.5 = 0.3295$

CHAPTER 2

Answers to Problems

1. a. $P(K) = 4/52 = 1/13$
   b. $P(B) = 26/52 = 1/2$
   c. $P(3 \le X \le 7) = 20/52 = 5/13$
2. $P(5 \text{ or } D) = P(5) + P(D) - P(5 \text{ and } D) = 4/36 + 6/36 - 0/36 = 10/36 = 5/18$
3. $P(12 \text{ or } D) = P(12) + P(D) - P(12 \text{ and } D) = 1/36 + 6/36 - 1/36 = 6/36 = 1/6$
4. $P(\bar{D}) = 1 - P(D) = 1 - 1/6 = 5/6$

5.

	B_1	B_2	Marginal
A_1	0.2	0.4	0.6
A_2	0.1	0.3	0.4
Marginal	0.3	0.7	1.0

6. a. $P(B_1 \mid A_1) = \dfrac{P(A_1 \text{ and } B_1)}{P(A_1)} = \dfrac{0.2}{0.6} = 0.33$ **b.** $P(A_1 \mid B_1) = \dfrac{P(A_1 \text{ and } B_1)}{P(B_1)} = \dfrac{0.2}{0.3} = 0.67$

7. The complement of a graduate student, given a male, is an undergraduate given a male, so
$P(B_2 \mid A_1) = 1 - P(B_1 \mid A_1) = 1 - 0.33 = 0.67$
or

$$P(B_2/A_1) = \frac{P(A_1 \text{ and } B_2)}{P(A_1)} = \frac{0.4}{0.6} = 0.67$$

8. $P(W_1 \text{ and } W_2) = P(W_1) \cdot P(W_2 \mid W_1) = (2/200) \cdot (1/199) = 1/19900 = 0.00005$
9. $P(W_1 \text{ and } W_2) = P(W_1) \cdot P(W_2) = (2/200) \cdot (2/200) = 1/10000 = 0.0001$
10. $P(M_1) = 0.4 \quad P(M_2) = 0.3 \quad P(M_3) = 0.3 \quad P(D \mid M_1) = 0.01 \quad P(D \mid M_2) = 0.02 \quad P(D \mid M_3) = 0.04$

$$P(M_2/D) = \frac{P(M_2) \cdot P(D \mid M_2)}{P(M_1) \cdot P(D \mid M_1) + P(M_2) \cdot P(D \mid M_2) + P(M_3) \cdot P(D \mid M_3)}$$

$$= \frac{(0.3) \cdot (0.02)}{(0.4) \cdot (0.01) + (0.3) \cdot (0.02) + (0.3) \cdot (0.04)}$$

$$= \frac{.006}{.022} = 0.273$$

11. $\quad$ 1st slot $\quad$ 2nd slot $\quad$ 3rd slot
$\quad\quad$ 26 $\quad \cdot \quad$ 10 $\quad \cdot \quad$ 10 $\quad$ = 2,600 possible codes
12. $n! = 6! = 720$ possible routes
13. a. $_{30}C_5 = \dbinom{30}{5} = \dfrac{30!}{(30-5)!5!} = 142{,}506$

   b. $_{30}P_5 = \dfrac{30!}{25!} = 17{,}100{,}720$

14. $P(3A) = \dfrac{\dbinom{4}{3}}{\dbinom{52}{3}} = \dfrac{4}{22100} = 0.00018$

Answers to Review Problems

1. a. $4/52 = 1/13$ **b.** $3/6 = 1/2$ **c.** $1/30$

2. a. The joint probability table is

	$\bar{E}$	E	Total
S	0.05	0.56	0.61
$\bar{S}$	0.35	0.04	0.39
Total	0.40	0.60	1.00

   b. $P(S \text{ and } E) = 0.56$ **c.** $P(S) = 0.61$ **d.** $P(E \mid S) = \dfrac{P(S \text{ and } E)}{P(S)} = \dfrac{0.56}{0.61} = 0.92$

   e. No. $P(E \mid S) = 0.92$ and $P(E) = 0.60$. For E and S to be independent, $P(E)$ must be the same as $P(E \mid S)$. So E and S are dependent.

   f. No. $P(S \text{ and } E) \neq 0$. So, E and S are not mutually exclusive.

3. $P(K) = 0.5,\quad P(J) = 0.6$ Independent

   a. $P(K \text{ and } J) = P(K) \cdot P(J) = (0.5)(0.6) = 0.3$

   b. $P(\bar{K} \text{ and } \bar{J}) = P(\bar{K}) \cdot P(\bar{J}) = (0.5)(0.4) = 0.2$

   c. $P(J \mid K) = P(J) = 0.6$

   d. $P(K \text{ or } J) = P(K) + P(J) - P(K \text{ and } J) = 0.5 + 0.6 - 0.3 = 0.8$

4. $P(A) = 0.3,\quad P(B) = 0.6$ Given the events are mutually exclusive, then $P(A \text{ and } B) = 0$.

   a. $P(A \mid B) = \dfrac{P(A \text{ and } B)}{P(B)} = \dfrac{0}{0.3} = 0$ **b.** $P(B \mid A) = \dfrac{P(A \text{ and } B)}{P(A)} = \dfrac{0}{0.6} = 0$

   c. $P(A \text{ and } B) = 0$ **d.** $P(A \text{ or } B) = P(A) + P(B) - P(A \text{ and } B) = 0.3 + 0.6 - 0 = 0.9$

5. $P(M) = 0.5,\quad P(W) = 0.7,\quad P(M \mid W) = 0.6$

   a. $P(M \text{ and } W) = P(W) \cdot P(M \mid W) = (0.7)(0.6) = 0.42$

   b. $P(W \mid M) = P(M \text{ and } W)/P(M) = 0.42/0.50 = 0.84$

   c. $P(M \text{ or } W) = P(M) + P(W) - P(M \text{ and } W) = 0.5 + 0.7 - 0.42 = .78$

   d. $P(\overline{M \text{ and } W}) = 1 - P(M \text{ or } W) = 1 - 0.78 = 0.22$

6. a. $P(R) = 3/10 = 0.3$

   b. Independent events; so $P(R_1 \text{ and } R_2) = P(R_1) \cdot P(R_2) = (0.3) \cdot (0.3) = 0.09$

   c. Dependent events; so $P(R_1 \text{ and } R_2) = P(R_1) \cdot P(R_2 \mid R_1) = (3/10) \cdot (2/9) = 0.067$

7. $P(P) = 0.9,\quad P(HD) = 0.6,\quad P(P \text{ and } HD) = 0.55$

   $P(P \text{ or } HD) = P(P) + P(HD) - P(P \text{ and } HD) = 0.4 + 0.6 - 0.55 = 0.95$

8. $P(B) = 0.3,\quad P(P) = 0.7,\quad P(M \mid B) = 0.02,\quad P(M \mid P) = 0.03$

   $P(B \mid M) = \dfrac{P(B) \cdot P(M \mid B)}{P(B) \cdot P(M \mid B) + P(P) \cdot P(M \mid P)} = \dfrac{(0.3)(0.02)}{(0.3)(0.02) + 0.7(0.03)} = 0.22$

9. a. $10 \cdot 10 \cdot 10 \cdot 26 \cdot 26 \cdot 26 = 17{,}576{,}000$ **b.** $36 \cdot 36 \cdot 36 \cdot 36 \cdot 36 \cdot 36 = 2{,}176{,}782{,}336$

10. $n! = 12! = 479{,}001{,}600$

11. $_{12}C_4 = \binom{12}{4} = \dfrac{12!}{(12-4)!4!} = 495$

CHAPTER 3

Answers to Problems

1. a. This is a probability distribution.

x	$f(x)$
1	1/10
2	2/10
3	3/10
4	4/10
	10/10 = 1

b. This is not a probability distribution: $f(0) = -1/2$. Probabilities cannot be negative.

x	$f(x)$
0	$-1/2$
1	$0/2$
2	$1/2$
3	$2/2$
	$2/2 = 1$

c. This is not a probability distribution: $\Sigma f(x) \neq 1$.

x	$f(x)$
1	$2/35$
2	$5/35$
3	$10/35$
4	$17/35$
	$34/35 \neq 1$

2. a. This is a probability distribution.   **b.** $P(x \leq 3) = 9/20$

x	$f(x)$
1	$2/20$
2	$3/20$
3	$4/20$
4	$5/20$
5	$6/20$
	$20/20 = 1$

3. Uniform: $f(x) = 1/s$; $f(x) = 1/26$ $x = 300, 301, \ldots, 325$.
    a. $1/26$ **b.** $11/26$ **c.** $15/26$ **d.** 0

4. Binomial; $P(\text{Information}) = P(S) = p = 0.3$, $n = 10$, $x = 4$

$$f(4) = \binom{10}{4}(0.3)^4(0.7)^6 = 0.2001$$

5. $n = 10$, $x = 4$; $P(S) = p = 0.3$ (From Table A-2); $P(x = 4) = 0.2001$

6. Binomial; $n = 10$, $P(S) = p = .25$
    a. $P(x = 3) = 0.2503$
    b. $P(x \geq 7) = 1 - P(x \leq 6) = 1 - 0.9965 = 0.0035$
    c. $P(x \leq 5) = 0.9803$
    d. $P(x < 6) = P(x \leq 5) = 0.9803$
    e. $P(2 \leq x \leq 4) = P(x \leq 4) - P(x \leq 1) = 0.9219 - 0.2440 = 0.6779$
    f. $P(x > 6) = P(x \geq 7) = 1 - P(x \leq 6) = 1 - 0.9965 = 0.0035$

7. Multinomial;

$$f(4, 1, 1) = \frac{6!}{4!1!1!}(0.92)^4(0.05)^1(0.03)^1 = 0.0322$$

$$f(5, 0, 1) = \frac{6!}{5!0!1!}(0.92)^5(0.05)^0(0.03)^1 = 0.1186$$

8. Hypergeometric;

$$f(1, 1, 1, 1) = \frac{\binom{4}{1}\binom{5}{1}\binom{3}{1}\binom{3}{1}}{\binom{15}{4}} = \frac{(4)(5)(3)(3)}{1,365} = 0.13$$

9. Hypergeometric;

$$f(4) = \frac{\binom{6}{2}\binom{4}{2}}{\binom{10}{4}} = \frac{15 \cdot 6}{210} = \frac{3}{7} = 0.429$$

10. Poisson; $\mu = 5$ (Table A-3)
   a. $P(x \le 5) = 0.616$
   b. $P(x = 5) = P(x \le 5) - P(x \le 4) = 0.616 - 0.440 = 0.176$
   c. $P(4 \le x \le 6) = P(x \le 6) - P(x \le 3) = 0.762 - 0.265 = 0.497$
   d. $P(x > 3) = P(x \ge 4) = 1 - P(x \le 3) = 1 - 0.265 = 0.735$

11. $E(X) = \Sigma x f(x) = -0.26$

x	$f(x)$	$xf(x)$
5	18/38	90/38
-5	20/38	-100/38
	38/38	-10/38

12. $f(x) = x/10 \quad x = 1, 2, 3, 4$

x	$f(x)$	$xf(x)$	$x^2f(x)$
1	1/10	1/10	1/10
2	2/10	4/10	8/10
3	3/10	9/10	27/10
4	4/10	16/10	64/10
	10/10	30/10 = 3	100/10 = 10

$E(X) = \mu = \Sigma x f(x) = 3$

$\sigma^2 = \Sigma x^2 f(x) - \mu^2 = 10 - (3)^2 = 1 \quad \sigma = 1$

13. $E(X_1 + X_2 + X_3 + X_4 + X_5) = 5(-0.26) = -1.30$

Answers to Review Problems

1.

x	$f(x)$	$xf(x)$	$x^2f(x)$
1	2/20	2/20	2/20
2	3/20	6/20	12/20
3	4/20	12/20	36/20
4	5/20	20/20	80/20
5	6/20	30/20	150/20
	20/20	70/20	280/20

$E(X) = \mu = 70/20 = 3.5 \qquad \sigma^2 = 1.75$

2. This is not a probability distribution. The mean and variance cannot be computed.

x	$f(x)$
1	1/9
2	2/9
3	3/9
4	4/9
	10/9 $\ne$ 1

3. $E(X) = \Sigma x f(x) = -160/36 = -4.44$

x	$f(x)$	$xf(x)$
90	2/36	180/36
−10	34/36	−340/36
	36/36	−160/36

4. $10(-4.444) = -44.44$

5. Multinomial

    a. $f(1, 2, 3) = \dfrac{6!}{1!2!3!}(0.05)^1(0.20)^2(0.75)^3 = 0.05$

    b. Binomial or multinomial;

$$\text{Binomial} \quad f(6) = \binom{6}{6}(0.75)^6(0.25)^0 = 0.18$$

$$\text{Multinomial} \quad f(0, 0, 6) = \frac{6!}{0!0!6!}(0.05)^0(0.20)^0(0.75)^6 = 0.18$$

6. Hypergeometric

    a. $f(4) = \binom{5}{4}\binom{45}{0}\Big/\binom{50}{4} = \dfrac{(5)(1)}{230,300} = 0.00002$

    b. $f(3) = \binom{5}{3}\binom{45}{1}\Big/\binom{50}{4} = \dfrac{(10)(45)}{230,300} = 0.00195$

7. Poisson; $\mu = 5$ (Table A-3)

    a. $P(X = 5) = p(X \le 5) - P(X \le 4) = 0.616 - 0.440 = 0.176$

    b. $P(X < 3) = P(X \le 2) = 0.125$

    c. $P(2 \le X \le 6) = P(X \le 6) - P(X \le 1) = 0.762 - 0.040 = 0.722$

    d. $P(X > 10) = 1 - P(X \le 10) = 1 - 0.986 = 0.014$

8. Binomial; $P(S) = p = 0.05$; $n = 10$ $P(x \le 2) = 0.9885$

9. Uniform; $f(x) = 1/16$ $(x = 50, 51, \ldots, 65)$

    a. 1/16   **b.** 10/16   **c.** 6/16

10. Binomial; $P(S) = p = 0.10$; $n = 10$

    a. $P(x = 3) = 0.0574$

    b. $P(x = 10) = 0^+$

    c. $P(x = 0) = 0.3487$

    d. $P(x \ge 6) = 1 - P(x \le 5) = 1 - .9999 = 0.0001$

11. Hypergeometric

    a. $\binom{26}{5}\binom{26}{0}\Big/\binom{52}{5} = \dfrac{65,780 \cdot 1}{2,598,960} = 0.025$

    b. $\binom{4}{3}\binom{4}{2}\binom{44}{0}\Big/\binom{52}{5} = \dfrac{4 \cdot 6 \cdot 1}{2,598,960} = 0.000009$

    c. $\binom{13}{3}\binom{39}{2}\Big/\binom{52}{5} = \dfrac{286 \cdot 741}{2,598,960} = 0.082$

    d. $\binom{13}{5}\binom{39}{0}\Big/\binom{52}{5} = \dfrac{1287 \cdot 1}{2,598,960} = 0.000495$

12. Binomial; $n = 5$, $p = 0.20$ (Tables A-1 and A-2)

    a. $P(X = 5) = 0.0003$

    b. $P(X = 0) = 0.3277$

    c. $P(X = 3) = 0.0512$

    d. $P(X \ge 3) = 1 - P(X \le 2) = 1 - 0.9421 = 0.0579$

    e. $P(2 \le X \le 4) = P(X \le 4) - P(X \le 1) = 0.9997 - 0.7373 = 0.2624$

13. Poisson; $\mu = 20$

    a. $P(x = 20) = P(x \le 20) - P(x \le 19) = 0.559 - 0.470 = 0.089$

    b. $P(x > 20) = 1 - P(x \le 20) = 1 - 0.559 = 0.441$

    c. $P(15 \le x \le 25) = P(x \le 25) - P(x \le 14) = 0.888 - 0.105 = 0.783$

CHAPTER 4

Answer to Problem

1. $\binom{N}{n} = \binom{4}{2} = 6$ 2, 4   4, 6
                       2, 6   4, 8
                       2, 8   6, 8

Answers to Review Problems

1. $\binom{N}{n} = \binom{15}{5} = 3{,}003$

2. $\binom{N}{n} = \binom{5}{3} = 10$
   $P(BCD) = 1/10 = 0.1$

3. $\binom{N}{n} = \binom{6}{3} = 20$ 1, 3, 5   1, 5, 7   1, 7, 11   3, 5, 11   5, 7, 9
                                   1, 3, 7   1, 5, 9   1, 9, 11   3, 7, 9   5, 7, 11
                                   1, 3, 9   1, 5, 11   3, 5, 7   3, 7, 11   5, 9, 11
                                   1, 3, 11   1, 7, 9   3, 5, 9   3, 9, 11   7, 9, 11

CHAPTER 5

Answers to Problems

1. $n = 5$ $P(S) = p = 0.30$ (Table A-2)

x	$f(x)$
0	0.1681
1	0.3602
2	0.3087
3	0.1323
4	0.0284
5	0.0024

2.

$\bar{p}$	$f(\bar{p})$
0.00	0.1681
0.20	0.3602
0.40	0.3087
0.60	0.1323
0.80	0.0284
1.00	0.0024

3. $\mu_{n\bar{p}} = 5(0.3) = 1.5$ $\sigma^2_{n\bar{p}} = 5(0.3)(0.7) = 1.05$

   $\sigma_{n\bar{p}} = 1.02$ $\mu_{\bar{p}} = 0.3$ $\sigma^2_{\bar{p}} = \dfrac{(0.3)(0.7)}{5} = 0.042$ $\sigma_{\bar{p}} = 0.2$

4. **a.** 0.0228   **b.** 0.49865   **c.** 0.49865   **d.** 0.9544   **e.** 0.9372   **f.** 0.2266
   g. 0.99865   **h.** 0.1359   **i.** 0.9537   **j.** 0.0744   **k.** 0.9826

5. $\mu = 12$; $\sigma = 0.2$
   a. $P(z \geq -1) = 0.8413$ **b.** $P(-2 \leq z \leq -1) = 0.1359$ **c.** $P(z > 0.5) = 0.3085$

6. $\mu = 100$; $\sigma = 10$; $n = 400$; $\sigma_{\bar{x}} = 0.5$
   $P(100 \leq \overline{X} \leq 101) = P(0 \leq z \leq 2) = 0.4772$

Answers to Review Problems

1. $n = 5$; $P(S) = p = 0.40$ (Table A-2)

x	$f(x)$
0	0.0778
1	0.2592
2	0.3456
3	0.2304
4	0.0768
5	0.0102
	1.0000

2.

$\bar{p}$	$f(\bar{p})$
0.00	0.0778
0.20	0.2592
0.40	0.3456
0.60	0.2304
0.80	0.0768
1.00	0.0102
	1.0000

3. $\mu_{n\bar{p}} = 5(0.4) = 2.0$; $\sigma^2_{n\bar{p}} = 5(0.4)(0.6) = 1.2$; $\sigma_{n\bar{p}} = 1.095$

4. $\mu_{\bar{p}} = 0.4$; $\sigma^2_{\bar{p}} = (0.4)(0.6)/5 = 0.048$; $\sigma_{\bar{p}} = 0.219$

5. $\mu = 70$; $\sigma = 5$
  a. $P(X > 72) = P(z > 0.4) = 0.3446$ **b.** $P(\bar{X} > 72) = P(z > 2) > 0.0228$

6. a. 0.5000   **b.** 0.5000   **c.** 0.1587   **d.** 0.7814   **e.** 0.8185   **f.** 0.15735

7. $N = 400$; $n = 16$; $\mu = 66$; $\sigma = 4$;

  $\sigma_{\bar{x}} = \sqrt{(N - n)/(N - 1)} \cdot \sigma/\sqrt{n} = 0.98(1) = 0.98$
  a. $P(z \geq 0) = 0.5000$
  b. $P(z \leq 2.04) = 0.9793$
  c. $P(-1.02 \leq z \leq 1.02) = 0.6922$

8. $\mu = 100$; $\sigma = 7$; $n = 49$; $\sigma_{\bar{x}} = 1$
  a. $P(z \geq -2) = 0.9772$
  b. $P(-1 \leq z \leq 1) = 0.6826$
  c. $P(z > 2) = 0.0228$
  d. $P(-2 \leq z \leq -1) = 0.1359$

9. $\mu = 100$; $\sigma = 7$; $n = 196$; $\sigma_{\bar{x}} = 0.5$
  a. $P(z \geq -4) = 0.99997$
  b. $P(-2 \leq z \leq 2) = 0.9544$
  c. $P(z > 4) = 0.00003$
  d. $P(-4 \leq z \leq -2) = 0.02277$

10. $\mu = 50$; $\sigma = 1$
  a. $P(z > 2) = 0.0228$
  b. $P(0 \leq z \leq 4) = 0.49997$
  c. $P(-2 \leq z \leq 3) = 0.97585$
  d. $P(z > -1) = 0.8413$
  e. $P(-0.5 \leq z \leq -0.2) = 0.1122$
  f. $P(-2 \leq z \leq 0) = 0.4772$

11. $\mu = 12$; $\sigma = 0.1$
  a. $P(z > 1.1) = 0.1357$
  b. $P(z < -1.3) = 0.0968$
  c. $P(1 \leq z \leq 2) = 0.1359$
  d. $P(1.5 < z < 2.5) = 0.0606$

12. $\mu = 50$; $\sigma = 5$

    a. $n = 16$; $\sigma_{\bar{x}} = 1.25$; $P(z > 0.8) = 0.2119$

    b. $n = 25$; $\sigma_{\bar{x}} = 1$; $P(z > 1) = 0.1587$

    c. $n = 64$; $\sigma_{\bar{x}} = 0.625$; $P(z > 1.6) = 0.0548$

CHAPTER 6

Answers to Problems

1. a. $z = 2.33$

  b. $z = 2.58$

2. $n = 400$; $\bar{X} = 20$ $s = 10$ $\alpha = 0.05$

$$s_{\bar{x}} = \frac{s}{\sqrt{n}} = \frac{10}{\sqrt{400}} = \frac{10}{20} = 0.50$$

$20 \pm 1.96(0.50) = 20 \pm 0.98$ or   19.02 to 20.98

3. $n = 200$ $\bar{p} = 0.05$ $\alpha = 0.02$

$$s_{\bar{p}} = \sqrt{\frac{(0.05)(0.95)}{200}} = 0.015$$

$0.05 \pm 2.33(0.015)$ or   0.015 to 0.085

4. $n_1 = 64$, $n_2 = 100$; $\bar{X}_1 = 14$, $\bar{X}_2 = 20$; $s_1 = 4$, $s_2 = 5$; $\alpha = 0.10$

$$s_{\bar{x}_1 - \bar{x}_2} = \sqrt{\frac{16}{64} + \frac{25}{100}} = 0.71 \qquad (14 - 20) \pm 1.65(0.71) \quad \text{or} \quad -7.17 \text{ to } -4.83$$

5. $n_1 = 100$, $n_2 = 64$; $\bar{p}_1 = 0.06$, $\bar{p}_2 = 0.04$; $\alpha = 0.05$

$$s_{\bar{p}_1 - \bar{p}_2} = \sqrt{\frac{(0.06)(0.94)}{100} + \frac{(0.04)(0.96)}{64}} = 0.034 \qquad (0.06 - 0.04) \pm 1.96(0.034) \quad \text{or} \quad -0.0467 \text{ to } 0.0867$$

6. $t = 2.567$

7. $t = 1.717$

8. $n = 25$; $\bar{X} = 90{,}000$ $s = 10{,}000$ $\alpha = 0.02$

$s_{\bar{x}} = 10{,}000/\sqrt{25} = 2{,}000$ (Use t)

$90{,}000 \pm 2.492(2{,}000)$ or   85,016 to 94,984

9. $D = 10$; $\alpha = 0.02$;   Range 210; $\sigma = 210/6 = 35$

$$n = \frac{(2.33)^2(35)^2}{10^2} = 66.5 = 67$$

10. $p = 0.02$ $D = 0.01$ $\alpha = 0.05$

$$n = \frac{(1.96)^2(0.02)(0.98)}{(0.01)^2} = 752.95 = 753$$

Answers to Review Problems

1. Range $= 120$; $\sigma = 20$; $D = 5$; $z = 2.33$

$$n = \frac{(2.33)^2(20)^2}{(5)^2} = 86.9 = 87$$

2. $n_1 = 30$, $n_2 = 50$; $x_1 = 3$, $x_2 = 7$; $\bar{p}_1 = 0.10$, $\bar{p}_2 = 0.14$; $z = 1.96$

$$s_{\bar{p}_1 - \bar{p}_2} = \sqrt{\frac{(0.10)(0.90)}{30} + \frac{(0.14)(0.86)}{50}} = 0.074 \qquad (0.10 - 0.14) \pm 1.96(0.074) \quad \text{or} \quad -0.185 \text{ to } 0.105$$

3. $n_1 = 30$, $n_2 = 30$; $\bar{X}_1 = 50{,}000$, $\bar{X}_2 = 30{,}000$; $s_1 = 10{,}000$, $s_2 = 6{,}000$; $z = 1.96$

$$s_{\bar{x}_1 - \bar{x}_2} = \sqrt{\frac{10{,}000^2}{30} + \frac{6{,}000^2}{30}} = 2{,}129 \qquad (50{,}000 - 30{,}000) \pm 1.96(2{,}129) \quad \text{or} \quad 15{,}827 \text{ to } 24{,}173$$

4. $n = 80$; $x = 75$; $\bar{p} = 0.9375$; $z = 1.96$

$$s_{\bar{p}} = \sqrt{\frac{(.9375)(.0625)}{80}} = 0.027 \qquad 0.9375 \pm 1.96(.027) \quad \text{or} \quad 0.8846 \text{ to } 0.9904$$

5. $n = 100$; $\bar{X} = 600$; $s = 200$; $z = 1.96$

$s_{\bar{x}} = 200/\sqrt{100} = 20$ $600 \pm 1.96(20)$ or   560.8 or 639.2

6. $z = 1.65$; $p = 0.25$; $D = 0.01$; $n = \dfrac{(1.65)^2(0.25)(0.75)}{(0.01)^2} = 5{,}104.7 = 5{,}105$

7. $n = 81$; $\bar{X} = 65$; $s = 9$; $z = 2.33$; $s_{\bar{x}} = s/\sqrt{n} = 9/\sqrt{81} = 1$ $65 \pm 2.33(1)$ or   62.67 to 67.33

8. $N = 200$; $n = 10$; $\bar{X} = 70$; $s = 8$; $t = 2.262$

$$s_{\bar{x}} = \sqrt{\frac{N-n}{N-1}} \cdot \frac{s}{\sqrt{n}} = \sqrt{\frac{200-10}{200-1}} \cdot \frac{8}{\sqrt{10}} = 2.47 \quad 70 \pm 2.262(2.47) \quad \text{or} \quad 64.41 \text{ to } 75.59$$

9. $n_1 = 50$; $n_2 = 50$; $\bar{X}_1 = 10,000$; $\bar{X}_2 = 11,000$; $s_1^2 = 20,000$; $s_2^2 = 25,000$; $z = 2.58$

$$s_{\bar{x}_1 - \bar{x}_2} = \sqrt{\left(\frac{20,000}{50}\right) + \left(\frac{25,000}{50}\right)} = 30 \quad (10,000 - 11,000) \pm 2.58(30) \quad \text{or} \quad (-1,077.4 \text{ to } -922.6)$$

10. $n = 10$; $\bar{X} = \dfrac{290}{10} = 29$; $s^2 = \dfrac{\Sigma(X - \bar{X})^2}{n-1} = \dfrac{310}{9} = 34.44$; $s = 5.87$; $t = 2.262$

$$s_{\bar{x}} = \frac{5.87}{\sqrt{10}} = 1.86 \quad 29 \pm 2.262(1.86) \quad \text{or} \quad 24.8 \text{ to } 33.2$$

11. $n_1 = 50$, $n_2 = 40$; $x_1 = 22$, $x_2 = 16$; $\bar{p}_1 = 0.44$, $\bar{p}_2 = 0.40$; $z = 1.65$

$$s_{\bar{p}_1 - \bar{p}_2} = \sqrt{\frac{(0.44)(0.56)}{50} + \frac{(0.4)(0.6)}{40}} = 0.10 \quad (0.44 - 0.40) \pm 1.65(0.10) \quad \text{or} \quad -0.13 \text{ to } 0.21$$

12. $n = 64$; $\bar{X} = 4$; $\sigma = 3$; $z = 2.33$

$$\sigma_{\bar{x}} = \frac{3}{\sqrt{64}} = .375 \quad 4 \pm 2.33(.375) \quad \text{or} \quad 3.13 \text{ to } 4.87$$

13. $n = 300$; $x = 140$; $\bar{p} = 140/300 = 0.467$; $z = 1.96$

$$s_{\bar{p}} = \sqrt{\frac{(0.467)(0.533)}{300}} = 0.0288 \quad 0.467 \pm 1.96(0.0288) \quad \text{or} \quad 0.411 \text{ to } 0.523$$

CHAPTER 7

Answers to Problems

1. The Type I error would be to return a good shipment. The Type II error would be to keep a bad shipment.

2. $n = 64$; $\bar{X} = 53$; $s = 8$; $\alpha = 0.02$; $s_{\bar{x}} = 8/\sqrt{64} = 1$

    $H_0: \mu \le 50$ $H_1: \mu > 50$ Critical value $= 50 + 2.05(1) = 52.05$ or $z = 2.05$

    Decision rule: Reject H_0 if $\bar{X} > 52.05$ or $z > 2.05$.

    $z = \dfrac{53 - 50}{1} = 3$ Since $\bar{X} = 53(z = 3)$, reject H_0. The statistical evidence supports the hypothesis that the average production of the workers is greater than 50 at $\alpha = .02$.

3. $\alpha = 0.0668$; $z = 1.5$; $n = 64$; $s_{\bar{x}} = 2$; $X_c = 97$

μ_T	β
98	0.6915
96	0.3085
95	0.1587
94	0.0668
92	0.0062

4. $\alpha = 0.0228$; $z = 2$; $n = 256$; $s_{\bar{x}} = 1$; $\bar{X}_c = 98$

μ_T	β
98	0.5000
96	0.0228
95	0.00135
94	0.00003
92	0+

5.

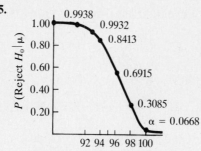

0.9938
0.9932
0.8413
0.6915
0.3085
$\alpha = 0.0668$

92 94 96 98 100

Values of the population parameter μ

H_0 is false | H_0 is true

6. $n = 500$ $x = 180$ $\bar{p} = \dfrac{180}{500} = 0.36$ $\alpha = 0.05$

$\sigma_{\bar{p}} = \sqrt{\dfrac{(0.4)(0.6)}{500}} = 0.02$

$H_0: p \geq 0.40$ $H_1: p < 0.40$ Critical value: $z = 1.65$

Decision rule: Reject H_0 if $z < -1.65$.

$z = \dfrac{0.36 - 0.40}{0.02} = -2$ Since $z = -2$, reject H_0. The statistical evidence does not support the hypothesis that at least 40 percent of the population likes the firm's product at $\alpha = 0.05$.

7. $n_1 = 40$, $n_2 = 40$; $\bar{X}_1 = 100$, $\bar{X}_2 = 90$; $s_1 = 20$, $s_2 = 8$; $\alpha = 0.05$

$s_{\bar{x}_1 - \bar{x}_2} = \sqrt{\dfrac{20^2}{40} + \dfrac{8^2}{40}} = 3.41$

$H_0: \mu_1 = \mu_2$ $H_1: \mu_1 \neq \mu_2$ Critical value: $z = 1.96$

Decision rule: Reject H_0 if $z < -1.96$ or $z > 1.96$.

$z = \dfrac{100 - 90}{3.41} = 2.93$ Since $z = 2.93$, reject H_0. The statistical evidence supports the hypothesis that there is a significant difference in the average output of the two shifts at $\alpha = 0.05$.

8. $n_1 = 200$, $n_2 = 200$; $x_1 = 120$, $x_2 = 100$; $\bar{p}_1 = 0.6$, $\bar{p}_2 = 0.5$; $\alpha = 0.05$

$\bar{p} = \dfrac{200(0.6) + 200(0.5)}{200 + 200} = 0.55$

$s_{\bar{p}_1 - \bar{p}_2} = \sqrt{(0.55)(0.45)\left(\dfrac{1}{200} + \dfrac{1}{200}\right)} = 0.05$

$H_0: p_1 = p_2$ $H_1: p_1 \neq p_2$ Critical value: $z = 1.96$

Decision rule: Reject H_0 if $z < -1.96$ or $z > 1.96$.

$z = \dfrac{0.6 - 0.5}{0.05} = 2$ Since $z = 2$, reject H_0. The statistical evidence supports the hypothesis that there is a difference in the candidate's appeal between genders at $\alpha = 0.02$.

9. $n = 25$; $\bar{X} = 22$; $s = 2$; $\alpha = 0.05$; $s_{\bar{x}} = \dfrac{2}{\sqrt{25}} = 0.4$

$H_0: \mu \leq 20$ $H_1: \mu > 20$ Critical value: $t = 1.711$

Decision rule: Reject H_0 if $t > 1.711$

$t = \dfrac{22 - 20}{0.4} = 5.$ Since $t = 5$, reject H_0. The statistical evidence supports the hypothesis that there is more than 20 peanuts on average in a bag at $\alpha = 0.05$.

10. $n_1 = 15$, $n_2 = 15$; $\bar{X}_1 = 100$, $\bar{X}_2 = 98$; $s_1 = 5$, $s_2 = 4$; $\alpha = 0.01$

$$\hat{s}^2 = \frac{(14)(25) + (14)(16)}{15 + 15 - 2} = 20.5 \quad \hat{s} = 4.53 \quad 4.53\sqrt{\frac{1}{15} + \frac{1}{15}} = 1.65$$

$H_0: \mu_1 \leq \mu_2$ $\quad H_1: \mu_1 > \mu_2$ $\quad$ Critical value: $t = 2.467$

Decision rule: Reject H_0 if $t > 2.467$.

$$t = \frac{100 - 98}{1.65} = 1.21 \qquad \text{Since } t = 1.21, \text{ accept } H_0.$$ The statistical evidence does not support the hypothesis that the cereal company on average puts more raisins in its cereal than its top competitor at $\alpha = 0.01$.

11. $n = 8$; $\quad \alpha = 0.025$

After (1)	100	98	95	102	115	101	88	91
Before (2)	92	96	94	100	113	98	85	88
d_{1-2}	8	2	1	2	2	3	3	3
$(d - \bar{d})$	5	-1	-2	-1	-1	0	0	0
$(d - \bar{d})^2$	25	1	4	1	1	0	0	0

$\Sigma d = 24$ $\quad \Sigma(d - \bar{d})^2 = 32$ $\quad \bar{d} = 24/8 = 3$ $\quad s_d = \sqrt{32}/7 = 2.14$ $\quad s_{\bar{d}} = 2.14/\sqrt{8} = 0.76$

$H_0: \mu_1 \leq \mu_2$ $\quad H_1: \mu_1 > \mu_2$ $\quad$ Critical value: $t = 2.365$

Decision rule: Reject H_0 if $t > 2.365$.

$$t = \frac{3 - 0}{0.76} = 3.95 \qquad \text{Since } t = 3.95, \text{ reject } H_0.$$ The statistical evidence supports the hypothesis that the training school increased productivity at $\alpha = 0.025$.

Answers to Review Problems

1. Let $1 = $ baseball and $2 = $ basketball.

$n_1 = 50$, $\quad n_2 = 30$; $\quad \bar{X}_1 = 300{,}000$, $\quad \bar{X}_2 = 270{,}000$; $\quad s_1^2 = 10{,}000{,}000$, $\quad s_2^2 = 5{,}000{,}000$; $\quad \alpha = 0.02$

$$s_{\bar{x}_1 - \bar{x}_2} = \sqrt{\frac{10{,}000{,}000}{50} + \frac{5{,}000{,}000}{30}} = 605.53$$

$H_0: \mu_1 \leq \mu_2$ $\quad H_1: \mu_1 > \mu_2$ $\quad$ Critical value: $z = 2.05$

Decision rule: Reject H_0 if $z > 2.05$.

$$z = \frac{300{,}000 - 270{,}000}{605.53} = 49.54 \qquad \text{Since } z = 49.54, \text{ reject } H_0.$$ The statistical evidence supports the hypothesis that the average earnings of baseball players are greater than the average earnings of basketball players at $\alpha = 0.02$.

2. $n = 25$; $\quad \bar{X} = 1.2$; $\quad s = 0.8$; $\quad \alpha = 0.05$; $\quad s_{\bar{x}} = 0.8/\sqrt{25} = 0.16$

$H_0: \mu = 1$ $\quad H_1: \mu \neq 1$ $\quad$ Critical value: $t = 2.064$

Decision rule: Reject H_0 if $t < -2.064$ or $t > 2.064$.

$$t = \frac{1.2 - 1}{0.16} = 1.25 \qquad \text{Since } t = 1.25, \text{ accept } H_0.$$ The statistical evidence supports the hypothesis that the watches do keep time on average within 1 minute per year at $\alpha = 0.05$.

3. $n = 100$; $\bar{X} = 1{,}980$; $s = 150$; $\alpha = 0.025$; $s_{\bar{x}} = 150/\sqrt{100} = 15$
$H_0: \mu \geq 2000$ $H_1: \mu < 2000$ Critical value: $z = 1.96$

Decision rule: Reject H_0 if $z < -1.96$.

$z = \dfrac{1{,}980 - 2{,}000}{15} = -1.33$ Since $z = -1.33$, accept H_0. The statistical evidence supports the hypothesis that the machine produces on average at least 2,000 an hour at $\alpha = 0.025$.

4. $n = 250$; $x = 150$; $\bar{p} = 150/250 = 0.6$; $\alpha = 0.05$; $\sigma_{\bar{p}} = \sqrt{\dfrac{(0.5)(0.5)}{250}} = 0.031$
$H_0: p \leq 0.50$ $H_1: p > 0.50$ Critical value: $z = 1.65$

Decision rule: Reject H_0 if $z > 1.65$.

$z = \dfrac{0.6 - 0.5}{0.031} = 3.23$ Since $z = 3.23$, reject H_0. The statistical evidence supports the hypothesis that a majority of the senator's constituents favor the bill at $\alpha = 0.05$.

5. $\alpha = 0.0228$; $z = 2$; $n = 100$; $\sigma_{\bar{x}} = 5$; $\bar{X}_c^{\,c} = 510$

μ_T	β
505	0.8413
510	0.5000
515	0.1587
520	0.0228
525	0.00135

6. $n_1 = 200$, $n_2 = 150$; $x_1 = 60$, $x_2 = 40$; $\bar{p}_1 = 60/200 = 0.3$, $\bar{p}_2 = 40/150 = 0.267$; $\alpha = 0.05$
$\hat{p} = \dfrac{200(0.3) + 150(0.267)}{200 + 150} = 0.286$

$s_{\bar{p}_1 - \bar{p}_2} = \sqrt{(0.286)(0.714)\left(\dfrac{1}{200} + \dfrac{1}{150}\right)} = 0.049$
$H_0: p_1 = p_2$ $H_1: p_1 \neq p_2$ Critical value: $z = 1.96$

Decision rule: Reject H_0 if $z < -1.96$ or $z > 1.96$.

$z = \dfrac{0.3 - 0.267}{0.049} = 0.67$ Since $z = 0.67$, accept H_0. The statistical evidence supports the hypothesis that there is a difference between the proportion of men and women who smoke at $\alpha = 0.05$.

7. $n = 64$; $\bar{X} = 147{,}000$; $\sigma = 8{,}000$; $\alpha = 0.02$; $\sigma_{\bar{x}} = \dfrac{8{,}000}{\sqrt{64}} = 1{,}000$

$H_0: \mu \geq 150{,}000$ $H_1: \mu < 150{,}000$ Critical value: $z = 2.05$

Decision rule: Reject H_0 if $z < -2.05$.

$z = \dfrac{147{,}000 - 150{,}000}{1{,}000} = -3$ Since $z = -3$, reject H_0. The statistical evidence supports the hypothesis that houses in the community sell on average for less than \$150,000 at $\alpha = 0.02$.

8. $n = 10$; $\alpha = 0.05$

New (1)	30	41	42	18	29	28	37	26	29	33
Old (2)	28	37	42	17	23	29	31	22	23	31
d_{1-2}	2	4	0	1	6	-1	6	4	6	2
$d - \bar{d}$	-1	1	-3	-2	3	-4	3	1	3	-1
$(d - \bar{d})^2$	1	1	9	4	9	16	9	1	9	1

$\Sigma d = 30$; $\bar{d} = 30/10 = 3$; $(d - \bar{d})^2 = 60$; $s_d = 60/9 = 2.58$; $s_{\bar{d}} = \dfrac{2.58}{\sqrt{10}} = 0.816$

$H_0: \mu_1 \leq \mu_2$ $\quad H_1: \mu_1 > \mu_2$ $\quad$ Critical value: $t = 1.833$

Decision rule: Reject H_0 if $t > 1.833$.

$t = \dfrac{3}{0.816} = 3.68$ $\quad$ Since $t = 3.68$, reject H_0. The statistical evidence supports the hypothesis that the new brand is better than the old at $\alpha = 0.05$.

9. $n = 60$; $x = 56$; $\bar{p} = 56/60 = 0.933$; $\alpha = 0.05$ $\quad \sigma_{\bar{p}} = \sqrt{\dfrac{(0.9)(0.1)}{60}} = 0.039$

$H_0: p \leq 0.90$ $\quad H_1: p > 0.90$ $\quad$ Critical value: $z = 1.65$

Decision rule: Reject H_0 if $z > 1.65$.

$z = \dfrac{0.933 - 0.90}{0.039} = 0.85$ $\quad$ Since $z = 0.85$, accept H_0. The statistical evidence does not support the hypothesis that more than 90% of the policemen live in the city at $\alpha = 0.05$.

10. $n_1 = 60$, $n_2 = 40$; $x_1 = 56$, $x_2 = 32$; $\bar{p}_1 = 56/60 = 0.933$, $\bar{p}_2 = 32/40 = 0.8$; $\alpha = 0.05$

$\hat{p} = \dfrac{60(0.933) + 40(0.8)}{60 + 40} = 0.89$

$s_{\bar{p}_1 - \bar{p}_2} = \sqrt{(0.89)(0.11)\left(\dfrac{1}{60} + \dfrac{1}{40}\right)} = 0.064$

$H_0: p_1 \leq p_2$ $\quad H_1: p_1 > p_2$ $\quad$ Critical value: $z = 1.65$

Decision rule: Reject H_0 if $z = 1.65$.

$z = \dfrac{0.933 - 0.8}{0.064} = 2.08$ $\quad$ Since $z = 2.08$, reject H_0. The statistical evidence supports the police commissioner's hypothesis that a greater proportion of policemen than firemen live in the city at $\alpha = 0.05$.

11. $n = 64$; $\bar{X} = 30$; $s = 12$; $\alpha = 10$; $s_{\bar{x}} = 12/\sqrt{64} = 1.5$

$H_0: \mu \leq 20$ $\quad H_1: \mu > 20$ $\quad$ Critical value: $z = 1.65$

Decision rule: Reject H_0 if $z > 1.65$.

$z = \dfrac{30 - 20}{1.5} = 6.67$ $\quad$ Since $z = 6.67$, reject H_0. The statistical evidence supports the hypothesis that the new model gets more than 50 miles per gallon at $\alpha = 0.10$.

12. $n = 25$; $\bar{X} = 18.2$; $s = 5$; $\alpha = 0.10$; $s_{\bar{x}} = 5/\sqrt{25} = 1$

$H_0: \mu = 20$ $\quad H_1: \mu \neq 20$ $\quad$ Critical value: $t = 1.711$

Decision rule: Reject H_0 if $t < -1.711$ or $t > 1.711$.

$t = \dfrac{18.2 - 20}{1} = -1.8$ $\quad$ Since $t = -1.8$, reject H_0. The statistical evidence does not support the hypothesis that the average employee has 20 years' experience at $\alpha = 0.10$.

13. $n = 25$; $\bar{X} = 18.2$; $s = 5$; $\alpha = 0.02$; $s_{\bar{x}} = 1$

$H_0 : \mu = 20$ $H_1 : \mu \neq 20$ Critical value: $t = 2.492$

Decision rule: Reject H_0 if $t < -2.492$ or $t > 2.492$

$t = \dfrac{18.2 - 20}{1} = -1.8$ Since $t = -1.8$, accept H_0. The statistical evidence supports the hypothesis that the average employee has 20 years' experience at $\alpha = 0.02$.

14. $n_1 = 25$, $n_2 = 25$; $\bar{X}_1 = 20{,}000$, $\bar{X}_2 = 25{,}000$; $s_1 = 1{,}000$, $s_2 = 2{,}000$; $\alpha = 0.05$

$s_{\bar{x}_1 - \bar{x}_2} = \sqrt{\dfrac{1{,}000^2}{25} + \dfrac{2{,}000^2}{25}} = 447.2$

$H_0 : \mu_1 = \mu_2$ $H_1 : \mu_1 \neq \mu_2$ Critical value: $z = 1.96$

Decision rule: Reject H_0 if $z < -1.96$ or $z > 1.96$.

$z = \dfrac{20{,}000 - 25{,}000}{447.2} = -11.2$ Since $z = -11.2$, reject H_0. The statistical evidence supports the hypothesis that the average sales are different at the two stores at $\alpha = 0.05$.

15. $n_1 = 12$, $n_2 = 15$; $\bar{X}_1 = 100$, $\bar{X}_2 = 90$; $s_1 = 10$, $s_2 = 8$; $\alpha = 0.05$

$\hat{s} = \sqrt{\dfrac{11(10)^2 + 14(8)^2}{12 + 15 - 2}} = 8.94$; $s_{\bar{x}_1 - \bar{x}_2} = 8.94 \sqrt{\dfrac{1}{12} + \dfrac{1}{15}} = 3.46$

$H_0 : \mu_1 = \mu_2$ $H_1 : \mu_1 \neq \mu_2$ Critical value: $t = 2.060$

Decision rule: Reject H_0 if $t < -2.060$ or $t > 2.060$

$t = \dfrac{100 - 90}{3.46} = 2.89$ Since $t = 2.89$, reject H_0. The statistical evidence supports the hypothesis that the average life of the lightbulbs is not the same at $\alpha = 0.05$.

CHAPTER 8

Answers to Problems

1. a. $\chi^2(18, 0.01) = 34.805$
   b. $\chi^2(28, 0.02) = 45.419$
   c. $\chi^2(14, 0.10) = 21.064$

2.

Brand	f_o	f_t	$f_o - f_t$	$(f_o - f_t)^2$	$\dfrac{(f_o - f_t)^2}{f_t}$
A	30	40	-10	100	2.5
B	10	40	-30	900	22.5
C	50	40	10	100	2.5
D	70	40	30	900	22.5
E	40	40	0	0	0
Total	200	200	0		50

$H_0 : p_1 = p_2 = p_3 = p_4 = p_5$ (uniform distribution)
H_1 : The proportions are not equal (not a uniform distribution).
Critical value: $\chi^2(4, 0.01) = 13.277$

Decision rule: Reject H_0 if $\chi^2 > 13.277$.

$\chi^2 = \sum \dfrac{(f_o - f_t)^2}{f_t} = 50$ χ^2 is 50; reject H_0. The statistical evidence supports the hypothesis that there is a difference in consumers' preference among coffee brands at $\alpha = 0.01$.

3. $n = 5$; $P(S) = p = 0.25$

x	f_o	f_t	$f_o - f_t$	$(f_o - f_t)^2$	$\dfrac{(f_o - f_t)^2}{f_t}$
0	10	24	-14	196	8.17
1	20	40	-20	400	10.00
2	40	26	14	196	7.54
3, 4 or 5	30	10	20	400	40.00
	100	100	0		65.71

$k = 4$; $m = 0$
H_0: We have a binomial distribution with $p = 0.25$.
H_1: We do not have a binomial distribution with $p = 0.25$.
Critical value: $\chi^2(k - 1 - m, \alpha) = \chi^2(3, 0.02) = 9.837$

Decision rule: Reject H_0 if $\chi^2 > 9.837$

$\chi^2 = \sum \dfrac{(f_o - f_t)^2}{f_t} = 65.71$ $\chi^2 = 65.71$; reject H_0. The statistical evidence does not support the hypothesis that sales is a binomial distribution with $p = 0.25$ at $\alpha = 0.02$.

4.

f_o	f_t	$f_o - f_t$	$(f_o - f_t)^2$	$\dfrac{(f_o - f_t)^2}{f_t}$
15	15	0	0	0
20	20	0	0	0
15	15	0	0	0
10	9	1	1	0.11
10	12	-2	4	0.33
10	9	1	1	0.11
5	6	-1	1	0.17
10	8	2	4	0.50
5	6	-1	1	0.17
100	100	0		1.39

H_0: The variables are independent.
H_1: The variables are not independent.
Critical value: $\chi^2(4, 0.02) = 11.668$

Decision rule: Reject H_0 if $\chi^2 > 11.668$.

$\chi^2 = \sum \dfrac{(f_o - f_t)^2}{f_t} = 1.39$ $\chi^2 = 1.39$; accept H_0. The statistical evidence supports the hypothesis that the variables are independent at $\alpha = 0.02$.

5. a. $F_{0.01}(5, 22) = 3.99$
   b. $F_{0.05}(7, 26) = 2.39$
6. ANOVA Table

Source of Variation	Sum of Square	Degrees of Freedom	Mean Square
Testing Method	18.53	2	9.27
Error	226.40	12	18.87
Total	244.93	14	

$$F = 9.27/18.87 = 0.49$$

$H_0: \mu_1 = \mu_2 = \mu_3$. The average grades of the students are equal regardless of testing method.
H_1: The means are not equal. The average grades of the students are not equal.
Critical value: $F_{0.01}(2, 12) = 6.93$

Decision rule: Reject H_0 if $F > 6.93$.

$F = 9.27/18.87 = 0.49$ $F = 0.49$; accept H_0. The statistical evidence supports the hypothesis that the average grades of the students are equal regardless of testing methods at $\alpha = 0.01$.

7. ANOVA Table

Source of Variation	Sum of Squares	Degrees of Freedom	Mean Square
Testing Method	18.53	2	9.27
Textbook	68.93	4	17.23
Error	157.47	8	19.68
Total	244.93		

$H_0: \mu_1 = \mu_2 = \mu_3$. The average grades of the students are equal regardless of testing method.
H_1: The means are not equal. The average grades of the students are not equal.
Critical value: $F_{0.01}(2, 8) = 8.65$

Decision rule: Reject H_0, if $F > 8.65$

$F = 9.27/19.68 = 0.47$ $F = 0.47$; accept H_0. The statistical evidence supports the hypothesis that the average grades of the students are equal regardless of testing methods at $\alpha = 0.01$.

$H_0: \mu_1 = \mu_2 = \mu_3 = \mu_4 = \mu_5$. The average grades of the students are equal regardless of the textbook used.
H_1: The means are not equal. The average grades of the students are not equal.
Critical value: $F_{0.01}(4, 8) = 7.01$

Decision rule: Reject H_0 if $F > 7.01$.

$F = 17.23/19.68 = 0.88$ $F = 0.88$; accept H_0. The statistical evidence supports the hypothesis that the average grades of the students are equal regardless of the textbook used at $\alpha = 0.01$.

Answers to Review Problems

1.

f_o	f_t	$f_o - f_t$	$(f_o - f_t)^2$	$\dfrac{(f_o - f_t)^2}{f_t}$
60	55	5	25	0.45
50	55	−5	25	0.45
40	45	−5	25	0.56
50	45	5	25	0.56
200	200	0		2.02

$r = 2; c = 2$
H_0: The variables are independent.
H_1: The variables are not independent.
Critical value: $\chi^2(1, 0.05) = 3.841$

Decision rule: Reject H_0 if $\chi^2 > 3.841$.

$\chi^2 = \sum \dfrac{(f_o - f_t)^2}{f_t} = 2.02 \qquad \chi^2 = 2.02$; accept H_0. The statistical evidence supports the hypothesis that a person's opinion and geographic area are independent at $\alpha = 0.05$.

2. ANOVA Table

Source of Variation	Sum of Squares	Degrees of Freedom	Mean Square
Shifts	280	2	140
Error	958	12	79.83
Total	1238		

$$F = 140/79.83 = 1.75$$

H_0: $\mu_1 = \mu_2 = \mu_3$. The average production is the same regardless of shift.
H_1: The means are not equal. The average production is not the same.
Critical value: $F_{0.01}(2, 12) = 6.93$

Decision rule: Reject H_0 if $F > 6.93$.

$F = 140/79.83 = 1.75$ $F = 1.75$, accept H_0. The statistical evidence supports the hypothesis that the average production is the same regardless of shift at $\alpha = 0.01$.

3.

f_o	f_t	$f_o - f_t$	$(f_o - f_t)^2$	$\dfrac{(f_o - f_t)^2}{f_t}$
60	60	0	0	0
40	60	−20	400	6.67
100	60	40	1600	26.67
50	60	−10	100	1.67
50	60	−10	100	1.67
300	300	0		36.68

$k = 5, m = 0$
H_0: $p_1 = p_2 = p_3 = p_4 = p_5$ (uniform distribution)

H_1: The proportions are not equal (not a uniform distribution).
Critical value: $\chi^2(k - 1 - m, \alpha) = \chi^2(4, 0.02) = 11.668$

Decision rule: Reject H_0, if $\chi^2 > 11.668$.

$\chi^2 = \sum \frac{(f_o - f_t)^2}{f_t} = 36.68$ $\chi^2 = 36.68$; reject H_0. The statistical evidence supports the hypothesis that there is a difference in consumer preference between brands of soap at $\alpha = 0.02$.

4. $n = 2$ $P(S) = p = 0.50$ Binomial $k = 3$ $m = 0$

x	f_o	f_t	$f_o - f_t$	$(f_o - f_t)^2$	$\dfrac{(f_o - f_t)^2}{f_t}$
0	10	25	-15	225	9
1	40	50	-10	100	2
2	50	25	25	625	25
	100	100	0		36

H_0: We have a binomial distribution with $p = 0.5$.
H_1: We do not have a binomial distribution with $p = 0.5$.
Critical value: $\chi^2(k - 1 - m, \alpha) = \chi^2(2, 0.05) = 5.991$

$\chi^2 = \sum \frac{(f_o - f_t)^2}{f_t} = 36$ $\chi^2 = 36$; reject H_0. The statistical evidence does not support the hypothesis that we have a binomial distribution with $p = 0.5$ at $\alpha = 0.05$.

5.

x	f_o	$x \cdot f_o$	f_t	$f_o - f_t$	$(f_o - f_t)^2$	$\dfrac{(f_o - f_t)^2}{f_t}$
0	3	0	5	-2	4	0.8
1	7	7	15	-8	64	4.27
2	12	24	22	-10	100	4.55
3	57	171	22	35	1225	55.68
4	10	40	17	-7	49	2.88
5	8	40	10	-2	4	0.4
6 or more	3	18	8	-5	25	3.13
	100	300	99*	-1		71.71

$$\bar{X} = 300/100 = 3 \text{ Poisson with } \mu = 3$$

* $\Sigma f_t = 99$ and not 100 because of rounding error. $f_o - f_t = -1$ because of rounding error.

$k = 7, m = 1$
H_0: We have a Poisson distribution with $\mu = 3$.
H_1: We do not have a Poisson distribution with $\mu = 3$.
Critical value: $\chi^2(k - 1 - m, \alpha) = \chi^2(5, 0.01) = 15.086$

Decision rule: Reject H_0 if $\chi^2 > 15.086$.

$\chi^2 = \sum \frac{(f_o - f_t)^2}{f_t} = 71.7$ $\chi^2 = 71.7$, reject H_0. The statistical evidence does not support the hypothesis that we have a Poisson distribution with $\mu = 3$ at $\alpha = 0.01$.

6. ANOVA Table

Sources of Variation	Sum of Squares	Degrees of Freedom	Mean Square
Diet	37.2	2	18.6
Error	647.7	9	72
Total	684.9		

$$F = 18.6/72 = 0.26$$

$H_0: \mu_1 = \mu_2 = \mu_3$. The average weight loss is equal regardless of diet.
H_1: The means are not equal. The average weight loss is not equal.
Critical value: $F_{0.05}(2, 9) = 4.26$

Decision rule: Reject H_0 if $F > 4.26$.

$F = 18.6/72 = 0.26$ $\qquad$ $F = 0.26$, accept H_0. The statistical evidence supports the hypothesis that the average weight loss is equal regardless of diet at $\alpha = 0.05$.

7.

f_o	f_t	$f_o - f_t$	$(f_o - f_t)^2$	$\dfrac{(f_o - f_t)^2}{f_t}$
20	20	0	0	0
17	20	-3	9	0.45
24	20	4	16	0.8
19	20	-1	1	0.05
25	20	5	25	1.25
17	20	-3	9	0.45
18	20	-2	4	0.2
20	20	0	0	0
160	160	0		3.2

$k = 8$ $\quad m = 0$
$H_0: p_1 = p_2 = p_3 = p_4 = p_5 = p_6 = p_7 = p_8$ (uniform distribution).
H_1: The proportions are not equal (not a uniform distribution).
Critical value: $\chi^2(k - 1 - m, \alpha) = \chi^2(7, 0.01) = 18.475$

Decision rule: Reject H_0 if $\chi^2 > 18.475$.

$\chi^2 = \sum \dfrac{(f_o - f_t)^2}{f_t} = 3.2$ $\qquad \chi^2 = 3.2$; accept H_0. The statistical evidence supports the hypothesis that the distribution is uniform and the game is fair at $\alpha = 0.01$.

8. ANOVA Table

Source of Variation	Sum of Squares	Degrees of Freedom	Mean Squares
Major	100.1	2	50.1
School	203.1	4	50.8
Error	24.5	8	3.1
Total	327.7		

$H_0: \mu_1 = \mu_2 = \mu_3$. The average starting salaries are equal regardless of major.
H_1: The means are not equal. The average starting salaries are not equal.
Critical value: $F_{0.01}(2, 8) = 8.65$

Decision rule: Reject H_0, if $F > 8.65$.

$F = 50.1/3.1 = 16.2$ $F = 16.2$; reject H_0. The statistical evidence does not support the hypothesis that the means are equal regardless of major at $\alpha = 0.01$.
$H_0: \mu_1 = \mu_2 = \mu_3 = \mu_4 = \mu_5$. The average starting salaries are equal regardless of school.
H_1: The means are not equal. The average starting salaries are not equal.
Critical value: $F_{0.01}(4, 8) = 7.01$.

Decision rule: Reject H_0 if $F > 7.01$.

$F = 50.8/3.1 = 16.4$ $F = 16.4$; reject H_0. The statistical evidence does not support the hypothesis that the means are equal regardless of school at $\alpha = 0.01$.

9.

f_o	f_t	$f_o - f_t$	$(f_o - f_t)^2$	$\dfrac{(f_o - f_t)^2}{f_t}$
250	200	50	2500	12.50
100	125	-25	625	5.00
100	70	30	900	12.86
50	105	-55	3025	28.81
150	200	-50	2500	12.50
150	125	25	625	5.00
40	70	-30	900	12.86
160	105	55	3025	28.81
1000	1000	0		118.34

$r = 4, c = 2$
H_0: The variables are independent.
H_1: The variables are not independent.
Critical value: $\chi^2(3, 0.02) = 9.837$.

Decision rule: Reject H_0 if $\chi^2 > 9.837$.

$\chi^2 = \sum \dfrac{(f_o - f_t)^2}{f_t} = 118.34$ $\chi^2 = 118.34$, reject H_0. The statistical evidence does not support the hypothesis that major field of study and gender are independent at $\alpha = 0.02$.

CHAPTER 9

Answers to Problems

1. a. $b = \dfrac{11541 - 10(30.3)(36.9)}{9413 - 10(30.3)^2} = 1.552$
$a = 36.9 - 1.552(30.3) = -10.13$
$\hat{Y} = -10.13 + 1.552X$
b. $\hat{Y} = -10.13 + 1.552(30)$
$\hat{Y} = 36.43 = \$36,430$

2. $s_{Y.x} = \sqrt{\dfrac{14{,}243 - (-10.13)(369) - 1.552(11{,}541)}{10 - 2}} = 2.94$

3. $s_Y = \sqrt{\dfrac{10(14{,}243) - (369)^2}{10(9)}} = 8.35$

4. $n = 10$ $\bar{Y} = 36.9$ $s_Y = 8.35$ $\alpha = 0.10$ $t = 1.833$ $s_{\bar{Y}} = 8.35/\sqrt{10} = 2.64$
   $36.9 \pm 1.833(2.64)$ or   32.1 to 41.7
5. $n = 10$ $\hat{Y} = 36.43$ $s_{Y.X} = 2.94$ $\alpha = 0.10$ $t = 1.860$ $s_{\hat{Y}} = 0.93$
   $36.43 \pm 1.86(0.93)$ or   34.70 to 38.16
6. $n = 10$ $\hat{Y} = 36.43$ $s_{Y.X} = 2.94$ $\alpha = 0.10$ $t = 1.860$ $s_{IND} = 3.32$
   $36.43 + 1.86(3.08)$ or   30.70 to 42.16
7. $r^2 = 1 - \dfrac{69.1488}{627.5025} = 0.89$ $n = 10$ $s_{Y.X} = 2.94$ $s_Y = 8.35$ $r = 0.94\ (r > 0,\ \text{because } b > 0)$
8. $a = -10.13$ $b = 1.552$ $\Sigma Y = 369$ $\Sigma XY = 11,541$ $\Sigma Y^2 = 14,243$
   $r^2 = \dfrac{(-10.13)(369) + 1.552(11,541) - 10(36.9)^2}{14,243 - 10(36.9)^2} = 0.89$
9. $n = 10$ $r = 0.94$ $\alpha = 0.10$ $t = 1.860$ $s_r = 0.117$
   $H_0: \rho = 0$ $H_1: \rho \neq 0$ Critical value: $t = 1.860$

Decision rule: Reject H_0 if $t < -1.860$ or $t > 1.860$.

   $t = (0.94 - 0)/0.117 = 8.03$ $t = 8.03$; reject H_0. The statistical evidence supports the hypothesis that age and income are related at $\alpha = 0.10$.
10. $n = 10$ $b = 1.552$ $\alpha = 0.10$ $t = 1.860$ $s_{Y.X} = 2.94$ $s_b = 0.19$
   $H_0: B = 2$ $H_1: B \neq 2$ Critical value: $t = 1.860$

Decision rule: Reject H_0 if $t < -1.860$ or $t > 1.860$.

   $t = (1.552 - 2)/0.19 = -2.36$ $t = -2.36$; reject H_0. The statistical evidence supports the hypothesis that $B \neq 2$ at $\alpha = 0.10$.
11. $n = 10$ $b = 1.552$ $\alpha = 0.10$ $t = 1.860$ $s_{Y.X} = 2.94$ $s_b = 0.19$
   $H_0: B = 0$ $H_1: B \neq 0$ Critical value: $t = 1.860$

Decision rule: Reject H_0 if $t < -1.860$ or $t > 1.860$.

   $t = (1.552 - 0)/0.19 = 8.17$ $t = 8.17$; reject H_0. The statistical evidence supports the hypothesis that there is a statistical relationship between age and income at $\alpha = 0.10$.

Answers to Review Problems

1. $r = -0.5$, because $b < 0$.
2. a. $b = \dfrac{200 - 10(5)(3)}{350 - 10(5)^2} = 0.5$ $a = 3 - (0.5)(5) = 0.5$ $\hat{Y} = 0.5 + 0.5X$

   b. $s_{Y.X} = \sqrt{\dfrac{420 - (0.5)(30) - (0.5)(200)}{10 - 2}} = 6.17$
   c. $n = 20$ $b = 0.5$ $s_b = 2$ $\alpha = 0.05$ $t = 2.306$
   $H_0: B = 0$ $H_1: B \neq 0$ Critical value: $t = 2.306$

   Decision rule: Reject H_0 if $t < -2.306$ or $t > 2.306$.

   $t = (0.5 - 0/2) = 0.25$ $t = 0.25$; accept H_0. The statistical evidence supports the hypothesis that X and Y are not related at $\alpha = 0.05$.
   d. Given that we do not have a valid regression equation, $\hat{Y}$ cannot be estimated for values of X.
3. a. $n = 20$ $b = -0.2$ $s_b = 0.05$ $\alpha = 0.05$ $t = 2.101$
   $H_0: B = 0$ $H_1: B \neq 0$ Critical value: $t = 2.101$

   Decision rule: Reject H_0 if $t < -2.101$ or $t > 2.101$.

   $t = (-0.2 - 0)/0.05 = -4$ $t = -4$, reject H_0. The statistical evidence supports the hypothesis that weight of a car and miles per gallon are related at $\alpha = 0.05$.
   b. 64% of the variation in miles per gallon can be explained by the variation in the weights of the cars.
   c. $r = -0.8$, because $b < 0$.

4. $n = 10$ $\Sigma X = 1,620$ $\Sigma Y = 2,860$ $\Sigma XY = 489,200$ $\Sigma X^2 = 282,800$ $\Sigma Y^2 = 860,600$

a. $b = \dfrac{489,200 - 10(162)(286)}{282,800 - 10(162)^2} = 1.271$ $a = 286 - 1.271(162) = 80.1$

$\hat{Y} = 80.1 + 1.271X$

b. $s_{Y \cdot X} = \sqrt{\dfrac{860,600 - 80.1(2,860) - 1.271(489,200)}{10 - 2}} = 34.89$

c. $s_Y^2 = \dfrac{10(860,600) - (2860)^2}{10(9)} = 4737.78$ $s_Y = 68.83$ $r^2 = 1 - \dfrac{8(34.89)^2}{9(68.83)^2} = 1 - 0.228 = 0.772$

5. $n = 10$ $\Sigma X^2 = 282,800$ $\Sigma X = 1,620$ $s_{Y \cdot X} = 34.89$ $b = 1.271$ $\alpha = 0.02$

$s_b = \dfrac{34.89}{\sqrt{\dfrac{10(282,800) - (1,620)^2}{10}}} = 0.245$

$H_0: B = 0$ $H_1: B \neq 0$ Critical value: $t = 2.896$

Decision rule: Reject H_0 if $t < -2.896$ or $t > 2.896$.

$t = (1.271 - 0)/0.245 = 5.19$ $t = 5.19$; reject H_0. The statistical evidence supports the hypothesis that advertising and sales are related at $\alpha = 0.02$.

6. a. $\hat{Y} = 80.1 + 1.271(150) = 270.75$

b. $270.75 \pm 2.896(11.42)$ or 237.68 to 303.82

$s_Y = 34.89 \sqrt{\dfrac{1}{10} + \dfrac{(150 - 162)^2}{282,800 - [(1620)^2/10]}} = 11.42$

c. $270.75 \pm 2.896(36.71)$ or 164.44 to 377.06

$s_{IND} = 34.89 \sqrt{1 + \dfrac{1}{10} + \dfrac{(150 - 162)^2}{282,800 - [(1620)^2/10]}} = 36.71$

7. $n = 42$ $b = 9.8$ $s_b = 2$ $\alpha = 0.01$

$H_0: B = 10$ $H_1: B \neq 10$ Critical value: $t = 2.704$

Decision rule: Reject H_0 if $t < -2.704$ or $t > 2.704$

$t = (9.8 - 10)/2 = -0.2/2 = -0.10$ $t = -0.10$; accept H_0. The statistical evidence supports the hypothesis that $B = 10$ at $\alpha = 0.01$.

8. $n = 10$ $\Sigma X = 56$ $\Sigma Y = 177$ $\Sigma XY = 779$ $\Sigma X^2 = 406$ $\Sigma Y^2 = 3,639$

a. $b = \dfrac{779 - 10(5.6)(17.7)}{406 - 10(5.6)^2} = -2.3$ $a = 17.7 - (-2.3)(5.6) = 30.58$ $\hat{Y} = 30.58 - 2.3X$

b. $s_{Y \cdot X} = \sqrt{\dfrac{3,639 - 30.58(177) - (-2.3)(779)}{10 - 2}} = 1.50$

c. $s_Y = \sqrt{\dfrac{10(3639) - (177)^2}{10(9)}} = 7.5$

$r^2 = 1 - \dfrac{8(2.25)}{9(56.25)} = 0.964$ $r = -0.982$

d. $t = 2.306$ $\alpha = 0.05$ $b = -2.3$

$s_b = \dfrac{1.5}{\sqrt{\dfrac{10(406) - (56)^2}{10}}} = 0.156$

$H_0: B = 0$ $H_1: B \neq 0$ Critical value: $t = 2.306$

Decision rule: Reject H_0, if $t < -2.306$ or $t > 2.306$

$t = (-2.3 - 0)/0.156 = -14.74$ $t = -14.74$; reject H_0. The statistical evidence supports the hypothesis that number of mistakes and years on the job are related at $\alpha = 0.05$.

9. $\bar{Y} = 17.7$ $t = 2.262$ $s_Y = 7.5$ $n = 10$ $s_{\bar{Y}} = 7.5/\sqrt{10} = 2.37$

$17.7 \pm 2.262(2.37)$ or 12.34 to 23.06

10. a. The relevant range for X is between 30 and 50. Thus, the $a = -10$ value is appropriate for the given range. Commissions over this range will not be negative.

b. $n = 122$ $\alpha = 0.05$ $t = 1.98$ $b = 1$ $s_b = 0.2$

$H_0: B = 0$ $H_1: B \neq 0$ Critical value: $t = 1.98$

Decision rule: Reject H_0 if $t < -1.98$ or $t > 1.98$.

$t = (1 - 0/0.2) = 5$ $t = 5$; reject H_0. The statistical evidence supports the hypothesis that age and commission are related at $\alpha = 0.05$.

c. $\hat{Y} = -10 + X = -10 + 45 = 35$ \$35,000

11. $\Sigma X = 99$ $\Sigma Y = 320$ $\Sigma XY = 3,225$ $\Sigma X^2 = 1,009$ $\Sigma Y^2 = 11,300$

a. $b = \dfrac{3,225 - 10(9.9)(32)}{1,009 - 10(9.9)^2} = 1.97$ $a = 32 - 1.97(9.9) = 12.5$ $\hat{Y} = 12.5 + 1.97X$

b. $s_{Y \cdot X} = \sqrt{\dfrac{11,300 - 12.5(320) - 1.97(3,225)}{10 - 2}} = 10.88$

c. $s_Y = \sqrt{\dfrac{10(11,300) - (320)^2}{10(9)}} = 10.85$

$r^2 = 1 - \dfrac{8(10.88)^2}{9(10.85)^2} = 1 - 0.894 = 0.106$

d. $n = 10$ $\alpha = 0.02$ $t = 2.896$ $s_b = \dfrac{10.88}{\sqrt{\dfrac{10(1,009) - (99)^2}{10}}} = 2.02$

$H_0: B = 0$ $H_1: B \neq 0$ Critical value: $t = 2.896$

Decision rule: Reject H_0 if $t < -2.896$ or $t > 2.896$.

$t = 1.97/2.02 = 0.98$ $t = 0.98$; accept H_0. The statistical evidence does not support the hypothesis that salary and shoe size are related at $\alpha = 0.02$.

CHAPTER 10

Answers to Problems

1. a. $\hat{Y} = -2,000 + 0.12(30,000) + 210(8) + 50(40) = \$5,280$
   b. $b_2 = 210$ $\Delta X_2 = 1$ $\Delta Y = b_2 \Delta X_2 = 210(1) = \$210$
   c. b_2 measures the change in savings ($\hat{Y}$) per unit change in the interest rate (X_2) holding X_1 and X_3 constant. Given $b_2 = 210$, then estimated savings will increase by \$210 per unit change in the interest rate, holding income and age constant.

2. $n = 20$ $\alpha = 0.05$ $b_1 = -4$ $b_2 = -16$ $s_{b_1} = 1$ $s_{b_2} = 5$ $t = 2.11$
   $H_0: B_1 = 0$ $H_1: B_1 \neq 0$ Critical value: $t = 2.11$

   Decision rule: Reject H_0 if $t_1 < -2.11$ or $t > 2.11$.

   $t_1 = (-4 - 0)/1 = -4$ $t_1 = -4$; reject H_0. The statistical evidence supports the hypothesis (H_1) that miles per gallon and engine size are related at $\alpha = 0.05$.

   $H_0: B_2 = 0$ $H_1: B_2 \neq 0$ Critical value: $t = 2.11$

   Decision rule: Reject H_0 if $t_2 < -2.11$ or $t > 2.11$.

   $t_2 = (-16 - 0)/5 = -3.2$ $t_2 = -3.2$; reject H_0. The statistical evidence supports the hypothesis (H_1) that miles per gallon and engine size are related at $\alpha = 0.05$.

3. H_0: All of the B_i values are equal to zero.
   H_1: Not all of the B_i values are equal to zero.
   Critical value: $F_{0.01}(4, 20) = 4.43$.

   Decision rule: Reject H_0 if $F > 4.43$.

   $F = 75/50 = 1.5$ $F = 1.5$; accept H_0. The statistical evidence supports the hypothesis that there is no relationship between the independent variables and the dependent variable at $\alpha = 0.01$.

4. $X_2 = 0$ for no air conditioning. $X_2 = 1$ for air conditioning.
   a. $\hat{Y} = 10,000 - 1000(5) + 450(0) = \$5,000$
   b. $\hat{Y} = 10,000 - 1000(5) + 450(1) = \$5,450$
   c. The estimated average price for a 5-year-old car is \$450 more with air conditioning than without air-conditioning.

Answers to Review Problems

1. a. $n = 20$ $k = 3$ $\alpha = 0.02$ $t = 2.567$
$H_0: B_1 = 0$ $H_1: B_1 \neq 0$ Critical value: $t = 2.567$

Decision rule: Reject H_0 if $t_1 < -2.567$ or $t > 2.567$.

$t_1 = (2 - 0)/0.5 = 4$ $t_1 = 4$, reject H_0. The statistical evidence supports the hypothesis (H_1) that income and age are related at $\alpha = 0.02$.

$H_0: B_2 = 0$ $H_1: B_2 \neq 0$ Critical value: $t = 2.567$

Decision rule: Reject H_0 if $t_2 < -2.567$ or $t > 2.567$.

$t_2 = (10 - 0/2) = 5$ $t_2 = 5$; reject H_0. The statistical evidence supports the hypothesis (H_1) that income and college degree are related at $\alpha = 0.02$.
b. $\hat{Y} = -40 + 2X_1 + 10X_2 = -40 + 80 + 10 = 50$ \$50,000
c. b_2 measures the value of a college education holding age constant. A person with a college degree is estimated to make on average \$10,000 more than a person of the same age without a college degree.
2. a. $n = 32$ $k = 4$ $\alpha = 0.05$ $t = 1.701$
$H_0: B_1 = 0$ $H_1: B_1 \neq 0$ Critical value: $t = 1.701$

Decision rule: Reject H_0 if $t_1 < -1.701$ or $t_1 > 1.701$.

$t_1 = (0.5 - 0)/0.5 = 1$ $t_1 = 1$; accept H_0. The statistical evidence does not support the hypothesis (H_1) that X_1 and Y are related at $\alpha = 0.10$.

$H_0: B_2 = 0$ $H_1: B_2 \neq 0$ Critical value: $t = 1.701$

Decision rule: Reject H_0 if $t_2 < -1.701$ or $t_2 > 1.701$.

$t_2 = (-0.8 - 0/0.2 = -4$ $t_2 = -4$; reject H_0. The statistical evidence supports the hypothesis (H_1) that X_2 and Y are related at $\alpha = 0.10$.

$H_0: B_3 = 0$ $H_1: B_3 \neq 0$ Critical value: $t = 1.701$

Decision rule: Reject H_0 if $t_3 < -1.701$ or $t_3 > 1.701$.

$t_3 = (6 - 0)/2 = 3$ $t_3 = 3$; reject H_0. The statistical evidence supports the hypothesis (H_1) that X_3 and Y are related at $\alpha = 0.10$.
b. This is not a valid regression equation. Given the regression equation is not valid, $\hat{Y}$ cannot be estimated using this equation.
3. H_0: All of the B_i values are equal to zero.
H_1: Not all of the B_i values are equal to zero.
Critical value: $F_{0.01}(3, 21) = 4.87$

Decision rule: Reject H_0 if $F > 4.87$.

$F = 100/2.62 = 38.2$ $F = 38.2$; reject H_0. The statistical evidence supports the hypothesis (H_1) that not all the B_i values are equal to zero at $\alpha = 0.05$.
4. a. $n = 25$ $\alpha = 0.02$ $t = 2.508$
$H_0: B_1 = 0$ $H_1: B_1 \neq 0$ Critical value: $t = 2.508$

Decision rule: Reject H_0 if $t_1 < -2.508$ or $t_1 > 2.508$.

$t_1 = (50 - 10)/10 = 5$ $t_1 = 5$; reject H_0. The statistical evidence supports the hypothesis (H_1) that sales and number of households within a three mile radius are related at $\alpha = 0.02$.

$H_0: B_2 = 0$ $H_1: B_2 \neq 0$ Critical value: $t = 2.508$

Decision rule: Reject H_0 if $t_2 < -2.508$ or $t_2 > 2.508$.

$t_2 = (10 - 0)/2 = 5$ $t_2 = 5$; reject H_0. The statistical evidence supports the hypothesis (H_1) that sales and location are related at $\alpha = 0.02$.
b. $\hat{Y} = 10 + 50X_1 + 10X_2 = 10 + 50X_1 + 10(1) = 20 + 50X_1$

5. a. $\hat{Y} = 2,000 - 100(10) - 25(10) = 750$
  b. $\hat{Y} = 2,000 - 100(9.5) - 25(10) = 800$
  c. $\hat{Y} = 2,000 - 100(10) - 25(8) = 800$

6. a. $n = 25 \quad k = 3 \quad \alpha = 0.05 \quad t = 2.074$
    $H_0: B_1 = 0 \quad H_1: B_1 \neq 0 \quad$ Critical value: $t = 2.074$

Decision rule: Reject H_0 if $t_1 < -2.074$ or $t_1 > 2.074$.

$t_1 = (2.2 - 0)/0.5 = 4.4 \quad t_1 = 4.4$; reject H_0. The statistical evidence supports the hypothesis (H_1) that age and income are related at $\alpha = 0.05$.

$H_0: B_2 = 0 \quad H_1: B_2 \neq 0 \quad$ Critical value: $t = 2.074$

Decision rule: Reject H_0 if $t_2 < -2.074$ or $t_2 > 2.074$.

$t_2 = (1.4 - 0)/0.3 = 4.67 \quad t_2 = 4.67$; reject H_0. The statistical evidence supports the hypothesis (H_1) that income and marital status are related at $\alpha = 0.05$.
  b. $\hat{Y} = -30 + 2.2X_1 + 1.4X_2 = -30 + 2.2(30) + 1.4(0) = 36 \quad \$36,000$

```
NUMBER OF INDEPENDENT VARIABLES = 3
NUMBER OF OBSERVATIONS          = 12
VARIABLE       AVERAGE        VARIANCE

  C           0.9999999      1.550275E-14
  1          32.83333       50.51515
  2           0.5            0.2727273
  3          45.25         234.3864

       CORRELATION COEFFICIENTS

VAR.I        VAR.J         CORRELATION

  1            2           0.2449245
  1            3           0.7088955
  2            3           0.1421304

VARIABLE     COEFFICIENT    ST.ERROR

  C          -4.975559      16.97527
  1           1.544671       0.5217812
  2          -0.9822347      7.101254

STANDARD ERROR OF THE ESTIMATE = 11.92511
COEFFICIENT OF MULTIPLE DETERMINATION = 0.5035874
F-VALUE = 4.565045
DURBIN-WATSON STATISTIC = 2.306522

  T          Y(T)          YEST(T)         ERROR

  1           50          39.81989        10.18012
  2           30          29.56963         0.4303742
  3           60          46.561          13.439
  4           25          27.46252        -2.462521
  5           40          50.63258       -10.63258
  6           75          55.82903        19.17098
  7           40          48.10567        -8.105671
  8           50          52.17725        -2.177246
  9           65          58.35593         6.64407
 10           42          48.10567        -6.105671
 11           37          55.82903       -18.82903
 12           29          30.55186        -1.551861
```

Computer printout of the data for Review Problem 7

7. See figure.
  a. $S_{Y.12} = 11.92511 = 11.93$
  b. $R^2 = 0.5035874 = 0.504$
  c. $n = 12 \quad \alpha = 0.05 \quad t = 2.262$
    $H_0: B_1 = 0 \quad H_1: B_1 \neq 0 \quad$ Critical value: $t = 2.262$

Decision rule: Reject H_0 if $t_1 < -2.262$ or $t_1 > 2.262$.

$t_1 = (1.54 - 0)/0.52 = 2.96 \quad t_1 = 2.96$; reject H_0. The statistical evidence supports the hypothesis (H_1) that salary and age are related at $\alpha = 0.05$.

$H_0: B_2 = 0 \quad H_1: B_2 \neq 0 \quad$ Critical value: $t = 2.262$

Decision rule: Reject H_0 if $t_2 < -2.262$ or $t_2 > 2.262$.

$t_2 = (-0.98 - 0)/7.1 = -0.14$ $\qquad t_2 = -0.14$; accept H_0. The statistical evidence does not support the hypothesis (H_1) that salary and sex are related at $\alpha = 0.05$.

8. See figure.

a. $a = 1.209658$ $\quad b_1 = 0.3762345$ $\quad b_2 = 0.001836727$

$\hat{Y} = 1.21 + 0.38X_1 + 0.002X_2$ $\quad s_{b_1} = 0.1401892 = 0.14$

$\qquad\qquad\qquad\qquad\qquad\qquad s_{b_2} = 0.0004899247 = 0.0005$

b. $S_{Y.12} = 0.1489525 = 0.15$

c. $R^2 = 0.8728116 = 0.87$

d. $n = 10$ $\quad \alpha = 0.10$ $\quad t = 1.895$

$H_0: B_1 = 0$ $\qquad H_1: B_1 \neq 0$ $\qquad$ Critical value: $t = 1.895$

Decision rule: Reject H_0 if $t_1 < -1.895$ or $t_1 > 1.895$.

$t_1 = (0.38 - 0)/0.14 = 2.7$ $\qquad t_1 = 2.7$; reject H_0. The statistical evidence supports the hypothesis (H_1) that graduate GPA and undergraduate GPA are related at $\alpha = 0.10$.

$H_0: B_2 = 0$ $\qquad H_1: B_2 \neq 0$ $\qquad$ Critical value: $t = 1.895$

Decision rule: Reject H_0 if $t_2 < -1.895$ or $t_2 > 1.895$.

$t_2 = (0.0018 - 0)/0.0005 = 3.6$ $\qquad t_2 = 3.6$; reject H_0. The statistical evidence supports the hypothesis (H_1) that graduate GPA and GMAT scores are related at $\alpha = 0.10$.

e. $\hat{Y} = 1.21 + 0.38(3.2) + 0.002(600) = 3.626$

```
NUMBER OF INDEPENDENT VARIABLES = 3
NUMBER OF OBSERVATIONS          = 10
VARIABLE      AVERAGE        VARIANCE

C               1            1.578984E-14
1               3.07         0.1845556
2             580          15111.11
3               3.43         0.1356667

        CORRELATION COEFFICIENTS

VAR.I       VAR.J        CORRELATION

1            2           0.565976
1            3           0.7857555
2            3           0.8613502

VARIABLE     COEFFICIENT   ST.ERROR

C            1.209658      0.3602199
1            0.3762345     0.1401892
2            1.836727E-03  4.899247E-04

STANDARD ERROR OF THE ESTIMATE = 0.1489525
COEFFICIENT OF MULTIPLE DETERMINATION = 0.8728116
F-VALUE = 24.01655
DURBIN-WATSON STATISTIC = 2.054839

T          Y(T)          YEST(T)        ERROR

1            3.4          3.440398      -4.039788E-02
2            3.6          3.548824       5.117607E-02
3            3.1          3.035429       6.457091E-02
4            3.2          3.331972      -0.1319721
5            4            4.092142      -9.214163E-02
6            2.8          3.014395      -0.2143951
7            3.6          3.440398       0.1596019
8            3.5          3.586447      -8.644724E-02
9            3.2          3.052019       0.1479814
10           3.9          3.757975       0.1420255
```

Computer printout of the data for Review Problem 8

```
NUMBER OF INDEPENDENT VARIABLES = 3
NUMBER OF OBSERVATIONS          = 14
VARIABLE      AVERAGE        VARIANCE

C          0.9999998     6.1216E-14
1          6.714286      1.912088
2          0.4285714     0.2637363
3          45.92857      45.14835

       CORRELATION COEFFICIENTS

VAR.I      VAR.J        CORRELATION

1          2           -3.094922E-02
1          3            0.8917746
2          3            0.299351

VARIABLE      COEFFICIENT    ST.ERROR

C          14.66773      3.196896
1          4.382558      0.4582609
2          4.281884      1.233905

STANDARD ERROR OF THE ESTIMATE = 2.283653
COEFFICIENT OF MULTIPLE DETERMINATION = 0.9022638
F-VALUE = 50.7725
DURBIN-WATSON STATISTIC = 1.059097

T          Y(T)          YEST(T)        ERROR

1          46           45.24496      0.7550392
2          38           36.58052      1.419479
3          48           45.34564      2.654366
4          55           54.01008      0.9899254
5          52           54.11075     -2.110748
6          39           40.86241     -1.862404
7          40           40.96308     -0.9630776
8          51           49.72819      1.271809
9          47           45.34564      1.654366
10         56           58.39263     -2.392632
11         37           40.96308     -3.963078
12         40           40.86241     -0.8624039
13         41           40.96308      3.692246E-02
14         53           49.62752      3.372482
```

Computer printout of the data for Review Problem 9

9. See figure.
   a. $a = 14.66773$ $b_1 = 4.382558$ $b_2 = 4.281884$ (rounding off)
   $\hat{Y} = 14.67 + 4.38X_1 + 4.28X_2$
   $s_{b_1} = 0.4582609 = 0.46$
   $s_{b_2} = 1.233905 = 1.23$
   b. $S_{Y.12} = 2.283653 = 2.28$
   c. $R^2 = 0.9022638 = 0.90$
   d. $n = 14$ $\alpha = 0.01$ $t = 3.106$
   $H_0: B_1 = 0$ $H_1: B_1 \neq 0$ Critical value: $t = 3.106$

   Decision rule: Reject H_0 if $t_1 < -3.106$ or $t_1 > 3.106$.

   $t_1 = (4.38 - 0)/0.46 = 9.52$ $t_1 = 9.52$; reject H_0. The statistical evidence supports the hypothesis (H_1) that height and age are related at $\alpha = 0.01$.

   $H_0: B_2 = 0$ $H_1: B_2 \neq 0$ Critical value: $t = 3.106$

   Decision rule: Reject H_0 if $t_2 < -3.106$ or $t_2 > 3.106$.

   $t_2 = (4.28 - 0)/1.23 = 3.48$ $t_2 = 3.48$; reject H_0. The statistical evidence supports the hypothesis (H_1) that height and sex are related at $\alpha = 0.01$.
   e. $n = 10$ $k = 3$ $k - 1 = 2$ $n - k = 7$
   H_0: All the B_i values are equal to zero.
   H_1: Not all the B_i values are equal to zero.
   Critical value: $F_{0.01}(2, 7) = 9.55$

Decision rule: Reject H_0 if $F > 9.55$.

$F = 50.7725 = 50.8$ $F = 50.8$; reject H_0. The statistical evidence does not support the hypothesis (H_1) that all the B_1 values are equal to zero at $\alpha = 0.01$.

CHAPTER 11

Answers to Problems

1. See table.

Answer to Problem 1

(1)	(2)	(3)	(4)	(5)	(6)	(7)
						Percentage of Trend
Year	x	Y	xY	x^2	Y_t	$(Y/Y_t) \cdot 100$
1970	-19	18	-342	361	17.0	105.9
1971	-17	22	-374	289	20.9	105.3
1972	-15	25	-375	225	24.8	100.8
1973	-13	30	-390	169	28.7	104.5
1974	-11	31	-341	121	32.6	95.1
1975	-9	37	-333	81	36.5	101.4
1976	-7	42	-294	49	40.4	104.0
1977	-5	47	-235	25	44.3	106.1
1978	-3	45	-135	9	48.2	93.4
1979	-1	50	-50	1	52.1	96.0
1980	1	53	53	1	56.0	94.6
1981	3	58	174	9	59.9	96.8
1982	5	62	310	25	63.8	97.2
1983	7	67	469	49	67.7	99.0
1984	9	74	666	81	71.6	103.4
1985	11	76	836	121	75.5	100.7
1986	13	82	1066	169	79.4	103.3
1987	15	80	1200	225	83.3	96.0
1988	17	87	1479	289	87.2	99.8
1989	19	95	1805	361	91.1	104.3
		1081	5,189	2,660		

Position of median year: $(20 + 1)/2 = 10.5$th year   ($x = 0$, July 1, 1979)
1. **a.** $a = 1,081/20 = 54.05$ $b = 5,189/2,660 = 1.9507 = 1.95$ $Y_t = 54.05 + 1.95x$
   b. See column (6): $Y_{1970} = 54.05 + 1.95(-19) = 17.0$
   c. See column (7): for 1970 $(18/17) \times 100 = 105.9$
2. $Y_{1990} = 54.05 + 1.95(21) = 95.0$
3. **a.** RCR $= 105.9\% - 100\% = 5.9\%$
   In 1970, the actual value is 5.9% above the trend value due to cyclical fluctuations and irregular movements.
   b. RCR $= 99\% - 100\% = -1\%$
   In 1983, the actual value is 1% below the trend value due to cyclical fluctuations and irregular movements.
4. See table.

Answer to Problem 4

Sales of gasoline by a service station by quarters, 1980–1984: Computations for seasonal indices and deseasonalizing of original data

(1) Quarter	(2) Sales (1,000 gal)	(3) Four- Quarter Moving Total	(4) Two-of a-Four- Quarter Moving Total	(5) Moving Average col 4 · $\frac{1}{8}$	(6) Original Data as a % of Moving Average $\frac{\text{col 2}}{\text{col 5}}$ · 100	(7) Seasonal Index	(8) Deseason- alized Sales $\frac{\text{col 2}}{\text{col 7}}$ · 100
1980							
I	40					91.0	44.0
II	42					93.2	45.1
III	60	187	381	47.625	126.0	125.5	47.8
IV	45	194	396	49.5	90.9	90.3	49.8
1981							
I	47	202	414	51.75	90.8	91.0	51.6
II	50	212	431	53.875	92.8	93.2	53.6
III	70	219	446	55.75	125.6	125.5	55.8
IV	52	227	461	57.625	90.2	90.3	57.6
1982							
I	55	234	480	60	91.7	91.0	60.4
II	57	246	500	62.5	91.2	93.2	61.2
III	82	254	517	64.625	126.9	125.5	65.3
IV	60	263	539	67.375	89.1	90.3	66.4
1983							
I	64	276	565	70.625	90.6	91.0	70.3
II	70	289	591	73.875	94.8	93.2	75.1
III	95	302	617	77.125	123.2	125.5	75.7
IV	73	315	642	80.25	91.0	90.3	80.8
1984							
I	77	327	669	83.625	92.1	91.0	84.6
II	82	342	697	87.125	94.1	93.2	88.0
III	110	355				125.5	87.6
IV	86					90.3	95.2

Percentage of Moving Averages Quarters

Year	I	II	III	IV
1980			126.0	90.9
1981	90.8	92.8	125.6	90.2
1982	91.7	~~91.2~~	~~126.9~~	~~89.1~~
1983	~~90.6~~	94.8	~~123.2~~	~~91.0~~
1984	~~92.1~~	94.1		
Modified means	91.25	93.45	125.8	90.55

Total of modified means = 401.05
Adjustment factor = 400/401.05 = 0.99738

	Seasonal Indices		
I	II	III	IV
91.0	93.2	125.5	90.3

5. See table.

Answer to Problem 5

	Actual Sales	Estimate $w = 0.5$	Estimate $w = 0.8$
1970	$18 = a_1$	$18 = F_2$	$18 = F_2$
1971	22	18	18
1972	25	20	21.2
1973	30	22.5	24.24
1974	31	26.25	28.85
1975	37	28.63	30.57
1976	42	32.81	35.71
1977	47	37.41	40.74
1978	45	42.20	45.75
1979	50	43.60	45.15
1980	53	46.80	49.03
1981	58	49.90	52.21
1982	62	53.95	56.84
1983	67	57.98	60.97
1984	74	62.49	65.79
1985	76	68.24	72.36
1986	82	72.12	75.27
1987	80	77.06	80.64
1988	87	78.53	80.13
1989	95	82.77	85.63

Answers to Review Problems

1. See table. $a = 1096/15 = 73.07$ $b = 2298/280 = 8.21$ $Y_t = 73.07 + 8.21x$

Answer to Review Problem 1

Year	x	Y	xY	x^2	Y_t	$(Y/Y_t) \cdot 100$
1975	-7	20	-140	49	15.60	128.2
1976	-6	25	-150	36	23.81	105.0
1977	-5	37	-185	25	32.02	115.6
1978	-4	33	-132	16	40.23	82.0
1979	-3	45	-135	9	48.44	92.9
1980	-2	52	-104	4	56.65	91.8
1981	-1	61	-61	1	64.86	94.0
1982	0	73	0	0	73.07	99.9
1983	1	82	82	1	81.28	100.9
1984	2	101	202	4	89.49	112.9
1985	3	97	291	9	97.70	99.3
1986	4	105	420	16	105.91	99.1
1987	5	111	555	25	114.12	97.3
1988	6	123	738	36	122.33	100.5
1989	7	131	917	49	130.54	100.4
		1096	2298	280		

---

2. $Y_{1984} = 73.07 + 8.21(2) = 89.49$ $Y_{1990} = 73.07 + 8.21(8) = 138.75$

3. See table.

Answer to Review Problem 3			
Year	Actual	$w = 0.3$	$w = 0.7$
1975	$20 = a_1$	$20 = F_2$	$20 = F_2$
1976	25	20	20
1977	37	21.5	23.5
1978	33	26.15	32.95
1979	45	28.21	32.99
1980	52	33.24	41.40
1981	61	38.87	48.82
1982	73	45.51	57.35
1983	82	53.76	68.30
1984	101	62.23	77.89
1985	97	73.86	94.07
1986	105	80.80	96.12
1987	111	88.06	102.34
1988	123	94.94	108.40
1989	131	103.36	118.62

4. See table.

Answer to Review Problem 4							
(1)	(2)	(3)	(4)	(5)	(6)	(7)	(8)
			Two-of-a-Four Quarter Moving Total		Original Data as a % of Moving Average $\dfrac{\text{Col 2}}{\text{Col 5}} \cdot 100$		Deseasonalized Sales $\dfrac{\text{Col 2}}{\text{Col 7}} \cdot 100$
Quarter	Sales ($000)	Four Quarter Moving Total		Moving Average Col 4 · $\frac{1}{8}$		Seasonal Index	
1980							
I	20					77.7	25.7
II	27					94.2	28.7
III	40	109	222	27.75	144.1	150.5	26.6
IV	22	113	231	28.875	76.2	77.6	28.4
1981							
I	24	118	246	30.75	78.0	77.7	30.9
II	32	128	261	32.625	98.1	94.2	34.0
III	50	133	271	33.875	147.6	150.5	33.2
IV	27	138	281	35.125	76.9	77.6	34.8
1982							
I	29	143	298	37.25	77.9	77.7	37.3
II	37	155	316	39.5	93.7	94.2	39.3
III	62	161	328	41	151.2	150.5	41.2
IV	33	167	342	42.75	77.2	77.6	42.5
1983							
I	35	175	363	45.375	77.1	77.7	45.0
II	45	188	383	47.875	94.0	94.2	47.8
III	75	195	397	49.625	151.1	150.5	49.8
IV	40	202	413	51.625	77.5	77.6	51.5

Answer to Review Problem 4 (*continued*)

(1) Quarter	(2) Sales ($000)	(3) Four Quarter Moving Total	(4) Two-of-a-Four Quarter Moving Total	(5) Moving Average Col 4 · $\frac{1}{8}$	(6) Original Data as a % of Moving Average $\frac{Col\ 2}{Col\ 5}$ · 100	(7) Seasonal Index	(8) Deseasonalized Sales $\frac{Col\ 2}{Col\ 7}$ · 100
1984							
I	42	211	437	54.625	76.9	77.7	54.1
II	54	226	461	57.625	93.7	94.2	57.3
III	90	235	478	59.75	150.6	150.5	59.8
IV	49	243	492	61.5	79.7	77.6	63.1
1985							
I	50	249	518	64.75	77.2	77.7	64.4
II	60	269	549	68.625	87.4	94.2	63.7
III	110	280				150.5	73.1
IV	60					77.6	77.3

Percentage of Moving Averages
Quarters

Year	I	II	III	IV
1980			~~144.1~~	~~76.2~~
1981	~~78.0~~	~~98.1~~	147.6	76.9
1982	77.9	93.7	~~151.2~~	77.2
1983	77.1	94.0	151.1	77.5
1984	~~76.9~~	93.7	150.6	~~79.7~~
1985	77.2	~~87.4~~		
Modified means	77.4	93.8	149.8	77.2

Total of modified means = 398.2
Adjustment factor = 400/398.2 = 1.0045

Seasonal Indices

I	II	III	IV
77.7	94.2	150.5	77.6

5. See table.

Answer to Review Problem 5

Percentage of Moving Average
Quarters

Year	I	II	III	IV
1978			~~95.0~~	97.2
1979	104.1	101.2	99.3	~~91.7~~
1980	~~110.2~~	~~95.6~~	97.1	94.2
1981	107.4	102.1	96.2	96.5
1982	~~103.2~~	~~106.7~~	~~103.1~~	~~98.1~~
1983	105.4	102.4	98.1	97.3
1984	103.5	103.1	97.0	96.0
Modified means	105.1	102.2	97.5	96.2

Total of modified means = 401

Adjustment factor = 400/401 = 0.9975

Seasonal Indices

I	II	III	IV
104.8	101.9	97.3	96.0

6.

Month	Deseasonalized (1000s)
October	60/0.8 = 75
November	120/1.5 = 80
December	90/1.05 = 85.714

7. See table.

Answer to Review Problem 7

Year	x	Y	xY	x^2	Y_t	$(Y/Y_t) \cdot 100$
1975	−15	20	−300	225	15.45	129.4
1976	−13	25	−325	169	23.69	105.5
1977	−11	37	−407	121	31.93	115.9
1978	−9	33	−297	81	40.17	82.2
1979	−7	45	−315	49	48.41	93.0
1980	−5	52	−260	25	56.65	91.8
1981	−3	61	−183	9	64.89	94.0
1982	−1	73	−73	1	73.13	99.8
1983	1	82	82	1	81.37	100.8
1984	3	101	303	9	89.61	112.7
1985	5	97	485	25	97.85	99.1
1986	7	105	735	49	106.09	99.0
1987	9	111	999	81	114.33	97.1
1988	11	123	1353	121	122.57	100.4
1989	13	131	1703	169	130.81	100.1
1990	15	140	2100	225	139.05	100.7
		1236	5600	1360		

$x = 0$, July 1, 1982 $a = 1236/16 = 77.25$ $b = 5,600/1360 = 4.12$ $Y_t = 77.25 + 4.12x$

8. $Y_t = 77.25 + 4.12(3) = 89.61$ $Y_t = 77.25 + 4.12(17) = 147.29$

9. See table.

Answer to Review Problem 9

Year	Actual	$w = 0.25$	$w = 0.50$
1975	$20 = a_1$	$20 = F_2$	$20 = F_2$
1976	25	20	20
1977	37	21.25	22.5
1978	33	25.19	29.75
1979	45	27.14	31.38
1980	52	31.61	38.19
1981	61	36.70	45.09
1982	73	42.78	53.05
1983	82	50.33	63.02
1984	101	58.25	72.51
1985	97	68.94	86.76
1986	105	75.95	91.88
1987	111	83.21	98.44
1988	123	90.16	104.72
1989	131	98.37	113.86
1990	140	106.53	122.43

10. Month

March 25,000(0.85) = 21,250

April 26,000(0.882) = 22,932

May 27,500(0.983) = 27,033

June 28,000(1.262) = 35,336

July 28,750(1.584) = 45,540

11. a. RCR = 91.8% − 100% = −8.2%   (1980)

  b. RCR = 112.7% − 100% = 12.7%   (1984)

CHAPTER 12

Answers to Problems

1. Index = $(74/65) \cdot 100 = 113.85$

2. Laspeyres = $(143/123) \cdot 100 = 116.26$

3. Paasche = $(217/188) \cdot 100 = 115.43$

4. Index = $1,348.00/11.13 = 121.11$

5. Index = $(3.44/3) \cdot 100 = 114.67$

6. Index = $14,300/123 = 116.26$

7. Index = $21,700/188 = 115.43$

8. Paasche = $(13.48/16.48) \cdot 100 = 81.8$

9. Laspeyres = $(188/123) \cdot 100 = 152.85$

10. Paasche = $(217/143) \cdot 100 = 151.75$

11. 25,000/0.97 = 25,773;   30,000/1 = 30,000;   32,000/1.05 = 30,476;   34,000/1.08 = 31,481;   35,000/1.10 = 31,818

12. Shift value = 100/110 = 0.909;   1979, 88.18; 1980, 90.90; 1981, 95.45; 1982, 98.17; 1983, 100.00.

Answers to Review Problems

1. Index = $(22.5/20.48) \cdot 100 = 109.86$

2. Laspeyres = $(54/48.92) \cdot 100 = 110.38$

3. Paasche = $(56.5/51.4) \cdot 100 = 109.92$

4. Index = $330.85/3 = 110.28$

5. Laspeyres = $(51.4/48.92) \cdot 100 = 105.07$

6. Paasche = $(56.5/54.0) \cdot 100 = 104.63$

7. 35,000/1.4 = 25,000   Your real income has not changed.

8. See table.

Answer to Review Problem 8

Year	Sales (in real dollars)	Year	Sales (in real dollars)
1979	$100,000/1.12 = 89,286$	1983	$160,000/1.35 = 118,519$
1980	$110,000/1.16 = 94,828$	1984	$175,000/1.37 = 127,737$
1981	$125,000/1.20 = 104,167$	1985	$200,000/1.40 = 142,857$
1982	$137,000/1.26 = 108,730$		

---

9. Shift value $= 100/138 = 0.7246$

Year	Price Index (1985 = 100)	Real Dollars (1985 = 100)
1977	72.46	125,587
1978	79.71	124,200
1979	84.78	150,979
1980	87.68	156,250
1981	90.58	174,431
1982	93.47	181,877
1983	96.37	197,157
1984	97.82	202,413
1985	100.00	210,000

---

10. Index $= (9.09/8.18) \cdot 100 = 111.12$

11. Index $= (4.448/4) \cdot 100 = 111.2$

12. Laspeyres $= (54.76/48.86) \cdot 100 = 112.08$

13. Paasche $= (54.55/48.79) \cdot 100 = 111.81$

CHAPTER 13

Answers to Problems

1. Let Tony's pizza being preferred be a $(+)$, then $(+) = 8$, $(-) = 12$, $(0) = 5$.

$$n = 20 \quad \bar{p} = 8/20 = 0.4 \quad \sigma_{\bar{p}} = \sqrt{\frac{(0.5)(0.5)}{20}} = 0.11$$

$$H_0: p = 0.50 \quad H_1: p \neq 0.50 \quad \text{Critical value: } z = 2.33$$

Decision rule: Reject H_0 if $z < -2.33$ or $z > 2.33$.

$z = (0.4 - 0.5)/0.11 = -0.909 \quad z = -0.909$; accept H_0. The statistical evidence supports the hypothesis that Tony's pizza is as good as the national brands at $\alpha = 0.02$.

2. See table.

Answer to Problem 2

| | | | | Signed Rank | |
After	Before	$d(A - B)$	Rank of $|d|$	Rank (+)	Rank (−)
40	35	5	8	8	
42	30	12	14	14	
50	45	5	8	8	
41	30	11	12	12	
25	10	15	18.5	18.5	
18	17	1	2	2	
22	23	−1	2		2
31	30	1	2	2	
25	18	7	10	10	
40	12	28	25	25	
35	21	14	16	16	
20	17	3	5	5	
45	20	25	24	24	
48	30	18	20.5	20.5	
32	18	14	16	16	
31	17	14	16	16	
26	15	11	12	12	
28	10	18	20.5	20.5	
32	30	2	4	4	
33	18	15	18.5	18.5	
41	21	20	23	23	
38	19	19	22	22	
25	20	5	8	8	
18	22	−4	6		6
41	30	11	12	12	
				317	$T = 8$

$T = 8$ $n = 25$ Use z $\alpha = 0.01$ $z = 2.33$

$\mu_T = (25)(26)/4 = 162.5$ $\sigma_T = \sqrt{25(26)(51)/24} = 37.17$

$H_0: \Sigma$ rank $(+) \leq \Sigma$ rank $(-)$ $H_1:$ rank $(+) > \Sigma$ rank $(-)$ Critical value: $z = 2.33$

Decision rule: Reject H_0 if $z < -2.33$.

$z = (8 - 162.5)/37.17 = -4.16$

$z = -4.16$; reject H_0. The statistical evidence supports the hypothesis that the students have learned at $\alpha = 0.01$.

3. See table.

Answer to Problem 3

Rank of Scores by Male and Female

Rank	Score	Sex	Rank	Score	Sex
1	250	M	16	495	F
2	275	M	17	505	M
3	280	F	18	510	F
4	300	F	19	520	F
5	305	F	20	525	M
6	320	F	21	535	M
7	325	M	22	540	F
8	355	M	23	570	F
9	400	F	24	600	F
10	405	M	25	605	M
11	430	M	26	660	M
12	450	F	27	720	M
13	455	M	28	725	F
14	470	M	29	740	F
15	475	F	30	790	M

Let Males $= 1$ $S_0, R_1 = 232$

$\mu_U = 15(15)/2 = 112.5$ $U = 15(15) + [(15)(16)/2] - 232 = 113$

$\sigma_U = \sqrt{[15(15)(31)]/12} = 24.1$

H_0: The samples were drawn from populations with equal means.

H_1: The samples were drawn from populations with unequal means.

Critical value: $z = 2.33$

Decision rule: Reject H_0 if $z < -2.33$ or $z > 2.33$.

$z = (113 - 112.5)/24.1 = 0.02$ $z = 0.02$; accept H_0. The statistical evidence supports the hypothesis that there is no difference between the average scores of males and females at $\alpha = 0.01$.

4. $r = 9$

5. $r = 16$ $n_1 = $ even $= 17$ $n_2 = $ odd $= 23$

$\mu_r = 2(17)(23)/(17 + 23) + 1 = 20.55$

$\sigma_r = \sqrt{2(17)(23)[(2)(17)(23) - 17 - 23]/(17 + 23)^2(17 + 23 - 1)} = 3.05$

H_0: The sample is random. H_1: The sample is not random.   Critical value: $z = 1.96$

Decision rule: Reject H_0 if $z < -1.96$ or $z > 1.96$.

$z = (16 - 20.55)/3.05 = -1.49$

$z = -1.49$; accept H_0. The statistical evidence supports the hypothesis that obtaining an odd or an even is random at $\alpha = 0.05$.

6.

Farmer A		Farmer B		Farmer C	
Yield	**Rank**	**Yield**	**Rank**	**Yield**	**Rank**
20	8.5	19	6.5	27	12.5
16	3	32	14	36	15
14	1	27	12.5	18	4.5
18	4.5	15	2	19	6.5
21	10	20	8.5	26	11
37	16	38	17	39	18
$R_1 = 43$		$R_2 = 60.5$		$R_3 = 67.5$	
$n_1 = 6$		$n_2 = 6$		$n_3 = 6$	

$$c = 3 \quad n = 18 \quad K = \frac{12}{(18)(18+1)}\left[\frac{43^2}{6} + \frac{60.5^2}{6} + \frac{67.5^2}{6}\right] - 3(18+1) = 1.86$$

H_0: The samples were drawn from populations having the same means.
H_1: The samples were drawn from populations having different means.
Critical value: $\chi^2(2, 0.02) = 7.824$

Decision rule: Reject H_0 if $\chi^2 > 7.824$.

$\chi^2 = K_c = 1.86/(1 - 0.009) = 1.88$
$\chi^2 = 1.88$; accept H_0. The statistical evidence supports the hypothesis that the samples are drawn from populations having the same mean at $\alpha = 0.02$.

7.

Ability		Difference	
Athletic	**Academic**	**in Rank**	
X	Y	$d = (X - Y)$	d^2
1	5	-4	16
2	7	-5	25
3	4	-1	1
4	2	2	4
5	1	4	16
6	8	-2	4
7	9	-2	4
8	3	5	25
9	10	-1	1
10	6	4	16
			$\Sigma d^2 = 112$

$$n = 10 \quad \alpha = 0.05 \quad t = 2.306 \quad r_r = 1 - \frac{6(112)}{10(10^2 - 1)} = 0.32 \quad r_r^2 = 0.10$$

H_0: The variables are not related. H_1: The variables are related.   Critical value: $t = 2.306$

Decision rule: Reject H_0, if $t < -2.306$ or $t > 2.306$

$$t = \frac{0.32}{\sqrt{\dfrac{1 - 0.10}{8}}} = 0.95$$

$t = 0.95$; accept H_0. The statistical evidence supports the hypothesis that athletic and academic ability are not related at $\alpha = 0.05$.

Answers to Review Problems

1.

Rank in Grade X	Rank in Completion Y	$d = (X - Y)$	d^2
1	12	-11	121
2	2	0	0
3	7	-4	16
4	5	-1	1
5	15	-10	100
6	6	0	0
7	11	-4	16
8	3	5	25
9	13	-4	16
10	10	0	0
11	4	7	49
12	14	-2	4
13	8	5	25
14	9	5	25
15	1	14	196

$$\Sigma d^2 = 594$$

$n = 15 \quad \alpha = 0.05 \quad t = 2.160 \quad r_r = 1 - \dfrac{6(594)}{15(15^2 - 1)} = -0.061$

H_0: The variables are not related. $\qquad H_1$: The variables are related. $\qquad$ Critical value: $t = 2.160$

Decision rule: Reject H_0 if $t < -2.16$ or $t > 2.16$.

$t = \dfrac{-0.061}{\sqrt{(1 - 0.004)/15 - 2}} = -0.22 \qquad t = -0.22$; accept H_0. The statistical evidence does not support the hypothesis that grade and time of completion of an exam are related at $\alpha = 0.05$.

2. $r = 24 \quad n_1 = $ number of $U = 29 \quad n_2 = $ number of $D = 31$

$\mu_r = \dfrac{2(29)(31)}{29 + 31} + 1 = 30.97 \qquad \sigma_r = \sqrt{\dfrac{2(29)(31)[2(29)(31) - 29 - 31]}{(29 + 31)^2(29 + 31 - 1)}} = 3.84$

H_0: The sample is random. $\qquad H_1$: The sample is not random. $\qquad$ Critical value: $z = 1.96$

Decision rule: Reject H_0 if $z < -1.96$ or $z > 1.96$.

$z = (24 - 30.97)/3.84 = -1.82$

$z = -1.82$; accept H_0. The statistical evidence supports the hypothesis that the movement of the stock is random at $\alpha = 0.05$.

3.

1st Course Grade	2nd Course Grade	d_{2-1}	Rank of $|d|$	Signed Ranks Rank (+)	Signed Ranks Rank (−)
78	82	4	5.5	5.5	
81	87	6	7.5	7.5	
94	98	4	5.5	5.5	
96	93	−3	4		4
87	89	2	2	2	
75	73	−2	2		2
65	72	7	9.5	9.5	
71	77	6	7.5	7.5	
62	70	8	11.5	11.5	
75	82	7	9.5	9.5	
84	92	8	11.5	11.5	
80	82	2	2	2	
				72	$T = 6$

$n = 12$ $\alpha = 0.01$ $T_{0.01} = 9$

$H_0: \Sigma$ rank $(+) \leq \Sigma$ rank $(-)$ $H_1: \Sigma$ rank $(+) > \Sigma$ rank $(-)$ Critical value: $T_{0.01} = 9$

Decision rule: Reject H_0 if $T \leq 9$.

$T = 6$ $T = 6$; reject H_0. The statistical evidence supports the hypothesis that the grades are better in the second course than in the first, at $\alpha = 0.01$.

4.

Bank A Score	Bank A Rank	Bank B Score	Bank B Rank	Bank C Score	Bank C Rank
70	5	74	7	95	15
80	9	83	11	87	12
65	2	71	6	67	3
90	13	94	14	81	10
50	1	68	4	75	8
97	16	98	17	100	18
$R_1 = 46$		$R_2 = 59$		$R_3 = 66$	
$n_1 = 6$		$n_2 = 6$		$n_3 = 6$	

$c = 3$ $n = 15$
H_0: The samples were drawn from populations having the same means.
H_1: The samples were drawn from populations having different means.
Critical value: $\chi^2(2, 0.05) = 5.991$

Decision rule: Reject H_0 if $\chi^2 > 5.991$.

$$\chi^2 = K = \frac{12}{18(18 + 1)}\left(\frac{46^2}{6} + \frac{59^2}{6} + \frac{66^2}{6}\right) - 3(18 + 1) = 1.20$$

$\chi^2 = 1.20$; accept H_0. The statistical evidence supports the hypothesis that the average ratings of the banks are the same at $\alpha = 0.05$.

5. Let A = being preferred be a $(+)$, then $(+) = 45$, $(-) = 40$, and $(0) = 15$.
$\bar{p} = 45/85 = 0.529$ $\sigma_{\bar{p}} = \sqrt{(0.5)(0.5)/85} = 0.054$
$H_0: p \leq 0.50$ $H_1: p > 0.50$ Critical value: $z = 2.05$

Decision rule: Reject H_0 if $z > 2.05$.

$$z = \frac{0.529 - 0.50}{0.054} = 0.54 \qquad z = 0.54; \text{ accept } H_0.$$ The statistical evidence does not support the hypothesis that bleach A is preferred to bleach B at $\alpha = 0.02$.

6.

Test Score X	Personnel Interview	$d = (X - Y)$	d^2
1	2	-1	1
2	1	1	1
3	4	-1	1
4	3	1	1
5	8	-3	9
6	9	-3	9
7	5	2	4
8	7	1	1
9	6	3	9
10	10	0	0
			$\Sigma d^2 = 36$

$$n = 10 \quad \alpha = 0.02 \quad t = 2.896 \quad r_r = \frac{1 - 6(36)}{10(10^2 - 1)} = 0.782$$

H_0: The variables are not related. H_1: The variables are related.   Critical value: $t = 2.896$

Decision rule: Reject H_0 if $t < -2.896$ or $t > 2.896$.

$$t = \frac{0.782}{\sqrt{\dfrac{1 - 0.612}{10 - 2}}} = 3.55$$

$t = 3.55$; reject H_0. The statistical evidence supports the hypothesis that test score and personnel interview rating are correlated at $\alpha = 0.02$.

7. See table.

Answer to Review Problem 7

Rank of Output by Machines A and B:

Rank	Output	Machine	Rank	Output	Machine
1	86	B	16	98	B
2	88	A	17.5	99	B
3.5	89	B	17.5	99	B
3.5	89	B	19.5	100	A
5	93	A	19.5	100	B
6	94	A	21.5	102	A
8.5	95	B	21.5	102	B
8.5	95	B	23.5	103	A
8.5	95	B	23.5	103	B
8.5	95	A	25	104	A
11	96	B	26	109	B
13.5	97	A	27	110	A
13.5	97	A	28	112	A
13.5	97	A	29	115	A
13.5	97	B	30	121	A

Let machine A = 1. So, $R_1 = 265.5$

$U = 15(15) + [15(15 + 1)/2] - 265.5 = 79.5 \quad \mu_u = 15(15)/2 = 112.5$

$\sigma_u = \sqrt{[15(15)(15 + 15 - 1)]/12} = 23.32$

H_0: The samples were drawn from populations with equal means.

H_1: The samples were drawn from populations with unequal means.

Critical value: $z = 1.96$

Decision rule: Reject H_0 if $z < -1.96$ or $z > 1.96$.

$z = (79.5 - 112.5)/23.32 = -1.42 \quad z = -1.42$; accept H_0.   The statistical evidence supports the hypothesis that the average output of the two machines are equal at $\alpha = 0.05$.

8. See table.

Answer to Review Problem 8

Worker A		Worker B		Worker C	
Output	Rank	Output	Rank	Output	Rank
50	16	45	11	35	1
48	14	40	6	38	4
46	12	47	13	41	7
51	17	42	8	44	10
49	15	43	9	37	3
52	18	39	5	36	2
$R_1 = 92$		$R_2 = 52$		$R_3 = 27$	
$n_1 = 6$		$n_2 = 5$		$n_3 = 6$	

$c = 3 \quad n = 18$

H_0: The samples were drawn from populations having the same means.

H_1: The samples were drawn from populations having different means.

Critical value: $\chi^2 (2, 0.01) = 9.210$

Decision rule: Reject H_0 if $\chi^2 > 9.210$.

$$\chi^2 = K = \frac{12}{18(18 + 1)}(92^2/6 + 52^2/6 + 27^2/6) - 3(18 + 1) = 12.57$$

$\chi^2 = 12.57$; reject H_0. The statistical evidence supports the hypothesis that the average output of the 3 workers is different at $\alpha = 0.01$.

9. See table.

Answer to Review Problem 9

		Rank of salary by school			
Rank	Salary	School	Rank	Salary	School
1	14	A	11.5	19	B
2.5	15	B	14.5	20	A
2.5	15	A	14.5	20	B
5	16	A	16	21	B
5	16	A	17	22	A
5	16	B	18.5	23	B
8	18	A	18.5	23	B
8	18	A	20.5	24	B
8	18	B	20.5	24	A
11.5	19	A	22.5	26	A
11.5	19	B	22.5	26	B
11.5	19	B	24	27	A

Let University $A = 1$. So, $R_1 = 139.5$.
$U = 12(12) + [(12)(12 + 1)/2] - 139.5 = 82.5$ $\mu_u = 12(12)/2 = 72$
$\sigma_u = \sqrt{[(12)(12)(12 + 12 + 1)]/12} = 17.3$
H_0: The samples were drawn from populations with equal means.
H_1: The samples were drawn from populations with unequal means.
Critical value: $z = 2.58$

Decision rule: Reject H_0 if $z < -2.58$ or $z > 2.58$.

$z = (82.5 - 72)/17.3 = 0.61$ $z = 0.61$; accept H_0.   The statistical evidence supports the hypothesis that average starting salaries are the same for students from both universities at $\alpha = 0.01$.

10. Let $A =$ being preferred be a $(+)$, then $(+) = 12$, $(-) = 10$, and $(0) = 8$.
$n = 22$ $\bar{p} = 12/22 = 0.545$ $\sigma_{\bar{p}} = \sqrt{(0.5)(0.5)/22} = 0.107$
H_0: $p = 0.50$
H_1: $p \neq 0.50$
Critical value: $z = 2.33$

Decision rule: Reject H_0 if $z < -2.33$ or $z > 2.33$.

$$z = \frac{0.545 - 0.50}{0.107} = 0.42$$

$z = 0.42$; accept H_0. The statistical evidence supports the hypothesis that there is no difference in preference between the two brands of bread at $\alpha = 0.02$.

11. See table.

Answer to Review Problem 11

(1)	(2)	(3)	(4)	(5)	
				Signed Ranks	
New Formula	Old Formula	d_{2-1}	Rank of $\|d\|$	Rank (+)	Rank (−)
500	600	100	24	24	
350	400	50	22	22	
100	125	25	17.5	17.5	
98	90	−8	2		2
1000	950	−50	22		22
500	640	140	25	25	
600	610	10	5.5	5.5	
450	410	−40	20		20
650	620	−30	19		19
100	120	20	12.5	12.5	
150	130	−20	12.5		12.5
179	159	−20	12.5		12.5
205	220	15	8	8	
721	730	9	3	3	
800	820	20	12.5	12.5	
650	670	20	12.5	12.5	
400	410	10	5.5	5.5	
250	270	20	12.5	12.5	
200	190	−10	5.5		5.5
190	200	10	5.5	5.5	
125	150	25	17.5	17.5	
650	700	50	22	22	
480	500	20	12.5	12.5	
460	440	−20	12.5		12.5
325	330	5	1	1	
				219	$T = 106$

Old($-$) New($+$) $T = 106$ $\mu_T = [25(25 + 1)]/4 = 162.5$ $\sigma_T = \sqrt{[(25)(26)(51)]/24}$
$= 37.17$

$H_0: \Sigma \text{ rank }(+) \leq \Sigma \text{ rank }(-)$ $H_1: \Sigma \text{ rank }(+) > \Sigma \text{ rank }(-)$ Critical value: $z = 2.05$

Decision rule: Reject H_0 if $z > 2.05$.

$z = (106 - 162.5)/37.17 = -1.52$ $z = -1.52$; accept H_0.   The statistical evidence does not support the hypothesis that the new formula has increased sales at $\alpha = 0.02$.

12. $r = 12$ $n_1 = \text{number of } U = 11$ $n_2 = \text{number of } O = 14$

$$\sigma_r = \sqrt{\frac{2(11)(14)[2(11)(14) - 11 - 14]}{(11 + 14)^2(11 + 14 - 1)}} = 2.41 \qquad \mu_r = \frac{2(11)(14)}{(11 + 14)} + 1 = 13.32$$

H_0: The sample is random
H_1: The sample is not random
Critical value: $z = 1.96$

Decision rule: Reject H_0 if $z < -1.96$ or $z > 1.96$.

$z = (12 - 13.32)/2.41 = -0.55$ $z = -0.55$; accept H_0. The statistical evidence supports the hypothesis that the overfilling or underfilling is random at $\alpha = 0.05$.

CHAPTER 14

Answers to Problems

1. See table. The best of the worst (maximin) is 100(A_2). Cold drinks should be sold using the maximin criterion.

Answer to Problem 1

Payoff Table

Weather	A_1: Hot Chocolate	A_2: Cold Drinks
O_1: Hot	-50	1,000
O_2: Cold	1,500	100
	-50	100

2. See table. Hot chocolate should be sold using the expected profit criterion.

Answer to Problem 2

Computations of Expected Profits
A_1: Hot Chocolate

Outcome	Probability	Profit	Weighted Profit
O_1: Hot	0.4	-50	-20
O_2: Cold	0.6	1,500	900
			880

Expected profit (A_1) = $\boxed{\$880}$

Answer to Problem 2 (*continued*)

A_2: Cold Drinks

Outcome	Probability	Profit	Weighted Profit
O_1: Hot	0.4	1,000	400
O_2: Cold	0.6	100	60
			460

Expected profit $(A_2) = \$460$

---

3. See table. Hot chocolate should be sold using the expected opportunity loss criterion.

Answer to Problem 3

	Payoff Table		Opportunity Loss	
	A_1: Hot Chocolate	A_2: Cold Drinks	A_1	A_2
O_1: Hot	−50	1,000*	1,050	0
O_2: Cold	1,500*	100	0	1,400

Computation of Expected Opportunity Loss
A_1: Hot Chocolate

	Probability	Opportunity Loss	Weighted Opportunity Loss
O_1: Hot	0.4	1,050	420
O_2: Cold	0.6	0	0
			420

Expected opportunity loss $(A_1) = \boxed{\$420}$

A_2: Cold Drinks

	Probability	Opportunity Loss	Weighted Opportunity Loss
O_1: Hot	0.4	0	0
O_2: Cold	0.6	1,400	840
			840

Expected opportunity loss $(A_2) = \$840$

4. Hot chocolate would be sold using the minimax opportunity loss criterion.

Opportunity Loss Table

	A_1: Hot Chocolate	A_2: Cold Drinks
O_1: Hot	1,050	0
O_2: Cold	0	1,400
	1,050	1,400

5. See table.

Answer to Problem 5

Calculation of Expected Profit with Perfect Information

Predicted Event	Profit	Probability	Weighted Profit
O_1: Hot	1,000	0.4	400
O_2: Cold	1,500	0.6	900
			1,300

Expected profit with perfect information = $1,300

$$\text{EVPI} = \begin{matrix}\text{Expected profit}\\\text{with perfect information}\end{matrix} - \begin{matrix}\text{Expected profit}\\\text{under uncertainty}\end{matrix}$$
$$= 1,300 - 880 = 420$$

This is the same as the EOL in Problem 3.

6. a. Investment 2 is chosen because it has the higher expected monetary value.
   b. Investment 2 is chosen because it has the higher expected utility.

Answer to Problem 6

a.   **Computation of Expected Monetary Value**

	Investment 1			Investment 2	
Prob.	Payoff	Weighted Payoff	Prob.	Payoff	Weighted Payoff
0.2	−20,000	−4,000	0.2	−40,000	−8,000
0.4	0	0	0.3	0	0
0.3	10,000	3,000	0.3	25,000	7,500
0.1	50,000	5,000	0.2	50,000	10,000
		4,000			9,500

Answer to Problem 6 (*continued*)

b. **Computation of Expected Utility**

	Investment 1			Investment 2	
Prob.	Utility	Weighted Utility	Prob.	Payoff	Weighted Utility
0.2	−20	−4	0.2	−50	−10
0.4	0	0	0.3	0	0
0.3	10	3	0.3	20	6
0.1	40	4	0.2	40	8
		3			4

Answers to Review Problems

1. Stock A should be bought using the maximin criterion.

Payoff Table ($000s)

Economic Activity	A_1 Stock A	A_2 Stock B	A_3 Stock C
O_1: Growth	50	75	110
O_2: Recession	20	−30	−65
	20	−30	−65

2. See table. Stock C should be bought using the expected profit criterion.

Answer to Review Problem 2

Computations of Expected Profits ($000s)
A_1: Stock A

Outcome	Probability	Profit	Weighted Profit
O_1: Growth	0.6	50	30
O_2: Recession	0.4	20	8
			38

Expected profit (A_1) = $38

A_2: Stock B

Outcome	Probability	Profit	Weighted Profit
O_1: Growth	0.6	75	45
O_2: Recession	0.4	−30	−12
			33

Expected profit (A_2) = $33

Answer to Review Problem 2 (*continued*)

A_3: Stock C

Outcome	Probability	Profit	Weighted Profit
O_1: Growth	0.6	110	66
O_2: Recession	0.4	−65	−26
			40

Expected profit $(A_3) = \boxed{\$40}$

---

3. See table. Stock C should be bought using the expected opportunity loss criterion.

Answer to Review Problem 3

	Payoff Table			Opportunity Loss		
	A_1 Stock A	A_2 Stock B	A_3 Stock C	A_1	A_2	A_3
O_1: Growth	50	75	110*	60	35	0
O_2: Recession	20*	−30	−65	0	50	85

Computation of Expected Opportunity Loss ($000s)
A_1: Stock A

	Probability	Opportunity Loss	Weighted Opportunity Loss
O_1: Growth	0.6	60	36
O_2: Recession	0.4	0	0
			36

Expected opportunity loss $(A_1) = \$36$

A_2: Stock B

	Probability	Opportunity Loss	Weighted Opportunity Loss
O_1: Growth	0.6	35	21
O_2: Recession	0.4	50	20
			41

Expected opportunity loss $(A_2) = \$41$

Answer to Review Problem 3 (*continued*)

A_3: Stock C

	Probability	Opportunity Loss	Weighted Opportunity Loss
O_1: Growth	0.6	0	0
O_2: Recession	0.4	85	34
			34

Expected opportunity loss (A_3) = $\boxed{\$34}$

4. Stock B should be chosen using the minimax expected opportunity loss criterion.

Opportunity Loss Table ($000s)

	A_1 Stock A	A_2 Stock B	A_3 Stock C
O_1: Growth	60	35	0
O_2: Recession	0	50	85
	60	$\boxed{50}$	85

5. Calculation of Expected Profit with Perfect Information ($000s)

Predicted Event	Profit	Probability	Weighted Profit
O_1: Growth	110	0.6	66
O_2: Recession	20	0.4	8
			74

Expected profit with perfect information = $74

6. The game show player should pick a door under the expected monetary value criterion.

Computation of Expected Monetary Value

Alternative 1 (keep the money)			Alternative 2 (pick a door)		
Prob.	Payoff	Weighted Payoff	Prob.	Payoff	Weighted Payoff
1	500	500	1/3	1,000	333.3
0	0	0	1/3	3,000	1,000.0
			1/3	5	1.7
		500			$\boxed{1,335.0}$

7. See table.

a. Investment 3 is chosen because it has the highest expected monetary value.

b. Investment 2 is chosen because it has the highest expected utility.

Answer to Review Problem 7

---

a. **Computation of Expected Monetary Value**
(payoffs in $000s)

	Investment 1			Investment 2			Investment 3	
Prob.	Payoff	Weighted Payoff	Prob.	Payoff	Weighted Payoff	Prob.	Payoff	Weighted Payoff
0.3	10	−3	0.4	−5	−2	0.5	−20	−10
0.6	10	6	0.4	10	4	0.4	25	10
0.1	30	3	0.2	20	4	0.1	100	10
		6			6			10

---

b. **Computation of Expected Utility**

	Investment 1			Investment 2			Investment 3	
Prob.	Utility	Weighted Utility	Prob.	Utility	Weighted Utility	Prob.	Utility	Weighted Utility
0.3	−20	−6	0.4	−8	−3.2	0.5	−70	−35
0.6	10	6	0.4	10	4	0.4	22	8.8
0.1	25	2.5	0.2	18	3.6	0.1	75	7.5
		2.5			4.4			−18.7

---

8. The inventor should sell the patent under the maximin criterion.

Payoff Table ($000s)

Outcome	A_1 Sell Patent	A_2 Manufacture the Product
O_1: Small demand	150	−100
O_2: Medium demand	300	500
O_3: Large demand	750	1,250
	150	−100

---

9. See table. The inventor should manufacture the product under the expected profit criterion.

Answer to Review Problem 9

Computations of Expected Profits ($000s)
A_1: Sell Patent

Outcome	Probability	Profit	Weighted Profit
O_1: Small	0.2	150	30
O_2: Medium	0.7	300	210
O_3: Large	0.1	750	75
			315

Expected profit $(A_1) = \$315$

A_2: Manufacture Product

Outcome	Probability	Profit	Weighted Profit
O_1: Small	0.2	−100	−20
O_2: Medium	0.7	500	350
O_3: Large	0.1	1250	125
			455

Expected profit $(A_2) = \boxed{\$455}$

---

10. See table. The inventor should manufacture the product under the expected opportunity loss criterion.

Answer to Review Problem 10

	Payoff Table		Opportunity Loss	
Outcome	A_1: Sell	A_2: Manufacture	A_1	A_2
O_1: Small	150*	−100	0	250
O_2: Medium	300	500*	200	0
O_3: Large	750	1,250*	500	0

Computation of Expected Opportunity Loss ($000s)
A_1: Sell

Outcome	Probability	Opportunity Loss	Weighted Opportunity Loss
O_1: Small	0.2	0	0
O_2: Medium	0.7	200	140
O_3: Large	0.1	500	50
			190

Expected opportunity loss $(A_1) = \$190$

Answer to Review Problem 10 (*continued*)

A_2: Manufacture

Outcome	Probability	Opportunity Loss	Weighted Opportunity Loss
O_1: Small	0.2	250	50
O_2: Medium	0.7	0	0
O_3: Large	0.1	0	0
			50

Expected opportunity loss $(A_2) = \boxed{\$50}$

---

11. The inventor should manufacture the product under the minimax opportunity loss criterion.

Opportunity Loss Table

Outcome	A_1 Sell	A_2 Manufacture
O_1: Small	0	250
O_2: Medium	200	0
O_3: Large	500	0
	500	$\boxed{250}$

---

12. Expected Value of Perfect Information (EVPI)
    EVPI = Expected Profit + Expected Opportunity Loss
    $$= 455 + 50 = 505$$

CHAPTER 15

Answers to Problems

1. See table. From Problem 2 (Chapter 14) the prior probabilities are $P(O_1) = 0.4$ and $P(O_2) = 0.6$
   The conditional probabilities are:

   $P(X_2|O_1) = 0.2$ The probability that the weatherman predicts cold given that it is actually hot.
   $P(X_2|O_2) = 0.8$ The probability that the weatherman predicts cold given that it is actually cold.

Answer to Problem 1

Computation of Posterior Probabilities

Event	Prior $P(O_i)$	Conditional $P(X_2\|O_i)$	Joint $P(O_i) \cdot P(X_2\|O_i)$	Posterior $P(O_i\|X_2)$
O_1: Hot	0.4	0.2	0.08	$\dfrac{0.08}{0.56} = 0.143$
O_2: Cold	0.6	0.8	0.48	$\dfrac{0.48}{0.56} = 0.857$
			0.56	1.000

---

2. See table. Hot chocolate should be sold using the expected posterior profits criterion.

Answer to Problem 2

Calculation of Posterior Expected Profits
A_1**: Hot Chocolate**

Event	Posterior Probability	Profit	Weighted Profit
O_1: Hot	0.143	−50	−7.15
O_2: Cold	0.857	1,500	1,285.5
			1,278.35

Expected posterior profits $(A_1) = \boxed{\$1,278.35}$

A_2**: Cold Drinks**

Event	Posterior Probability	Profit	Weighted Profit
O_1: Hot	0.143	1,000	143
O_2: Cold	0.857	100	85.7
			228.7

Expected posterior profits $(A_2) = \$228.70$

---

3. See table.

Answer to Problem 3

**Calculation of Posterior Expected Profit with
Perfect Information**

Event	Profit	Posterior Probability	Weighted Profit
O_1: Hot	1,000	0.143	143
O_2: Cold	1,500	0.857	1,288.5
			1,431.5

Posterior expected profit with perfect
information = \$1,431.50

Calculation of Posterior Expected Value of Perfect Information

Posterior expected profit with perfect information	\$1,431.50
Less: Posterior expected profit under uncertainty	−1,278.35
Posterior expected value of perfect information	\$ 153.15

4. See table. The shipment should be accepted using the prior expected opportunity loss criterion.

Answer to Problem 4

Prior Expected Opportunity Losses
A_1: Reject the Shipment

Event p	Prior Probability $P_0(p)$	Opportunity Loss	Weighted Opportunity Loss
0.05	0.70	50	35
0.10	0.30	0	0
			35

EOL (A_1) = \$35

A_2: Accept the Shipment

Event p	Prior Probability $P_0(p)$	Opportunity Loss	Weighted Opportunity Loss
0.05	0.70	0	0
0.10	0.30	100	30
			30

EOL (A_2) = $\boxed{\$30}$

---

5. See table. The shipment should be rejected using the posterior expected opportunity loss criterion.

Answer to Problem 5

Computation of Posterior Probabilities Incorporating Evidence Based on a Sample of Size 20

Event p	Prior Probability $P_0(p)$	Conditional Probability $P(X = 2 \mid n = 20, p)$	Joint Probability $P_0(p) \cdot P(X = 2 \mid n = 20, p)$	Posterior Probability $P_1(p)$
0.05	0.70	0.1887	0.13	0.59
0.10	0.30	0.2852	0.09	0.41
	1.00		0.22	1.00

Posterior Expected Opportunity Losses
A_1: Reject the Shipment

Event p	Posterior Probability $P_1(p)$	Opportunity Loss	Weighted Opportunity Loss
0.05	0.59	50	29.5
0.10	0.41	0	0
			29.5

Posterior EOL (A_1) = \$29.5

Answer to Problem 5 (*continued*)

A_2: Accept the Shipment

Event p	Posterior Probability $P_1(p)$	Opportunity Loss	Weighted Opportunity Loss
0.05	0.59	0	0
0.10	0.41	100	41
			41

Posterior EOL $(A_2) = \$41$

---

6. See table.

Answer to Problem 6

Calculation of the Prior Mean for the Proportion of Defectives

Event p	Prior Probability $P_0(p)$	$pP_0(p)$
0.05	0.70	0.035
0.10	0.30	0.03
		0.065

Prior mean: $E_0(p) = 0.065$

Calculation of the Posterior Mean for the Proportion of Defectives

Event p	Posterior Probability $P_1(p)$	$pP_1(p)$
0.05	0.59	0.030
0.10	0.41	0.041
		0.071

Posterior mean: $E_1(p) = 0.071$

Answers to Review Problems

1. See table. The conditional probabilities are:
   $P(X_1 \mid O_1) = 0.90$
   $P(X_1 \mid O_2) = 0.20$
   From Review Problem 1 in Chapter 14
   $P(O_1) = 0.6$
   $P(O_2) = 0.4$

Answer to Review Problem 1

Computation of Posterior Probabilities

Event	Prior $P(O_i)$	Conditional $P(X_1 \mid O_i)$	Joint $P(O_i) \cdot P(X_1 \mid O_i)$	Posterior $P(O_i \mid X_1)$
O_1: Growth	0.6	0.9	0.54	0.871
O_2: Recession	0.4	0.2	0.08	0.129
			0.62	1.000

2. See table. The professor should purchase Stock C using the expected posterior profits criterion.

Answer to Review Problem 2

Calculations of Posterior Expected Profits ($000s)

A_1: Stock A

Event	Posterior Probability	Profit	Weighted Profit
O_1: Growth	0.871	50	43.55
O_2: Recession	0.129	20	2.58
			46.13

Expected posterior profits $(A_1) = \$46.13$

A_2: Stock B

Event	Posterior Probability	Profit	Weighted Profit
O_1: Growth	0.871	75	65.33
O_2: Recession	0.129	-30	-3.87
			61.46

Expected posterior profits $(A_2) = \$61.46$

A_3: Stock C

Event	Posterior Probability	Profit	Weighted Profit
O_1: Growth	0.871	110	95.81
O_2: Recession	0.129	-65	-8.39
			87.42

Expected posterior profits $(A_3) = \boxed{\$87.42}$

3. See Table.

Answer to Review Problem 3

Calculation of Posterior Expected Profit with Perfect Information

Event	Profit	Posterior Probability	Weighted Profit
O_1: Growth	110	0.871	95.81
O_2: Recession	20	0.129	2.58
			98.39

Posterior Expected Profit with Perfect Information = $98.39

Calculation of Posterior Expected Value with Perfect Information ($000s)

Posterior expected profit with perfect information	$98.39
Less: Posterior expected profit under uncertainty	−87.42
Posterior expected value with perfect information	$10.97

4. See Table. The shipment should be rejected using the prior expected opportunity loss criterion.

Answer to Review Problem 4

Prior Expected Opportunity Losses
A_1: Reject the Shipment

Event p	Prior Probability $P_0(p)$	Opportunity Loss	Weighted Opportunity Loss
0.10	0.60	50	30
0.15	0.30	0	0
0.20	0.10	0	0
			30

$$EOL(A_1) = \boxed{\$30}$$

A_2: Accept the Shipment

Event p	Prior Probability $P_0(p)$	Opportunity Loss	Weighted Opportunity Loss
0.10	0.60	0	0
0.15	0.30	100	30
0.20	0.10	200	20
			50

$$EOL(A_2) = \$50$$

5. See table. The shipment should be rejected using the posterior expected opportunity loss criterion.

Answer to Review Problem 5

Computation of Posterior Probabilities Incorporating Evidence, Based on a Sample of Size 20

Event p	Prior Probability $P_0(p)$	Conditional Probability $P(X = 3 \mid n = 20, p)$	Joint Probability $P_0(p) \cdot P(X = 3 \mid n = 20, p)$	Posterior Probability $P_1(p)$
0.10	0.60	0.1901	0.114	0.55
0.15	0.30	0.2428	0.073	0.35
0.20	0.10	0.2054	0.021	0.10
			0.208	1.00

Posterior Expected Opportunity Losses

A_1: Reject the Shipment

Event p	Posterior Probability $P_1(p)$	Opportunity Loss	Weighted Opportunity Loss
0.10	0.55	50	27.5
0.15	0.35	0	0
0.20	0.10	0	0
			27.5

Posterior EOL $(A_1) = \boxed{\$27.5}$

A_2: Accept the Shipment

Event p	Posterior Probability $P_1(p)$	Opportunity Loss	Weighted Opportunity Loss
0.10	0.55	0	0
0.15	0.35	100	35
0.20	0.10	200	20
			55

Posterior EOL $(A_2) = \$55$

---

6. See table.

Answer to Review Problem 6

**Calculation of the Prior Mean for the
Proportion of Defectives**

Event p	Prior Probability $P_0(p)$	$pP_0(p)$
0.10	0.60	0.06
0.15	0.30	0.045
0.20	0.10	0.02
		0.125

Prior mean: $E_0(p) = 0.125$

**Calculation of the Posterior Mean for the
Proportion of Defectives**

Event p	Posterior Probability $P_1(p)$	$pP_1(p)$
0.10	0.55	0.055
0.15	0.35	0.053
0.20	0.10	0.02
		0.128

Posterior mean: $E_1(p) = 0.128$

---

7. See table. The shipment should be rejected using the prior expected opportunity loss criterion.

Answer to Review Problem 7

**Prior Expected Opportunity Loss
A_1: Reject the Shipment**

Event p	Prior Probability $P_0(p)$	Opportunity Loss	Weighted Opportunity Loss
0.10	0.40	50	20
0.20	0.60	0	0
			20

EOL $(A_1) = \boxed{\$20}$

Answer to Review Problem 7 (*continued*)

A_2: Accept the Shipment

Event p	Prior Probability $P_0(p)$	Opportunity Loss	Weighted Opportunity Loss
0.10	0.40	0	0
0.20	0.60	150	90
			90

EOL (A_2) = $90

---

8. See table. The shipment should be rejected using the posterior expected opportunity loss criterion.

Answer to Review Problem 8

Computation of Posterior Probabilities Incorporating Evidence Based on a Sample of Size 10

Event p	Prior Probability $P_0(p)$	Conditional Probability $P(X = 1 \mid n = 10, p)$	Joint Probability $P_0(p) \cdot P(X = 1 \mid n = 10, p)$	Posterior Probability $P_1(p)$
0.10	0.40	0.3874	0.155	0.49
0.20	0.60	0.2684	0.161	0.51
			0.316	1.00

Posterior Expected Opportunity Loss
A_1: Reject the Shipment

Event p	Posterior Probability $P_1(p)$	Opportunity Loss	Weighted Opportunity Loss
0.10	0.49	50	24.5
0.20	0.51	0	0
			24.5

Posterior EOL (A_1) = $24.5

A_2: Accept the Shipment

Event p	Posterior Probability $P_1(p)$	Opportunity Loss	Weighted Opportunity Loss
0.10	0.49	0	0
0.20	0.51	150	76.5
			76.5

Posterior EOL (A_2) = $76.5

9. See table.

Answer to Review Problem 9

Calculation of the Prior Mean for the Proportion of Defectives

Event p	Prior Probability $P_o(p)$	$pP_o(p)$
0.10	0.40	0.04
0.20	0.60	0.12
		0.16

Prior mean: $E_0(p) = 0.16$

Calculation of the Posterior Mean for the Proportion of Defectives

Event p	Posterior Probability $P_1(p)$	$pP_1(p)$
0.10	0.49	0.049
0.20	0.51	0.102
		0.151

Posterior mean: $E_1(p) = 0.151$

---

10. See table. The conditional probabilities are:

$$P(X_2 \mid O_1) = 0.2 \quad P(X_2 \mid O_2) = 0.8 \quad P(X_2 \mid O_3) = 0.1$$

From Review Problem 8, Chapter 14, $P(O_1) = 0.2$, $P(O_2) = 0.7$, $P(O_3) = 0.1$.

Answer to Review Problem 10

Computation of Posterior Probabilities

Event	Prior $P(O_i)$	Conditional $P(X_2 \mid O_i)$	Joint $P(O_i) \cdot P(X_2 \mid O_i)$	Posterior $P(O_i \mid X_2)$
O_1: Small	0.2	0.2	0.04	0.066
O_2: Medium	0.7	0.8	0.56	0.918
O_3: Large	0.1	0.1	0.01	0.016
			0.61	1.000

---

11. See table. The inventor should manufacture the product under the expected posterior profits criterion.

Answer to Review Problem 11

Calculation of Posterior Expected Profits ($000s)
A_1: Sell

Event	Posterior Probabilities	Profit	Weighted Profit
O_1: Small	0.066	150	9.9
O_2: Medium	0.918	300	275.4
O_3: Large	0.016	750	12.0
			297.3

Expected posterior profits (A_1) = $297.3

A_2: Manufacture

Event	Posterior Probabilities	Profit	Weighted Profit
O_1: Small	0.066	-100	-6.6
O_2: Medium	0.918	500	459.0
O_3: Large	0.016	1,250	20.0
			472.4

Expected posterior profits (A_2) = $472.4

---

12. See table.

Answer to Review Problem 12

Calculation of Posterior Expected Profit with Perfect Information

Event	Profit	Posterior Probability	Weighted Profit
O_1: Small	150	0.066	9.9
O_2: Medium	500	0.918	459.0
O_3: Large	1250	0.016	20.0
			488.9

Posterior expected profit with perfect information = $488.90

Calculation of Posterior Expected Value with Perfect Information

Posterior expected profit with perfect information	$488.90
Less: Posterior expected profit under uncertainty	-472.40
Posterior expected value with perfect information	$ 16.50

CHAPTER 16

Answers to Problems

1. See diagram; see table. Using the prior expected opportunity loss criterion, Dr. Egan should enter, as shown in part (a) of the table. Using the posterior expected opportunity loss criterion, Dr. Egan should enter if the survey indicates a success, as shown in part (b) of the table. Using the posterior expected opportunity loss criterion, Dr. Egan should enter if the survey is inconclusive, as shown in part (c) of the table. Using the posterior expected opportunity loss criterion, Dr. Egan should not enter if the survey indicates a failure, as shown in part (d) of the table. The survey should not be taken, and Dr. Egan should enter the business, as shown in part (e) of the table.

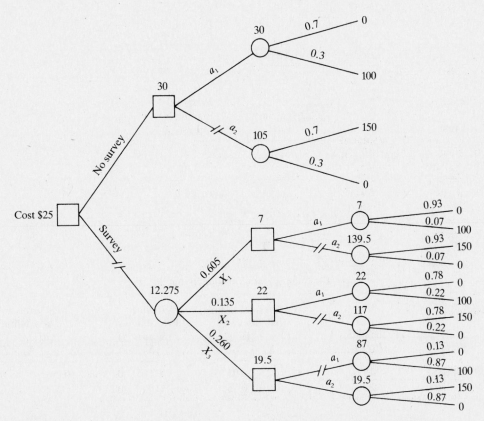

Answer to Problem 1: Decision diagram for preposterior analysis for Dr. Egan problem

a.

Answer to Problem 1

Calculation of Prior Expected Opportunity Losses ($000s)
A_1: Enter

Event	Probability	Opportunity Loss	Weighted Opportunity Loss
O_1: Success	0.7	0	0
O_2: Failure	0.3	100	30
	1.0		30

Prior EOL (A_1) = $\boxed{\$30}$

A_2: Don't Enter

Event	Probability	Opportunity Loss	Weighted Opportunity Loss
O_1: Success	0.7	150	105
O_2: Failure	0.3	0	0
	1.0		105

Prior EOL (A_2) = $105

b.

Computation of Posterior Probabilities

Event	Prior Probabilities $P(O_i)$	Conditional Probabilities $P(X_i \mid O_i)$ X_1	X_2	X_3	Joint Probabilities $P(X_i \text{ and } O_i)$ X_1	X_2	X_3	Posterior Probabilities $P(O_i \mid X_i)$ X_1	X_2	X_3
O_1: Success	0.7	0.80	0.15	0.05	0.56	0.105	0.035	0.93	0.78	0.13
O_2: Failure	0.3	0.15	0.10	0.75	0.045	0.03	0.225	0.07	0.22	0.87
					0.605	0.135	0.260			

Posterior Expected Opportunity Losses for Survey Indicating a Success
A_1: Enter

Event	Posterior Probability	Opportunity Loss	Weighted Opportunity Loss
O_1: Success	0.93	0	0
O_2: Failure	0.07	100	7
			7

Posterior EOL (A_1) = $\boxed{\$7}$

Answer to Problem 1 (*continued*)

A_2: Don't Enter

Event	Posterior Probability	Opportunity Loss	Weighted Opportunity Loss
O_1: Success	0.93	150	139.5
O_2: Failure	0.07	0	0
			139.5

Posterior EOL $(A_2) = \$139.5$

c.

Posterior Expected Opportunity Losses for Inconclusive Survey
A_1: Enter

Event	Posterior Probability	Opportunity Loss	Weighted Opportunity Loss
O_1: Success	0.78	0	0
O_2: Failure	0.22	100	22
			22

Posterior EOL $(A_1) = \boxed{\$22}$

A_2: Don't Enter

Event	Posterior Probability	Opportunity Loss	Weighted Opportunity Loss
O_1: Success	0.78	150	117
O_2: Failure	0.22	0	0
			117

Posterior EOL $(A_2) = \$117$

d.

Posterior Expected Opportunity Losses for Survey
Indicating a Failure
A_1: Enter

Event	Posterior Probability	Opportunity Loss	Weighted Opportunity Loss
O_1: Success	0.13	0	0
O_2: Failure	0.87	100	87
			87

Posterior EOL $(A_1) = \$87$

Answer to Problem 1 (*continued*)

A_2: Don't Enter

Event	Posterior Probability	Opportunity Loss	Weighted Opportunity Loss
O_1: Success	0.13	150	19.5
O_2: Failure	0.87	0	0
			19.5

Posterior EOL(A_2) = $\boxed{\$19.5}$

---

e.

Calculation of Expected Opportunity Loss of Taking the Survey

Survey Outcome	$P(X_i)$	EOL(X_i)	Weighted Opportunity Loss
X_1: Success	0.605	7	4.235
X_2: Inconclusive	0.135	22	2.97
X_3: Failure	0.260	19.5	5.07
	1.000		12.275

EOL when survey is taken = $12.275

EVSI = EOL without a survey (prior EOL) − EOL with a sample = 30 − 12.275 = $17.725

ENGS = EVSI − cost of survey = $17.725 − 25 = $−7.275

2. See table. Strategies s_2 and s_4 are the only feasible ones as shown in part (a) of the table. Strategy s_2 minimizes the EOL with a sample, as shown in part (b) of the table.

Note: The EOL with a survey in Problem 1 is $12.275 and in Problem 2 it is $12.75. As stated before, these values should be equal. However, due to rounding error, they are not. The actual EOL with a survey is $12.75. The EOL with a survey is $30. This was computed in Problem 1 as the Prior EOL. EVSI = 30 − 12.75 = 17.25; ENGS = 17.25 − 25 = −7.75. Thus, as in Problem 1, the sample survey should not be taken, and Dr. Egan should enter the business.

a.

Answer to Problem 2

A List of All Possible Strategies

Survey Outcome	s_1	s_2	s_3	s_4	s_5	s_6	s_7	s_8
X_1	a_1	a_1	a_1	a_1	a_2	a_2	a_2	a_2
X_2	a_1	a_1	a_2	a_2	a_1	a_1	a_2	a_2
X_3	a_1	a_2	a_1	a_2	a_1	a_2	a_1	a_2

Answer to Problem 2 (*continued*)

Calculation of Risks, or Conditional Expected Opportunity Losses, for Strategies s_2 and s_4 ($000s)

s_2

State of Nature	Opportunity Loss		Probability of Action $s_2(a_1, a_1, a_2)$			Risk (conditional expected loss) $R(s_2 \mid O_i)$
	a_1	a_2	a_1	a_1	a_2	
O_1	0	150	0.80	0.15	0.05	7.5
O_2	100	0	0.15	0.10	0.75	25.0

$R(s_2 \mid O_1) = 0.8(0) + 0.15(0) + 0.05(150) = 7.5$

$R(s_2 \mid O_2) = 0.15(100) + 0.10(100) + 0.75(10) = 25$

---

s_4

State of Nature	Opportunity Loss		Probability of Action $s_4(a_1, a_2, a_2)$			Risk (conditional expected loss) $s_4(a_1, a_2, a_2)$ $R(s_4 \mid O_i)$
	a_1	a_2	a_1	a_2	a_2	
O_1	0	150	0.80	0.15	0.05	30
O_2	100	0	0.15	0.10	0.75	15

$R(s_4 \mid O_1) = 0.80(0) + (0.15)(150) + 0.05(150) = 30$

$R(s_4 \mid O_2) = 0.15(100) + (0.10)(10) + 0.75(0) = 15$

$$\text{EOL}(s_2) = 0.7(7.5) + 0.3(25) = \boxed{\$12.75}$$

$$\text{EOL}(s_4) = 0.7(30) + 0.3(15) = \$25.5$$

---

3. From Problem 2: $R(s_2 \mid O_1) = 7.5$, $R(s_2 \mid O_2) = 25$, $R(s_4 \mid O_1) = 30$, $R(s_4 \mid O_2) = 15$

$$p(7.5) + (1 - p)25 = p(30) + (1 - p)15$$
$$10 = 32.5p$$
$$p = 10/32.5 = 0.30769$$

If $p(O_1) < 0.30769$, then follow s_4. If $p(O_1) > 0.30769$, then follow s_2.

4. See table. If there are no defectives in the sample, you should accept the shipment, as shown in part (a) of the table. If there is one defective in the sample, you should reject the shipment, as shown in part (b) of the table. If there are two defectives in the sample, you should reject the shipment, as shown in part (c) of the table. Part (d) of the table demonstrates that $P(X_i)$ is the sum of the joint probabilities for each X_i. A sample should not be taken. This is the same result as we obtained using the normal-form analysis, except for some rounding error.

$$\text{EOL without a sample} = \quad 45$$
$$\text{Less: EOL with a sample} = \underline{-42.56}$$
$$\text{EVSI} = \quad \$2.44$$

$$\text{ENGS} = \text{EVSI} - \text{cost of sample} = 2.44 - 10 = \$-7.56$$

Answer to Problem 4

Basic Data for Acceptance Sampling for the Orange Example

Event p (lot proportion of defectives)	Prior Probability $P_0(p)$	Opportunity Loss a_1	Opportunity Loss a_2
0.05	0.10	150	0
0.10	0.60	75	0
0.15	0.30	0	150

Prior EOL(A_1) = \$60

Prior EOL(A_2) = $\boxed{\$45}$

Computations of Posterior Probabilities

Event	Prior Probabilities $P_0(p)$	Conditional Probabilities $P(X\|p)$ $X = 0$	$X = 1$	$X = 2$	Joint Probabilities $P(p \text{ and } X)$ $X = 0$	$X = 1$	$X = 2$	Posterior Probabilities $P(p\|X)$ $X = 0$	$X = 1$	$X = 2$
0.05	0.10	0.9025	0.095	0.0025	0.09025	0.0095	0.00025	0.114	0.05	0.02
0.10	0.60	0.81	0.18	0.01	0.486	0.108	0.006	0.613	0.56	0.46
0.15	0.30	0.7225	0.255	0.0225	0.21675	0.0765	0.00675	0.273	0.39	0.52
					0.793	0.194	0.013	1.000	1.00	1.00

The conditional probabilites are found using Table A-2.

---

a.

Posterior EOL for $X = 0$ (no defectives)
A_1: Reject

Event	Posterior Probability	Opportunity Loss	Weighted Opportunity Loss
$p = 0.05$	0.114	150	17.1
$p = 0.10$	0.613	75	46.0
$p = 0.15$	0.273	0	0
			63.1

Posterior EOL (A_1) = \$63.1

Answer to Problem 4 (*continued*)

A_2: Accept

Event	Posterior Probability	Opportunity Loss	Weighted Opportunity Loss
$p = 0.05$	0.114	0	0
$p = 0.10$	0.613	0	0
$p = 0.15$	0.273	150	40.95
			40.95

Posterior EOL (A_2) = $\boxed{\$40.95}$

b.

Posterior EOL for $X = 1$ (one defective)
A_1: Reject

Event	Posterior Probability	Opportunity Loss	Weighted Opportunity Loss
$p = 0.05$	0.05	150	7.5
$p = 0.10$	0.56	75	42.0
$p = 0.15$	0.39	0	0
			49.5

Posterior EOL (A_1) = $\boxed{\$49.5}$

A_2: Accept

Event	Posterior Probability	Opportunity Loss	Weighted Opportunity Loss
$p = 0.05$	0.05	0	0
$p = 0.10$	0.56	0	0
$p = 0.15$	0.39	150	58.5
			58.5

Posterior EOL (A_2) = \$58.5

c.

Posterior EOL for $X = 2$ (two defectives)
A_1: Reject

Event	Posterior Probability	Opportunity Loss	Weighted Opportunity Loss
$p = 0.05$	0.02	150	3
$p = 0.10$	0.46	75	34.5
$p = 0.15$	0.52	0	0
			37.5

Posterior EOL (A_1) = $\boxed{\$37.5}$

Answer to Problem 4 (*continued*)

A_2: Accept

Event	Posterior Probability	Opportunity Loss	Weighted Opportunity Loss
$p = 0.05$	0.02	0	0
$p = 0.10$	0.46	0	0
$p = 0.15$	0.52	150	78
			78

Posterior EOL $(A_2) = \$78$

---

d.

EOL of Taking the Sample

X_i	$P(X_i)$	$EOL \mid X_i$	Weighted Opportunity Loss
X_1	0.793	40.95	32.47
X_2	0.194	49.5	9.60
X_3	0.013	37.5	0.49
	1.000		42.56

EOL of taking a sample $= \$42.56$

Answers to Review Problems

1. See table. Using the Prior EOL criterion, shown in part (a), the firms should merge.

   X_1 = She predicts that it will be allowed.
   X_2 = She predicts that it will not be allowed.

   If the consultant predicts the merger will be allowed, you should merge as indicated in part (b) of the table.

   If the consultant predicts the merger will not be allowed, you should not merge as indicated in part (c) of the table.

   According to part (d) of the table, the consultant should be hired.

a.

Answer to Review Problem 1

Calculation of Prior EOL ($000s)
A_1: Merge

Event	Probability	Opportunity Loss	Weighted Opportunity Loss
O_1: Allowed	0.7	0	0
O_2: Disallowed	0.3	200	60
			60

Prior EOL $(A_1) = \boxed{\$60}$

Answer to Review Problem 1 (*continued*)

A_2: Don't Merge

Event	Probability	Opportunity Loss	Weighted Opportunity Loss
O_1: Allowed	0.7	150	105
O_2: Disallowed	0.3	0	0
			105

Prior EOL $(A_2) = \$105$

b.

Computation of Posterior Probabilities

Event	Prior Prob. $P(O_i)$	Conditional Prob. $P(X_i\|O_i)$		Joint Prob. $P(X_i \text{ and } O_i)$		Posterior Prob. $P(O_i\|X_i)$	
		X_1	X_2	X_1	X_2	X_1	X_2
O_1: Allowed	0.7	0.9	0.1	0.63	0.07	0.91	0.23
O_2: Disallowed	0.3	0.2	0.8	0.06	0.24	0.09	0.77
				0.69	0.31	1.00	1.00

c.

Posterior EOL When She Predicts It Will Be Allowed ($000s)
A_1: Merge

Event	Posterior Probability	Opportunity Loss	Weighted Opportunity Loss
O_1: Allowed	0.91	0	0
O_2: Disallowed	0.09	200	18
			18

Posterior EOL $(A_1) = \boxed{\$18}$

A_2: Don't Merge

Event	Posterior Probability	Opportunity Loss	Weighted Opportunity Loss
O_1: Allowed	0.91	150	136.5
O_2: Disallowed	0.09	0	0
			136.5

Posterior EOL $(A_2) = \$136.5$

Answer to Review Problem 1 (*continued*)

Posterior EOL When She Predicts It Will Not Be Allowed ($000s)
A_1: Merge

Event	Posterior Probability	Opportunity Loss	Weighted Opportunity Loss
O_1: Allowed	0.23	0	0
O_2: Disallowed	0.77	200	154
			154

Posterior EOL $(A_1) = \$154$

A_2: Don't Merge

Event	Posterior Probability	Opportunity Loss	Weighted Opportunity Loss
O_1: Allowed	0.23	150	34.5
O_2: Disallowed	0.77	0	0
			34.5

Posterior EOL $(A_2) = \boxed{\$34.5}$

---

d.

Computation of the EOL When Consultant Is Hired ($000s)

X_i	$P(X_i)$	$EOL \mid X_i$	Weighted Opportunity Loss
X_1: Predicts allowed	0.69	18	12.42
X_2: Predicts disallowed	0.31	34.5	10.70
			23.12

EOL when consultant is hired = $23.12

EOL without consultant = 60
Less: EOL with consultant = −23.12
EVSI = 26.88

ENGS = EVSI − Cost of consultant = $26.88 − $5 = $21.88

---

2. See table. A listing of all possible strategies in merger problem (see part (a) of the table) shows that s_2 is the only feasible strategy. According to part (b) of the table, the consultant should be hired.

a.

Answer to Review Problem 2

Sample Outcome	Strategy			
	s_1	s_2	s_3	s_4
X_1: Predicts allowed	a_1	a_1	a_2	a_2
X_2: Predicts not allowed	a_1	a_2	a_1	a_2

b.

Answer to Review Problem 2 (*continued*)

Calculation of Risks, or Conditional EOL of s_2 ($000s)

State of Nature	Opportunity Loss a_1	a_2	Probability Action $s_2(a_1, a_2)$ a_1	a_2	Risk (conditional expected loss) $R(s_2 \mid O_i)$
O_1: Allowed	0	150	0.9	0.1	15
O_2: Disallowed	200	0	0.2	0.8	40

$$\text{EOL}(s_2) = 0.7(15) + 0.3(40) = \$22.5$$

Note: The difference in EOL (s_2) and EOL when consultant is hired is due to rounding error.

$$
\begin{array}{ll}
\text{EOL without consultant} = & 60 \text{ (see answer to Review Problem 1)} \\
\text{Less: EOL } (s_2) \text{ with consultant} = & -22.5 \\
\hline
\text{EVSI} = & 27.5
\end{array}
$$

$$\text{ENGS} = \text{EVSI} - \text{cost of consultant} = \$27.5 - \$5 = \$22.5$$

3. $p(5) + (1 - p)12 = 10p + (1 - p)6$
$$p = 6/11$$
If $P(O_1) > 0.54545$, follow s_1.   If $P(O_1) < 0.54545$, follow s_5.

4. See table. Normal-form analysis: A listing of all possible strategies (see part (a) of table) reveals that s_5 and s_7 are the only feasible strategies. As part (b) of the table shows, s_5 is the optimal strategy. EOL with a sample is $40.175. EOL without a sample is $30. Strategy s_1 is the strategy that will actually minimize EOL $[\text{EOL}(s_1) = 30]$. However, under s_1, no matter what the sample outcome is, you will reject the shipment. Thus, there is no need to take a sample, and the shipment should be rejected.

Answer to Review Problem 4

Basic Data for Acceptance Sampling

Event p (lot proportion of defectives)	Prior Probability $P_0(p)$	Opportunity Loss a_1 Reject	a_2 Accept
0.10	0.60	50	0
0.15	0.30	0	100
0.20	0.10	0	200

Prior EOL $(A_1) = \boxed{\$30}$ Prior EOL $(A_2) = \$50$

a.

Sample Outcome (number of defectives)	s_1	s_2	s_3	s_4	s_5	s_6	s_7	s_8
$X = 0$	a_1	a_1	a_1	a_1	a_2	a_2	a_2	a_2
$X = 1$	a_1	a_1	a_2	a_2	a_1	a_1	a_2	a_2
$X = 2$	a_1	a_2	a_1	a_2	a_1	a_2	a_1	a_2

Answer to Review Problem 4 (*continued*)

b.

Calculation of Risks, Conditional EOL, for s_5 and s_7 ($000s)

s_5

Event p(lot proportion of defectives)	Opportunity Loss a_1	a_2	Probability of Action $s_5(a_2, a_1, a_1)$ X = 0 a_2	X = 1 a_1	X = 2 a_1	Risk (conditional expected loss) $R(s_7 \mid p, n = 2)$
0.10	50	0	0.81	0.18	0.01	9.5
0.15	0	100	0.7225	0.2550	0.0225	72.25
0.20	0	200	0.64	0.32	0.04	128

$R(s_5 \mid p = 0.10, n = 2) = 0.81(0) + 0.18(50) + 0.01(50) = 9.5$

$R(s_5 \mid p = 0.15, n = 2) = 0.7225(100) + 0.2550(0) + 0.0225(0) = 72.25$

$R(s_5 \mid p = 0.20, n = 2) = 0.64(200) + 0.32(0) + 0.04(0) = 128$

s_7

Event p(lot proportion of defectives)	Opportunity Loss a_1	a_2	Probability of Action $s_7(a_2, a_2, a_1)$ X = 0 a_2	X = 1 a_2	X = 2 a_1	Risk (conditional expected loss) $R(s_7 \mid p, n = 2)$
0.10	50	0	0.81	0.18	0.01	0.5
0.15	0	100	0.7225	0.2550	0.0225	97.75
0.20	0	200	0.64	0.32	0.04	192.0

$R(s_7 \mid p = 0.10, n = 2) = 0.81(0) + 0.18(0) + 0.01(50) = 0.5$

$R(s_7 \mid p = 0.15, n = 2) = 0.7225(100) + 0.2550(100) + 0.0225(0) = 97.75$

$R(s_7 \mid p = 0.20, n = 2) = 0.64(200) + 0.32(200) + 0.04(0) = 192$

$EOL(s_5) = 0.6(9.5) + 0.3(72.25) + 0.1(128) = \boxed{\$40.175}$

$EOL(s_7) = 0.6(0.5) + 0.3(97.75) + 0.1(192) = \$48.825$

5. See table. A listing of all possible strategies (see part (a) of the table) shows that s_5 and s_7 are the only feasible strategies. As part (b) of the table shows, strategy s_5 is the optimal strategy.

However, EOL with a sample is $61.40. EOL without a sample is $30. The optimal decision is to not take a sample and to reject the shipment.

Answer to Review Problem 5

Basic Data for Acceptance Sampling

Event p (lot proportion of defectives)	Prior Probability $P_0(p)$	Opportunity Loss a_1 Reject	a_2 Accept
0.10	0.40	50	0
0.20	0.60	0	150

$EOL\,(A_1) = \boxed{\$20}$ $EOL\,(A_2) = \$90$

Answer to Review Problem 5 (*continued*)

a.

Sample Outcome (number of defectives)	Strategies							
	s_1	s_2	s_3	s_4	s_5	s_6	s_7	s_8
$X = 0$	a_1	a_1	a_1	a_1	a_2	a_2	a_2	a_2
$X = 1$	a_1	a_1	a_2	a_2	a_1	a_1	a_2	a_2
$X = 2$	a_1	a_2	a_2	a_1	a_1	a_2	a_1	a_2

b.

Calculation of Risks, Conditional EOL, for s_5 and s_7 ($000s)

s_5

Event p(lot proportions of defectives)	Opportunity loss		Probability of Action $s_5(a_2, a_1, a_1)$			Risk (conditional expected loss)
	a_1	a_2	$X = 0$ a_2	$X = 1$ a_1	$X = 2$ a_1	$R(s_5 \mid p, n = 2)$
0.10	50	0	0.81	0.18	0.01	9.5
0.20	0	150	0.64	0.32	0.04	96

$R(s_5 \mid p = 0.10, n = 2) = 0.81(0) + 0.18(50) + 0.01(50) = 9.5$

$R(s_5 \mid p = 0.20, n = 2) = 0.64(150) + 0.32(0) + 0.04(0) = 96$

s_7

Event p(lot proportions of defectives)	Opportunity Loss		Probability of Action $s_7(a_2, a_2, a_1)$			Risk (conditional expected loss)
	a_1	a_2	$X = 0$ a_2	$X = 1$ a_2	$X = 2$ a_1	$R(s_7 \mid p, n = 2)$
0.10	50	0	0.81	0.18	0.01	0.5
0.20	0	150	0.64	0.32	0.04	144

$R(s_7 \mid p = 0.10, n = 2) = 0.81(0) + 0.18(0) + 0.01(50) = 0.5$

$R(s_7 \mid p = 0.20, n = 2) = 0.64(150) + 0.32(150) + 0.04(0) = 144$

$EOL(s_5) = 0.4(9.5) + 0.6(96) = \boxed{\$61.4}$ $EOL(s_7) = 0.4(0.5) + 0.6(144) = \$86.6$

6. See table. According to part (a) of the table, with the prior EOL criterion, the parade should be postponed. Normal-form analysis: A list of all possible strategies (see part (b) of the table) shows that strategies s_5 and s_7 are the only feasible strategies. Part (c) shows that strategy s_5 is the optimal strategy. Part (d) shows that the meteorologist should be hired. If he predicts rain, then the parade should be postponed; if he is unsure or predicts no rain, the parade should be allowed.

a.

Answer to Review Problem 6

Calculation of Prior EOL ($000s)
A_1: Allow

Event	Probability	Opportunity Loss	Weighted Opportunity Loss
O_1: Rain	0.6	5	3
O_2: Don't rain	0.4	0	0
			3

EOL (A_1) = $3

A_2: Postpone

Event	Probability	Opportunity Loss	Weighted Opportunity Loss
O_1: Rain	0.6	0	0
O_2: Don't rain	0.4	3	1.2

EOL (A_2) = $1.2

b.

Outcome	s_1	s_2	s_3	s_4	s_5	s_6	s_7	s_8
X_1: Predicts rain	a_1	a_1	a_1	a_1	a_2	a_2	a_2	a_2
X_2: Not sure	a_1	a_1	a_2	a_2	a_1	a_1	a_2	a_2
X_3: Predicts no rain	a_1	a_2	a_1	a_2	a_1	a_2	a_1	a_2

c.

Calculation of Risks, or Conditional EOL for s_5 and s_7 ($000s)
s_5

State of Nature	Opportunity Loss		Probability of Action $s_5 (a_2, a_1, a_1)$			Risk (Conditional EOL) $R(s_5 \mid O_i)$
	a_1	a_2	a_2	a_1	a_1	
O_1	5	0	0.90	0.05	0.05	0.5
O_2	0	3	0.30	0.20	0.50	0.9

$R(s_5 \mid O_1) = 0.9(0) + 0.05(5) + 0.05(5) = 0.5$

$R(s_5 \mid O_2) = 0.3(3) + 0.2(0) + 0.2(0) = 0.9$

Answer to Review Problem 5 (*continued*)

State of Nature	Opportunity Loss		Probability of Action $s_7 (a_2, a_2, a_1)$			Risk (Conditional EOL) $R(s_7 \mid O_i)$
	a_1	a_2	a_2	a_2	a_1	
O_1	5	0	0.90	0.05	0.05	0.25
O_2	0	3	0.30	0.20	0.50	1.5

$R(s_7 \mid O_1) = 0.9(0) + 0.05(0) + 0.05(5) = 0.25$

$R(s_7 \mid O_2) = 0.3(3) + 0.2(3) + 0.5(0) = 1.5$

---

d.

The EOL without a sample is 1.2. The EOL with a sample is 0.66.

$$\text{EVSI} = 1.2 - 0.66 = 0.54 \qquad \text{ENGS} = 0.54 - 0.5 = 0.04$$

---

7. $p(0.5) + (1 - p)(0.9) = p(0.25) + (1 - p)(1.5)$

$\qquad p = 0.6/0.85 = 0.70588$

If $p(O_1) > 0.70588$, follow s_7. If $p(O_1) < 0.70588$, follow s_5.

CHAPTER 17

Answer to Problem 1

See table. Solved by normal-form analysis, strategies s_3 and s_4 are the only feasible strategies, as shown in part (a) of the table. Strategy s_4 is the optimal strategy, as shown in part (b) of the table.

Classical Hypothesis Test: $H_0 : p = 0.02 \qquad H_1 : p \neq 0.04 \quad \text{or} \quad p \neq 0.06$

Type I Error of s_3 and s_4: $s_3 = 0.06 \qquad s_4 = 0.25$

Using hypothesis testing, we would follow s_3. Thus, Bayesian and classical result in different optimal strategies.

Answer to Problem 1

Calculations for Prior EOL

State of Nature p (lot proportion of defectives)	Prior Probability $P_0(p)$	Act	
		a_1 Reject	a_2 Accept
0.02	0.8	200	0
0.04	0.15	0	300
0.06	0.05	0	600

$\text{EOL}(A_1) = 0.8(200) + 0.15(0) + 0.05(0) = \$160$

$\text{EOL}(A_2) = 0.8(0) + 0.15(300) + 0.05(600) = \boxed{\$75}$

Answer to Problem 1 (*continued*)

a.

Possible Decision Rules Based on Information Derived from Single Samples of Size n

Strategy

Sample Information	s_1	s_2	s_3	s_4	s_5	s_6	s_7	s_8
Type E $(X \leq C_1)$	R	A	A	A	A	R	R	R
Type F $(C_1 < X \leq C_2)$	R	A	A	R	R	A	R	A
Type G $(X > C_2)$	R	A	R	R	A	A	A	R

R: Reject the lot

A: Accept the lot

b.

Calculation of Conditional Probability for Type of Sample Information. Given p

State of Nature p (lot proportion of defectives)	Prior Probability $P_0(p)$	Conditional Probability $P(E \mid p)$	$P(F \mid p)$	$P(G \mid p)$
0.02	0.8	0.75	0.19	0.06
0.04	0.15	0.53	0.33	0.13*
0.06	0.05	0.20	0.40	0.40

* The row doesn't add to 1 because of rounding.

Calculations of Risk, or Conditional EOL for s_3 and s_4

s_3

State of Nature p (lot proportion of defectives)	Opportunity Loss R	A	Probability of Action $s_3(A, A, R)$ A	A	R	Risk (conditional losses) $R(s_3 \mid p_i, n)$
0.02	200	0	0.75	0.19	0.06	12
0.04	0	300	0.53	0.33	0.13	258
0.06	0	600	0.20	0.40	0.40	360

$R(s_3 \mid p = 0.02, n) = 0.75(0) + 0.19(0) + 0.06(200) = 12$

$R(s_3 \mid p = 0.04, n) = 0.53(300) + 0.33(300) + 0.13(0) = 258$

$R(s_3 \mid p = 0.06, n) = 0.20(600) + 0.40(600) + 0.40(0) = 360$

Answer to Problem 1 (*continued*)

$$s_4$$

State of Nature p (lot proportion of defectives)	Opportunity Loss R	A	Probability of Action $s_4(A, R, R)$ A	R	R	Risk (conditional expected losses) $R(s_4 \mid p_i, n)$
0.02	200	0	0.75	0.19	0.06	50
0.04	0	300	0.53	0.33	0.13	159
0.06	0	600	0.20	0.40	0.40	120

$R(s_4 \mid p = 0.02, n) = 0.75(0) + 0.19(200) + 0.06(200) = 50$

$R(s_4 \mid p = 0.04, n) = 0.53(300) + 0.33(0) + 0.13(0) = 159$

$R(s_4 \mid p = 0.06, n) = 0.20(600) + 0.40(0) + 0.40(0) = 120$

$EOL(s_3) = 0.8(12) + 0.15(258) + 0.05(360) = \$166.3$

$EOL(s_4) = 0.8(50) + 0.15(159) + 0.05(120) = \boxed{\$33.85}$

Answers to Review Problems

1. See table. Solved by normal-form analysis: Possible decision rules based on information derived from single samples of size *n*. Strategies s_3 and s_4 are the only feasible strategies, as shown in part (a) of the table. Strategy s_3 is the optimal strategy, as shown in part (b) of the table.
   Classical hypothesis test: $H_0: p = 0.01$ $H_1: p = 0.02$ or $p = 0.03$
   Type I Error of s_3 and s_4: $s_3 = 0.08$ $s_4 = 0.25$
   Using hypothesis test, we would follow s_3. Thus, Bayesian and classical result in the same optimal strategy.

Answer to Review Problem 1

Calculations for Prior EOL

State of Nature p (lot proportion of defectives)	Prior Probability	Act a_1 Reject	a_2 Accept
0.01	0.60	100	0
0.02	0.30	200	0
0.03	0.10	0	400

$EOL(A_1) = 0.6(100) + 0.3(200) + 0.1(0) = \$120$

$EOL(A_2) = 0.6(0) + 0.3(0) + 0.1(400) = \boxed{\$40}$

a.

Sample Information	Strategy s_1	s_2	s_3	s_4	s_5	s_6	s_7	s_8
Type E ($X \leq C_1$)	R	A	A	A	A	R	R	R
Type F ($C_1 < X \leq C_2$)	R	A	A	R	R	A	R	A
Type G ($X > C_2$)	R	A	R	R	A	A	A	R

R: Reject the lot

A: Accept the lot

Answer to Review Problem 1 (*continued*)

b.

Calculation of Conditional Probability for Type of Sample Information, Given *p*

State of Nature p (lot proportion of defectives)	Prior Probability $P_0(p)$	$P(E\mid p)$	Conditional Probability $P(F\mid p)$	$P(G\mid p)$
0.01	0.6	0.75	0.17	0.08
0.02	0.3	0.67	0.20	0.13
0.03	0.1	0.20	0.30	0.50

Calculation of Risk, or Conditional EOL for s_3 and s_4

s_3

State of Nature p (lot proportion of defectives)	Opportunity Loss R	Opportunity Loss A	Probability of Action $s_3(A, A, R)$ A	A	R	Risk (conditional expected losses) $R(s_3\mid p_i, n)$
0.01	100	0	0.75	0.17	0.08	8
0.02	200	0	0.67	0.20	0.13	26
0.03	0	400	0.20	0.30	0.50	200

$R(s_3\mid p = 0.01, n) = 0.75(0) + 0.17(0) + 0.08(100) = 8$

$R(s_3\mid p = 0.02, n) = 0.67(0) + 0.20(0) + 0.13(200) = 26$

$R(s_3\mid p = 0.03, n) = 0.20(400) + 0.30(400) + 0.50(0) = 200$

s_4

State of Nature p (lot proportion of defectives)	Opportunity Loss R	Opportunity Loss A	Probability of Action $s_4(A, R, R)$ A	R	R	Risk (conditional expected losses) $R(s_4\mid p_i, n)$
0.01	100	0	0.75	0.17	0.08	25
0.02	200	0	0.67	0.20	0.13	66
0.03	0	400	0.20	0.30	0.50	80

$R(s_4\mid p = 0.01, n) = 0.75(0) + 0.17(100) + 0.08(100) = 25$

$R(s_4\mid p = 0.02, n) = 0.67(0) + 0.20(200) + 0.13(200) = 66$

$R(s_4\mid p = 0.03, n) = 0.20(400) + 0.30(0) + 0.50(0) = 80$

$EOL(s_3) = 0.6(8) + 0.3(26) + 0.1(200) = \boxed{\$32.6}$

$EOL(s_4) = 0.6(25) + 0.3(66) + 0.1(80) = \$42.8$

2. See table. Solve by normal-form analysis: Strategies s_3 and s_4 are the only feasible strategies, as shown in part (a) of the table. Strategy s_4 is the optimal strategy, as shown in part (b) of the table.
Classical Hypothesis Test: $H_0: p = 0.01$ $H_1: p = 0.03$ or $p = 0.05$
Type I Error of s_3 and s_4: $s_3 = 0.02$ $s_4 = 0.11$
Strategy s_3 is the optimal strategy using classical hypothesis analysis. Thus, Bayesian and classical result in different optimal strategies.

Answer to Review Problem 2

Calculations for Prior EOL

State of Nature p (lot proportion of defectives)	Prior Probability	Act a_1 Reject	a_2 Accept
0.01	0.90	50	0
0.03	0.06	0	100
0.05	0.04	0	200

EOL $(A_1) = 0.9(50) + 0.06(0) + 0.04(0) = \$45$

EOL $(A_2) = 0.9(0) + 0.06(100) + 0.04(200) = \boxed{\$14}$

---

a.

Possible Decision Rules Based on Information Derived from Single Samples of Size n

Strategy

Sample Information	s_1	s_2	s_3	s_4	s_5	s_6	s_7	s_8
Type E $(X \le C_1)$	R	A	A	A	A	R	R	R
Type F $(C_1 < X \le C_2)$	R	A	A	R	R	A	R	A
Type G $(X > C_2)$	R	A	R	R	A	A	A	R

R: Reject the lot

A: Accept the lot

Calculations of Conditional Probability for Type of Sample Information, Given p

State of Nature p (lot proportion of defectives)	Prior Probability	$P(E \mid p)$	Conditional Probability $P(F \mid p)$	$P(G \mid p)$
0.01	0.90	0.89	0.09	0.02
0.03	0.06	0.50	0.33	0.17
0.05	0.04	0.50	0.25	0.25

Calculation of Risk, or Conditional EOL for s_3 and s_4

s_3

State of Nature p (lot proportion of defectives)	Opportunity Loss R	A	Probability of Action $s_3(A, A, R)$ A	A	R	Risk (conditional expected losses) $R(s_3 \mid p_i, n)$
0.01	50	0	0.89	0.90	0.02	10
0.03	0	100	0.50	0.33	0.17	83
0.05	0	200	0.50	0.25	0.25	150

$R(s_3 \mid p = 0.01, n) = 0.89(0) + 0.09(0) + 0.02(50) = 10$

$R(s_3 \mid p = 0.03, n) = 0.50(100) + 0.33(100) + 0.17(0) = 83$

$R(s_3 \mid p = 0.05, n) = 0.50(200) + 0.25(200) + 0.25(0) = 150$

Answer to Review Problem 2 (*continued*)

State of Nature p (lot proportion of defectives)	Opportunity Loss		s_4 Probability of Action $s_4(A, R, R)$			Risk (conditional expected losses) $R(s_4 \mid p_i, n)$
	R	A	A	R	R	
0.01	50	0	0.89	0.09	0.02	5.5
0.03	0	100	0.50	0.33	0.17	50
0.05	0	200	0.50	0.25	0.25	100

$R(s_4 \mid p = 0.01, n) = 0.89(0) + 0.09(50) + 0.02(50) = 5.5$

$R(s_4 \mid p = 0.03, n) = 0.50(100) + 0.33(0) + 0.17(0) = 50$

$R(s_4 \mid p = 0.05, n) = 0.50(200) + 0.25(0) + 0.25(0) = 100$

$\text{EOL}(s_3) = 0.90(10) + 0.06(83) + 0.04(150) = \$19.98$

$\text{EOL}(s_4) = 0.90(5.5) + 0.06(50) + 0.04(100) = \boxed{\$11.95}$